Life-Cycle Cost
and Economic
Analysis

PRENTICE HALL INTERNATIONAL SERIES
IN INDUSTRIAL AND SYSTEMS ENGINEERING

W. J. Fabrycky and J. H. Mize, Editors

ALEXANDER *The Practice and Management of Industrial Ergonomics*
AMOS AND SARCHET *Management for Engineers*
ASFAHL *Industrial Safety and Health Management, 2/E*
BABCOCK *Managing Engineering and Technology*
BANKS AND CARSON *Discrete-Event System Simulation*
BANKS AND FABRYCKY *Procurement and Inventory Systems Analysis*
BEIGHTLER, PHILLIPS, AND WILDE *Foundations of Optimization, 2/E*
BLANCHARD *Logistics Engineering and Management, 3/E*
BLANCHARD AND FABRYCKY *Systems Engineering and Analysis, 2/E*
BROWN *Systems Analysis and Design for Safety*
BUSSEY *The Economic Analysis of Industrial Projects*
CANADA AND SULLIVAN *Economic and Multi-Attribute Evaluation of Advanced
    Manufacturing Systems*
CHANG AND WYSK *An Introduction to Automated Process Planning Systems*
CHANG, WYSK, AND WANG *Computer Aided Manufacturing*
CLYMER *Systems Analysis Using Simulation and Markov Models*
ELSAYED AND BOUCHER *Analysis and Control of Production Systems*
FABRYCKY AND BLANCHARD *Life-Cycle Cost and Economic Analysis*
FABRYCKY, GHARE, AND TORGERSEN *Applied Operations Research and Management
    Science*
FABRYCKY AND THUESEN *Economic Decision Analysis, 2/e*
FRANCIS AND WHITE *Facility Layout and Location: An Analytical Approach*
GIBSON *Modern Management of the High-Technology Enterprise*
HALL *Queing Methods: For Services and Manufacturing*
HAMMER *Occupational Safety Management and Engineering, 4/E*
HUTCHINSON *An Integrated Approach to Logistics Management*
IGNIZIO *Linear Programming in Single- and Multiple-Objective Systems*
KUSIAK *Intelligent Manufacturing Systems*
MUNDEL *Improving Productivity and Effectiveness*
MUNDEL *Motion and Time Study: Improving Productivity, 6/E*
OSTWALD *Cost Estimating, 2/E*
PHILLIPS AND GARCIA-DIAZ *Fundamentals of Network Analysis*
SANDQUIST *Introduction to System Science*
SMALLEY *Hospital Management Engineering*
TAHA *Simulation Modeling and SIMNET*
THUESEN AND FABRYCKY *Engineering Economy, 7/E*
TURNER, MIZE, AND CASE *Introduction to Industrial and Systems Engineering, 2/E*
WHITEHOUSE *Systems Analysis and Design Using Network Techniques*
WOLFF *Stochastic Modeling and the Theory of Queues*

Life-Cycle Cost and Economic Analysis

Wolter J. Fabrycky
*Virginia Polytechnic Institute
and State University*

Benjamin S. Blanchard
*Virginia Polytechnic Institute
and State University*

PRENTICE HALL
Englewood Cliffs, New Jersey 07632

Library of Congress Cataloging-in-Publication Data

Fabrycky, W. J. (Wolter J.)
    Life-cycle cost and economic analysis / Wolter J. Fabrycky,
Benjamin S. Blanchard.
       p.   cm. -- (Prentice Hall international series in industrial
and systems engineering)
    Includes bibliographical references and index.
    ISBN 0-13-538323-4
    1. Cost effectiveness. ·I. Blanchard, Benjamin S. II. Title.
III. Series.
HD47.4.F33 1991
658.15'53--dc20   90-49461
                                                             CIP

Editorial/production supervision and interior design: *Kathleen Schiaparelli*
Manufacturing buyers: *Linda Behrens and Patrice Fraccio*
Series logo design: *Judith Winthrop*

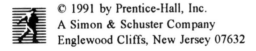 © 1991 by Prentice-Hall, Inc.
A Simon & Schuster Company
Englewood Cliffs, New Jersey 07632

Printed in the United States of America

10 9 8 7 6 5 4 3 2

ISBN 0-13-538323-4

Prentice-Hall International (UK) Limited, *London*
Prentice-Hall of Australia Pty. Limited, *Sydney*
Prentice-Hall Canada Inc., *Toronto*
Prentice-Hall Hispanoamericana, S.A., *Mexico*
Prentice-Hall of India Private Limited, *New Delhi*
Prentice-Hall of Japan, Inc., *Tokyo*
Simon & Schuster Asia Pte. Ltd., *Singapore*
Editora Prentice-Hall do Brasil, Ltda., *Rio de Janeiro*

Contents

Preface

In these times of intensifying international economic competition, producers are searching for ways to gain a sustainable market advantage for their products, systems, and structures. Acquisitions, mergers, and advertising campaigns seem unable to create the intrinsic wealth so essential for long-term corporate health. Economic competitiveness is essential for the viability of private and public sector organizations worldwide.

The purpose of technical activities of design and analysis is to determine how physical factors may be altered to create the most benefit for the least cost, in terms of product cost, product support cost, and social cost. An overarching goal is to bring high-quality products, systems, and structures into being in response to established needs. Engineering with an emphasis on economic competitiveness must become co-equal with concerns for advertising, finance, production, and distribution. It is through a concurrent life-cycle approach that economic competitiveness can be enhanced.

Our title, *Life-Cycle Cost and Economic Analysis,* might incorrectly imply that the benefit side has been ignored in this book. Effectiveness, worth, profit, and other tangeable and intangeable benefit measures are essential and central to the subject. When these measures are economic in nature, the methodology is straightforward. We treat these straightforward cases, as well as the more difficult situations embracing noneconomic benefits factors.

This book is organized around the concurrent life-cycle concept fully recognizing that superior product attributes are quality "effects" resulting from design "causes". These attributes have their genesis in the early conceptual stage, where a large percentage of the life-cycle cost is committed. Accordingly, life-cycle cost and life-cycle economic analysis are merged in this text. Our objective is to provide a complete treatment of the subject, originating with the identification of a need and ending with phaseout and disposal.

This text progresses from conceptual and theoretical material, to methodology, and then to applications. It includes two comprehensive case studies. Part I presents life-cycle economic concepts and provides the theoretical underpinning needed to formulate and analyze economic decisions. Part II sets forth life-cycle costing methodology, presents cost estimation and the treatment thereof, addresses the economic evaluation and optimization of alternatives, and introduces the managerial aspects of life-cycle costing. Part III provides two chapter-length case studies bringing together many of the ideas and approaches presented earlier in the text. Finally, Part IV provides supporting material in five appendices.

A full range of concepts, theory, methodology, and applications makes this book usable in the classroom as well as by the practicing professional. We have opted for generality in the types of products and systems to which this subject may be applied. Economic factors permeate all aspects of the technological process of bringing products and systems into being. Accordingly, those who are striving to enhance the economic stature of their organization will find this book to be well suited to their endeavor. Numerous examples and problems are presented to help the reader gain an in-depth understanding of the process of life-cycle economic analysis.

Many students have helped us in the development and refinement of this material. Gregory Barrett, Bill Hoehn, Merlin Lee, Brian Platnick, and Shashi Rao made specific contributions. Special credit is due Dinesh Verma for his direct help with several sections and for his overall contribution to the manuscript. Finally, Joni Chambers and Nicole Lively put it all together with their excellent word processing skills.

Wolter J. Fabrycky
Benjamin S. Blanchard

System Life-Cycle Concepts

Emerging technologies are revealing unprecedented opportunities for bringing new and improved products and systems into being that will be more cost-effective in private and public sectors worldwide. These technologies are acting to expand physically realizable design options and to enhance capabilities for developing more competitive consumer and producer goods. In this chapter we introduce a technologically-based process involving the extension of engineering and engineering economics to embrace all phases of the system life cycle: design and development, production or construction, utilization, operational support, phaseout, and disposal.

1.1 PLANNING FOR ECONOMIC COMPETITIVENESS

In these times of intensifying international competition, producers are searching for ways to gain a sustainable competitive advantage in the marketplace. Acquisitions, mergers, and advertising campaigns seem unable to create the intrinsic wealth so essential for long-term corporate health. Economic competitiveness is desired by corporations and nations alike.

Engineering and Economic Competitiveness

The purpose of the engineering activities of design and analysis is to determine how physical factors may be altered to create the most utility for the least cost, in terms of product cost, product support cost, and social cost. An overarching goal is to bring high-quality products and systems into being in response to established needs. In the defense sector, this means deploying weapon systems that are competitive in both performance and life-cycle cost. In the nondefense sector, this means bringing products into being that will compete successfully in the world marketplace.[1]

Engineering with an emphasis on economic competitiveness must become coequal with concerns for advertising, finance, production, and distribution. Accordingly, engineering viewed in this context implies a life-cycle orientation. It is through a life-cycle approach to engineering that economic competitiveness can be enhanced.

The Consumer-to-Consumer Process

Fundamental to the application of engineering for the life cycle is an understanding of the consumer-to-consumer process illustrated in Figure 1.1. This process begins with the identification of a need and extends through planning, research, design, production or construction, evaluation, consumer use, maintenance and support, and ultimate retirement (phaseout). The process is "generic" in nature and represents the life-cycle activities of most products and systems. Although these activities may vary somewhat from one program to the next, they reflect a process common to all.

Figure 1.2 is presented to illustrate the product life cycle in simple form. The program activities identified in Figure 1.1 have been classified into two basic phases: the *acquisition phase* and the *utilization phase*. Activities progress from the identified need through conceptual/preliminary design, detail design and development, production and/or construction, and product utilization.

In general, engineers have focused mainly on the acquisition phase of the product life cycle and have been involved in early design and analysis activities alone. Product performance has been a main objective, versus the development of an overall system with economic factors in mind. However, experience in recent decades indicates that a properly functioning product, which is competitive in the marketplace, cannot be achieved through efforts applied largely after it comes into being. Accordingly, it is essential that engineers be sensitive to operational outcomes during the early stages of product development, and that they assume the responsibility for *life-cycle engineering*, which has been largely neglected in the past.

Designing for the Life Cycle

The life-cycle or concurrent design approach for bringing competitive products into being must go beyond consideration of the life cycle of the

---

[1] A strong defense sector depends directly on a strong economy, with a strong economy derived from economic competitiveness in the world marketplace.

Consumer-to-Consumer Process	Consumer	Identification of need	"Wants or desires" for systems (because of obvious deficiences/problems or made evident through basic research).
	Producer	System planning function	Marketing analysis; feasibility study; advanced system planning (system selection, specifications and plans, acquisition plan research/design/production, evaluation plan, system use and logistic support plan); planning review; proposal
		System research function	Basic research; applied research ("need" oriented); research methods; results of research; evolution from basic research to system design and development.
		System design function	Design requirements; conceptual design; preliminary system design; detail design; design support; engineering model/prototype development; engineering test; transition from design to production.
		Production and/or construction function	Production and/or construction requirements; industrial engineering and operations analysis (plant engineering, manufacturing engineering, methods engineering, production control); quality control; production operations.
	Consumer	System evaluation function	Evaluation requirements; categories of test and evaluation; test preparation phase (planning, resource requirements, etc.); formal operational test and evaluation; data collection, analysis, reporting, and corrective action; retesting.
		System use and logistic support function	System distribution and operational use; elements of logistics and life cycle maintenance support; system evaluation; modifications; product phaseout; material disposal, reclamation, and/or recycling.

Figure 1.1   The consumer-to-consumer process.

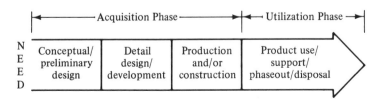

Figure 1.2   The product life cycle.

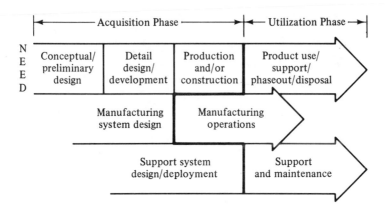

Figure 1.3   Product, process, and support life cycles.

product itself.[2] It must simultaneously embrace the life cycle of the manufacturing process as well as the life cycle of the product support system. Thus there are three coordinated life cycles progressing in parallel, as illustrated in Figure 1.3.[3]

The need for the product comes into focus first. This recognition initiates conceptual design activity to meet the need. Then, during conceptual/preliminary design of the product, consideration should be given simultaneously to its ease of manufacture. This gives rise to a parallel life cycle for bringing a manufacturing capability into being, requiring many production-related activities to "make ready" for manufacturing.

Also shown in Figure 1.3 is another life cycle of great importance which is often neglected until product and production design is completed. This is the life cycle for the logistic support activities needed to service the product during use and to support the manufacturing facility during its duty cycle. Logistics and maintenance requirements planning should begin during product conceptual/preliminary design in a coordinated manner.

The objective behind engineering for the life cycle (in a concurrent manner) is to ensure that the entire life of a system is considered from inception. An engineering design should not only transform a need into a definitive product configuration for customer use, but should ensure the design's compatibility with related physical and functional requirements. Further, it should take into account life-cycle outcomes as measured by performance, effec-

---

[2]A "product," for example, may be a television set, an automobile, or a child's toy. The product by itself cannot function properly without an operator, a support capability, and so on. Therefore, in dealing with "systems," the product, its manufacturing process, consumer use, and sustaining life-cycle maintenance and support must be considered jointly.

[3]Concurrent or simultaneous engineering is an integrated approach that depends on life-cycle thinking.

tiveness, producibility, reliability, maintainability, supportability, quality, and cost.

Concern for the entire life cycle is very strong within the Department of Defense (DoD). This may be attributed to the fact that acquired defense systems are owned, operated, and maintained by the DoD. This is unlike the situation most often encountered in the private sector, where the consumer or user is usually not the producer. Those private firms serving as defense contractors are obliged to design and develop in accordance with DoD directives, specifications, and standards. Since the DoD is the customer and also the user of the resulting system, considerable interaction takes place during the acquisition phase. This interaction is guided by DoD Directive 5000.1 and a host of subordinate directives and documentation.[4]

Many firms that produce for private-sector markets have chosen to design with the life cycle in mind. For example, design for energy efficiency is now quite common in appliances such as water heaters and air conditioners. Fuel efficiency is a required design characteristic of automobiles. Some truck manufacturers promise that life-cycle maintenance requirements will be within stated limits. These developments are commendable, but they do not go far enough. When the producer is not the consumer, it is less likely that potential operational problems will be addressed during development. Undesirable outcomes too often end up with the user of the product instead of with the producer.

All other factors remaining equal, people will meet their needs by procuring goods and services that offer the highest value/cost ratio, subjectively evaluated. This ratio can be increased by giving more attention to the resource-constrained world within which engineering is practiced. To ensure economic competitiveness with regard to the end item, engineering must become more closely associated with economics and economic feasibility. This is best accomplished through a concurrent life-cycle approach, as illustrated in Figure 1.3.

Systems Engineering and Analysis[5]

Systems engineering relates primarily to the design and development activities depicted in Figures 1.1, 1.2, and 1.3. Specifically, systems engineering is a process that has only recently been recognized to be essential in the orderly evolution of people-made systems. It involves the application of efforts to:

[4] "Acquisition of Major Defense Systems," DoD Directive 5000.1 (Washington, DC.: U.S. Department of Defense, July 1971). The requirement for life-cycle costing in the procurement of major defense systems was established by this directive.

[5] Systems engineering and analysis is treated completely in B. S. Blanchard and W. J. Fabrycky, *Systems Engineering and Analysis* (Englewood Cliffs, NJ: Prentice-Hall, Inc., 1990).

1. Transform an operational need into a description of system performance parameters and a preferred system configuration through the use of an iterative process of functional analysis, synthesis, optimization, definition, design, test, and evaluation.

2. Incorporate related technical parameters and assure compatibility of all physical, functional, and program interfaces in a manner that optimizes the total system definition and design.

3. Integrate performance, producibility, reliability, maintainability, human factors, supportability, quality, and other specialties into the overall engineering effort.

Systems engineering per se is not considered to be an engineering discipline in the same context as the technical specialties it represents. Actually, systems engineering is a process employed in the evolution of systems from the point when a need is identified through production and/or construction and ultimate deployment of that system for consumer use. This process involves a series of steps accomplished in a logical manner and directed toward the development of an effective product or system. It views the system from a top-down, integrated, life-cycle perspective. The requirement for systems engineering is brought about because many of the engineering specialists in one or more of the conventional engineering areas (e.g., aeronautical engineering, civil engineering, electrical/electronic engineering) are not sufficiently broad based to ensure that all elements are considered in a coordinated and timely manner.

1.2 THE SYSTEM LIFE-CYCLE PROCESS

The process of system design evolution is illustrated in Figure 1.4. It is "tailored" to meet a specific system requirement. Tailoring refers to the application of the proper level of engineering effort to the system being developed. The application of too much or too little effort could be quite costly. Thus the steps presented in Figure 1.4 should be considered as a thought process, with each step being addressed to the extent and depth necessary to fulfill the requirement.

Regardless of the system type and size, one begins with an identified need and a completed feasibility study for the purposes of establishing a set of requirements, constraints, and design criteria. Based on the results, functional analyses and allocations are generated to apportion the appropriate system-level requirements down to the subsystem, unit, and lower levels of the system.

System analyses are accomplished to evaluate various alternative approaches that are considered feasible in meeting the identified need. The output reflects a preferred system configuration. Identification, analysis, and system definition are inherent feedback provisions, as shown in Figure 1.4.

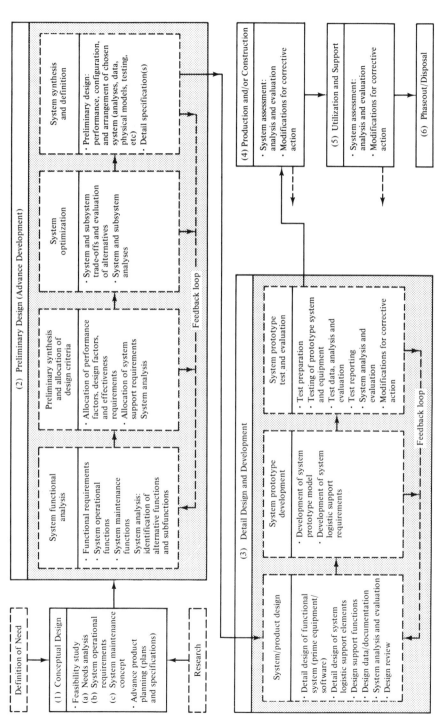

Figure 1.4 The system life-cycle process.

Definition of Need

(1) Conceptual Design
· Feasibility study
(a) Needs analysis
(b) System operational requirements
(c) System maintenance concept
· Advance product planning (plans and specifications)

Research

(2) Preliminary Design (Advance Development)

System functional analysis
· Functional requirements
· System operational functions
· System maintenance functions
· System analysis: identification of alternative functions and subfunctions

Preliminary synthesis and allocation of design criteria
· Allocation of performance factors, design factors, and effectiveness requirements
· Allocation of system support requirements
· System analysis

System optimization
· System and subsystem trade-offs and evaluation of alternatives
· System and subsystem analyses

System synthesis and definition
· Preliminary design: performance, configuration, and arrangement of chosen system (analyses, data, physical models, testing, etc)
· Detail specification(s)

Feedback loop

(3) Detail Design and Development

System/product design
· Detail design of functional system (prime equipment/ software)
· Detail design of system logistic support elements
· Design support functions
· Design data/documentation
· System analysis and evaluation
· Design review

System prototype development
· Development of system prototype model
· Development of system logistic support requirements

System prototype test and evaluation
· Test preparation
· Testing of prototype system and equipment
· Test data, analysis and evaluation
· Test reporting
· System analysis and evaluation
· Modifications for corrective action

Feedback loop

(4) Production and/or Construction
· System assessment: analysis and evaluation
· Modifications for corrective action

(5) Utilization and Support
· System assessment: analysis and evaluation
· Modifications for corrective action

(6) Phaseout/Disposal

7

Definition of System Requirements

The system life-cycle approach stems from the identification of a need that develops as a result of a problem or deficiency, and the subsequent "want" or "desire" for a system of some type. From the identification of a given need, one must define the basic requirements for the system in terms of input criteria for design. To facilitate this process, the following questions should be addressed:

1. What is the system to accomplish in terms of operations and functional performance characteristics (e.g., range, accuracy, speed, power output, flow in gallons per hour, units processed per month, etc.)?
2. When is the system needed? What are the consumer requirements? What is the expected operational life of the system?
3. How is the system to be utilized in terms of hours of operation per day, number of "on–off" cycles per month, and so on?
4. How is the system to be distributed and deployed? Where are the various elements of the system to be located, and for how long?
5. What effectiveness characteristics should the system exhibit? Effectiveness requirements may include factors for cost-effectiveness, system effectiveness, availability, dependability, reliability, maintainability, supportability, and others.
6. What are the environmental requirements for the system (e.g., temperature, humidity, shock and vibration, etc.)? Will the system be operated in arctic or tropical areas, mountainous or flat terrain, and what are the anticipated transportation, handling, maintenance, and/or storage modes?
7. How is the system to be supported throughout its life cycle, and who is responsible for its support? This includes a definition of levels of maintenance, functions at each level, and anticipated logistic support requirements (i.e., test and support equipment, supply support and spare/repair parts, personnel skills, training, transportation and handling requirements, facilities, software, and technical data).

8. When the system becomes obsolete and/or when items are removed from the inventory, what are the requirements for disposal? Can specific items be reclaimed and recycled? What are the effects on the environment?

Regardless of the size and type of the product or system (large or small, mechanical, electrical or electronic, chemical, commercial, or defense), the foregoing questions apply to varying degrees and must be addressed. Answers to these questions generally evolve from feasibility studies, the development of operational requirements and the maintenance concept, and the preparation of the system specification. This activity, constituting the baseline on which the systems engineering process depends, is reflected in block 1 of Figure 1.4 (conceptual design).

Design and Development

The design process proceeds from a set of stated requirements for a given product or system and evolves through (1) conceptual design (i.e., the establishment of performance parameters, operational requirements, and support policies), (2) preliminary systems design (sometimes called advanced development), and (3) detail design. This process generally begins with a visualization of what is required and extends through the development, test, and evaluation of an engineering or prototype model of the system. The output constitutes a configuration that can be produced or constructed directly from specifications, supporting documents, and a data base.

The engineer's role in design and development involves a variety of functions that are dependent on the type of system and the extent of new development necessary. These functions may include all or any combination of the following, which are inherent in blocks 2 and 3 of Figure 1.4:

1. Accomplishing functional analyses and allocations to identify the major operational and maintenance support functions that the system is to perform.

2. Establishing criteria (i.e., qualitative and quantitative technical parameters, bounds, and constraints) for system design.

3. Evaluating alternative design approaches through the accomplishment of cost-effectiveness analyses and trade-off studies.

4. Preparing system, development, product, process, and material specifications.

5. Selecting components for the system and recommending supplier sources.

6. Assisting the purchasing and contracting functions in the preparation of supplier specifications and contractual documentation.

7. Preparing functional design layouts, drawings, parts and material lists, standards, and so on, with the objective of thoroughly defining the product or process through documentation.

8. Assessing the design through predictions, analyses, and the performance of periodic design reviews.

9. Developing breadboards, engineering models, and prototypes for system test and evaluation purposes.

10. Developing system software (computer programs), associated data

bases, and related documentation required to define, design, test, produce, operate, and maintain the system.

11. Developing system and component test specifications and procedures, and accomplishing specific tests to ensure that all design requirements are met.

12. Performing design modifications as necessary to correct deficiencies and/or to improve the system design.

Production and/or Construction

Production and/or construction may constitute (1) the production of a multiple quantity of like items (i.e., mass production), (2) the production of small quantities of a wide variety of different items (i.e., a job shop type of operation), and/or (3) the construction of a single item, such as a large structure of some type. In production and/or construction operations, material and personnel resources must be combined in such a manner as to provide the necessary product/system output in an effective and efficient manner. Production actually begins from the point where system design is considered fixed and includes the total flow of materials, from the acquisition of raw materials to delivery of the finished product for evaluation, and ultimate consumer use. The production flow process, regardless of the product type, involves inventories, material acquisition and control provisions, tooling and test equipment, transportation and handling methods, facilities, personnel, and data.

Engineering is directly required in the design and development of a production capability and for defining the resources necessary for a large construction project. These engineering functions may entail the following:

1. Design of facilities for product fabrication, assembly, and test. This includes determining the capacity and location of both manufacturing and storage facilities, utility requirements, capital equipment needs, and material-handling provisions.

2. Selection of manufacturing processes (e.g., sequencing of tasks, human–machine operations, process specifications).

3. Selection of materials and the determination of inventory requirements.

4. Design of special tools, numerical-control (NC) equipment, test equipment, and transportation and handling capability.

5. Establishment of work methods and processes, time and cost standards, and the subsequent evaluation of production/construction operations in terms of the established parameters.

6. Evaluation of production/construction operations to ensure that product performance, quality, reliability, maintainability, safety, and other desired features are maintained throughout the production/construction process.

These activities are represented by block 4 (production and/or construction) in Figure 1.4. Emphasis at this point is to ensure that those characteristics which have been designed into the system during the earlier phases of a program are indeed maintained throughout the production/construction process.

Utilization and Support

Functions during the utilization phase constitute (1) consumer use of the system throughout its intended life cycle, (2) incorporation of product or system modifications for improvement, (3) the logistic support requirements necessary to ensure that the product or system is deployed and operationally available when needed, and (4) planning for the ultimate phaseout and disposal of the product or system due to obsolescence or wear-out. These functions may be accomplished by the consumer alone, by the consumer with the support of the producer in certain areas, or by the consumer with the support of an outside organization (other than the producer) performing specific activities.

Regardless of the organizations represented, the engineering role may encompass the following:

1. Providing engineering assistance in the initial deployment, installation, and checkout of the system in preparation for consumer operational use.
2. Providing field service or customer service engineers at strategic geographical locations to assist the consumer in the day-to-day operation and maintenance support of the system.
3. Providing engineering support in the design and incorporation of system modifications and in the subsequent checkout of the system to ensure satisfactory operation.
4. Providing engineering assistance in the collection and analysis of data covering system operations in the field, the conductance of special tests, and in the actual assessment of system operations.

Referring to block 5 in Figure 1.4 (utilization and support), systems engineering activities primarily involve customer service and the ongoing overall assessment of the system in the user environment. Based on experience during use, feedback to initiate modifications and corrections should take place.

Phaseout, Retirement, and Disposal

Phaseout, and especially disposal, can be a costly activity. Provision for disposal can be included in product design. Often an economic benefit can be captured through reclamation and recycling of product and system components. From an economic perspective, the cost of disposal is often an externality to the producer and sometimes to the consumer. Steps are needed to make this external cost internal. Only then will design for disposability take its rightful place among other design considerations in the trade-off process.

1.3 COST COMMITMENT OVER THE LIFE CYCLE

Many systems and products are planned, designed, produced, and operated with very little concern for their life-cycle cost. Although different aspects of cost have been considered in the development of new systems, these costs have often been viewed in a fragmented manner. The costs associated with activities such as research, design, testing, production or construction, consumer use, and support have been isolated and addressed at various stages in the system life cycle, and not viewed on an integrated basis.

Experience has indicated that a large portion of the total cost for many systems is the direct result of activities associated with their operation and support, while the commitment of these costs is based on decisions made in the early stages of the system life cycle. Further, costs associated with the different phases of the life cycle are interrelated. Thus in addressing the economic aspects of a system, one must look at total cost in the context of the overall life cycle, particularly during the early stages of conceptual design and advanced system planning. Life-cycle cost, when included as a parameter in the system development process, provides the opportunity to design for economic feasibility.

Figure 1.5 illustrates a characteristic cumulative life-cycle cost curve related to actions occurring during the various phases of the life cycle. The life-cycle phases presented in Figure 1.5 are translated to reflect emphasis on the early planning and design stages of a program. As illustrated, more than half of the projected life-cycle cost is committed by the end of the system planning and conceptual design, even though actual expenditures are relatively minimal by this point in time. This curve varies from one application to the next; however, it does show a trend relative to the effects of decisions on ultimate life-cycle cost.

1.4 LIFE-CYCLE ECONOMIC ANALYSIS

Economic considerations are very important in systems engineering, the process of bringing systems into being. For systems already in existence, economic considerations often provide a basis for the analysis of system operation, support, and retirement. There are numerous examples of structures, processes, and systems that exhibit excellent physical design but have little economic merit. The essential prerequisite of successful engineering application is economic feasibility.

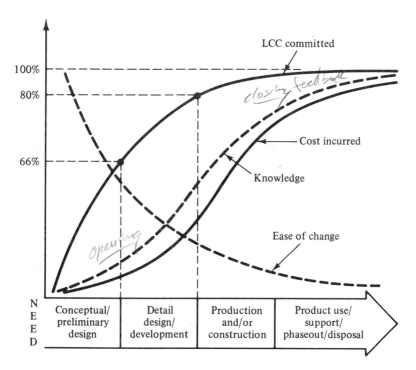

Figure 1.5 LCC committed, cost incurred, knowledge, and ease of change.

Engineers are confronted with two important interconnected environments: the physical and the economic. Their success in altering physical factors to create consumer and producer goods depends on a knowledge of physical laws. However, the worth of these products and systems lies in their utility measured in economic terms. Engineering economics is an essential ingredient in successful engineering application.[6]

Engineering economics has always been closely associated with time: the time value of money, receipts and disbursements over time, and so on. The central model in engineering economics is the money flow diagram, depicting estimates of receipts and disbursements over time. Accordingly, engineering economics and the product/process life cycle are on the same "dimension." Missing from much work in engineering economics, however, is a view of the entire life cycle. Like many functions, engineering economics has come into play only after the detail design is being finalized. This is too late.

Life-cycle economic analysis is an approach that should originate early in the product life cycle, during the conceptual/preliminary design phase. Economic considerations are essential in the final outcome. This outcome

---

[6]Economic considerations in engineering are presented in G. J. Thuesen and W. J. Fabrycky, *Engineering Economy* (Englewood Cliffs, NJ: Prentice-Hall, Inc., 1989).

cannot be influenced much after the design is completed, as was illustrated in Figure 1.5. Furthermore, economic considerations must be applied during manufacturing system design and support system design in accordance with the structure depicted in Figure 1.3.[7]

Opportunities for the more effective application of engineering economics derive from the life-cycle process by which products, systems, and structures are brought into being. Attention directed to this process holds great promise for helping engineering economics reach its full potential in design, in manufacturing, and in operations. The purpose of this book is to present the concepts, theory, and methodology for achieving this desirable end.

QUESTIONS AND PROBLEMS

1. Name some of the emerging technologies providing new opportunities for bringing improved products and systems into being.
2. Explain the role of economic considerations in product competitiveness.
3. The various phases of the consumer-to-consumer process shown in Figure 1.1 are applicable to all systems. True or false? Explain.
4. Select a system of your choice and define the system life cycle (construct a detailed flow diagram).
5. Describe what is meant by "designing for the life cycle."
6. Why is concern for the life cycle greater within DoD than by firms producing for private-sector markets?
7. Describe the interrelationships among the three coordinated "life cycles" shown in Figure 1.3.
8. Define *systems engineering*. What is included? Why is it important?
9. What are some of the basic objectives of *systems engineering* (identify at least three)?
10. How is systems engineering affected by political factors? Economic factors? Technological factors? Social factors? Explain.
11. What are the major systems engineering functions in conceptual design? Preliminary design? Detail design and development? Production/construction? Utilization and life-cycle support?
12. What is the significance of the feedback process in Figure 1.4?
13. What is meant by *tailoring* to meet specific need? Why is it important?
14. Contrast and explain life-cycle cost committed and cost incurred over the life cycle.
15. What is the significance of the "gap" between the knowledge curve and the life-cycle cost committed in Figure 1.5?
16. What is the economic cost significance of the "ease of change" curve in Figure 1.5?
17. Time is a common dimension in engineering economics and the life-cycle concept. Explain.

---

[7] The life-cycle cost analysis process is presented in "generic" terms in Appendix A. It adds a deeper economic dimension to the life-cycle concepts presented in this chapter.

2

Economic and Cost Concepts

Concepts are crystallized thoughts that have withstood the test of time. They are usually qualitative in nature and not necessarily universal in application. Economic and cost concepts, when carefully related to fact, may be useful in suggesting approaches to economic analysis. The ability to arrive at correct decisions depends jointly on a sound conceptual understanding and the ability to handle the quantitative aspects of the analysis needed in life-cycle costing studies. In this chapter special attention is given to selected concepts needed in the life-cycle economic evaluation of alternatives.

2.1 THE VALUE AND UTILITY OF GOODS

Two classes of goods are recognized by economists: consumer goods and producer goods. *Consumer goods* are products and services that directly satisfy human wants. Examples of consumer goods are television sets, shoes, books, orchestras, and health services. *Producer goods* also satisfy human wants, but do so indirectly as a part of the production or construction process. Broadly speaking, the ultimate end of all production activity is to supply goods and services that people may consume to satisfy their needs and desires.

Value and Utility Defined

The term *value* has a variety of meanings. In economics, value designates the worth that a person attaches to a good or service. Thus the value of an object is inherent not in the object but in the regard that a person has for it. Value should not be confused with the cost or price. There may be little or no relation between the value a person ascribes to an article and the cost of providing it, or the price that is asked for it.

The general economic meaning of the term *utility* is the power to satisfy human wants. The utility that an object has for a person is determined by the person. Thus the utility of an object, like its value, is inherent not in the object itself but in the regard that a person has for it. Utility and value as used here are closely related. The utility that an object has for a person is the satisfaction that he or she derives from it. Value is an appraisal of utility in terms of a medium of exchange.

The evaluation of the utility of various items is not ordinarily constant but may be expected to change with time. Each person also possesses either goods or services that he or she may offer in exchange. These have the utility for the person that he or she regards them to have. These same goods and possible services may also be desired by others, who may ascribe to them very different utilities. The possibility for exchange exists when each of two persons possesses utilities desired by the other.

Utility of Consumer Goods

People will consider two types of utility. One kind embraces the utility of goods and services that they intend to consume personally for the satisfaction they derive from them. Thus is seems reasonable to believe that the utility a person ascribes to goods and services that are consumed directly is in large measure a result of subjective, nonlogical mental processes. This may be inferred from the fact that sellers of consumer goods apparently find emotional appeals more effective than factual information.

An analysis of advertising and sales practices used in selling consumer goods will reveal that they appeal primarily to the senses rather than to reason, and perhaps rightly so. If the enjoyment of consumer goods stems almost exclusively from how one feels about them rather than what one reasons about them, it seems logical to make sales presentations on the basis of the utility consumers ascribe to the product.

Some kinds of human wants are much more predictable than others. The demand for food, clothing, and shelter, needed for bare physical existence, is much more stable and predictable than the demand for those items that satisfy human emotional needs. The amount of foodstuffs needed for existence is ascertainable within reasonable limits in terms of calories of energy, and the clothing and shelter requirement may be fairly accurately determined from climate data. But once human beings are assured of physical existence, they reach out for satisfactions related to being a person rather than merely to being a physical organism.

Utility of Producer Goods

The second kind of utility that a good or service may have for a person is as a means to an end. Producer goods are not consumed for direct satisfaction, but as a means of producing consumer goods, usually by facilitating the alteration of the physical environment. Accordingly, the utility of a producer good is ordinarily ascribed by an organization rather than an individual.

Although the utility of consumer goods is determined primarily subjectively, the utility of producer goods as a means to an end may be, and usually is, in large measure considered objectively. In this connection, consider the satisfaction of the human want for harmonic sounds, as in a concert of recorded music. Suppose it has been decided that the desire for a certain recorded concert can be met by 100,000 copies of a compact disc (CD). Then the organization of the artists, the technicians, and the equipment necessary to produce the CD's becomes predominantly objective in character. The amount of material that must be procured and processed to form one CD is calculable to a high degree of accuracy. If a company has been making CDs for some time, it will know the various operations that are to be performed and the unit times of performing them. From these data, the kind and amount of producer services, the amount and kind of labor, and the number of various equipment types are determinable within rather narrow limits.

Whereas the determination of the kinds and amounts of consumer goods needed at any one time may depend on the most subjective of human considerations, the problems associated with their production are quite objective by comparison. The extent to which producer utility may be considered by logical processes is limited only by factual knowledge and the ability to reason technically.

2.2 ECONOMIC INPUTS AND OUTPUTS

All that has utility is physically manifested. This statement is readily accepted in regard to physical objects that have utility, such as an automobile, a tractor, a house, or a steak dinner. But this statement is equally true with regard to the more intangible things. Music, which is regarded as pleasing to people, is manifested to them as air waves that strike their ears. Pictures are manifested as light waves. Even friendship is realized only through the five senses and must therefore have its physical aspects. It follows that utilities must be created by altering physical factors through production and/or construction.

The Production Process

Any project or activity that is undertaken requires an input of thought, effort, material, and other elements for its performance. In a purposeful activity, an input of some value is surrendered in the hope of securing an output of greater value. The terms *input* and *output* as used here have the same meanings as when they are used to designate, for instance, the number of heat units that are supplied to an engine and the number of energy units it contributes for a defined purpose.

The *production process* may be described as a system for converting some combination of inputs to one or more forms of output. This conversion process may be quite simple, but is usually very complex. An essential feature of the process is the conversion of inputs through altering physical factors, thus creating an output of increased utility. This concept is shown schematically in Figure 2.1.

The purpose of much engineering effort is to determine how physical factors may be altered through production and/or construction to create the most utility for the least cost in terms of the utilities that must be given up. It is the relationship between economic inputs and economic outputs that determines the outcome of an activity in economic terms. This outcome can be evaluated by life-cycle economic analysis with the time value of money taken into consideration. A listing of these outputs and inputs is an essential first step in the analysis.

Economic Outputs

Structures, processes, systems, and activities are normally proposed in response to a need or requirement. Outputs should therefore be considered first and in conjunction with the need. Benefit, effectiveness, worth, and other terms are used to describe outputs in relationship to needs.

The outputs of commercial organizations and governmental agencies are endless in variety. Commercial outputs are differentiated from governmental outputs by the fact that it is usually possible to evaluate the former accurately, but not the latter. A commercial organization offers its products to the public. Each item of output is evaluated by its purchaser at the point of exchange.

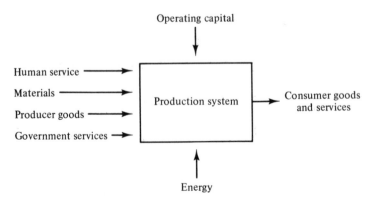

Figure 2.1   Economic and physical inputs and outputs.

Thus the monetary values of past and present outputs of commercial concerns are accurately known item by item.

Information on two subjects is needed to come to a sound conclusion. One of these is the physical output that may be expected from a certain input. This is a matter for engineering analysis. The second is a measure of output that may be expressed in terms of monetary income.

Monetary income is dependent on two factors: the volume of output and the monetary value of the output per unit. The determination of each of these items for the future must of necessity be based upon estimates. Market surveys and similar techniques are widely used for estimating the future output of commercial firms. In the case of large-scale systems or projects the monetary income to the contractor is determined through contractual agreement.

Under some circumstances, for example, if the income is presented by the saving resulting from an improvement in a process for manufacturing a product made at a constant rate, an estimate of income is easily made. But estimating income for new products with reasonable accuracy may be very difficult. Extensive market surveys and even trial sales campaigns over experimental areas may be necessary to determine volume. When work is done on contract, as is the case with much construction work, the necessity for estimating income is eliminated. Under these circumstances the income to be received is known in advance with certainty from.the terms of the contract.

Internal intermediate outputs of commercial organizations are determined with great difficulty and are usually estimated by judgment. For example, the value of the contribution of an engineer, a maintenance technician, or a foreman to a final output is rarely known with reasonable accuracy to either the employee or his superior. Similarly, it is difficult to determine the value of the contributions of most intermediate activities to the final result.

The outputs of many governmental activities are distributed without regard to the amount of taxes paid by the recipient. When there is no evaluation at the point of exchange, it appears almost impossible to evaluate many governmental activities. A person may recognize the desirability of the Department of Defense, the Forest Service, or Public Health activities, but may find it impossible to demonstrate their worth in monetary terms. However, some government outputs, particularly those that are localized, such as highways, irrigation, and power projects, may be fairly accurately evaluated in monetary terms by calculating the reduction in cost or the increase in income they bring about for the user.

Economic Inputs

Primary among the list of economic inputs are producer goods, due to the advent of large investments in automated capital equipment. Producer goods are, in the long run, used as a means to an end—that of producing consumer goods and services for human consumption. These goods are an intermediate step in people's efforts to satisfy their wants. They are not desired for themselves but because they may be instrumental in producing something that can be consumed.

A most important item of input is the services of people, for which salaries and wages are paid. In a commercial organization the total input of human services, as measured by the cost for a given period of time, is ordinarily reflected quite accurately. The input of human services may be classified under the headings of direct labor, indirect labor, and research and development. Of these, direct labor is the only item whose amount is known with reasonable accuracy and whose identify is preserved until it becomes a part of output.

Input devoted to investigation and research is particularly hard to relate to particular units of output. Much research is conducted with no particular specified goal in mind, and much of it results in no appreciable benefit that can be associated with a particular output. Expenditures for people engaged in research and development may be made for some period of time before this type of service has a concrete effect on output. Successful research of the past may continue to affect output for a long time in the future.

Indirect labor, supervision, and management have characteristics falling between those of direct labor and those of investigation and research. The input of indirect labor and, to a lesser extent, that of supervision parallel the output fairly closely in time, but their effects can ordinarily be identified only with broad classes of output items. Management is associated with the operations of an organization as a whole. Its important function of seeking out desirable opportunities and providing direction is similar in character to research. Input in the form of management effort is difficult to associate with output in relation either to time or to classes of product.

As difficult as it may be to associate certain inputs with a final measurable output, such as units of product sold on the market, input can ordinarily be identified closely with intermediate ends that may or may not be measurable in concrete terms. For example, the costs of the input of human effort assigned to the engineering department, the legal department, the labor relations department, and the production department are reflected with a high degree of accuracy by the payrolls of each. However, the worth of the output of the personnel assigned to these departments may defy even reasonably accurate measurement.

A second major category of input is that of material. Many items of material are acquired to meet the objectives of commercial and governmental enterprises. For convenience, material items may be classified as direct material, indirect material, equipment, land, and buildings.

Inputs of direct material are allocated directly to final and measurable outputs. The measure of material items of input is their purchase price plus cost for purchasing, storage, and the like. This class of input is subject to reasonably accurate measurement and may be quite definitely related to final output, which in the case of commercial organizations is easily measurable.

Indirect material and power inputs are measurable in much the same way and with essentially the same accuracy as direct material and power inputs. One of the important functions of accounting is to allocate this class of input in concrete terms to items of output or classes of output. This may ordinarily be done with reasonable accuracy.

An input in the form of an item of equipment requires that an immediate expenditure be made, but its contribution to output takes place piecemeal over a period in the future that may vary from a short time to many years, depending on the useful life of the equipment. Inputs of equipment are accurately measurable and can often be accurately allocated to definite output items, except in amount. The latter limitation is imposed by the fact that the number and kinds of output to which any equipment may contribute are often not known until years after many units of the product have been distributed. One function of depreciation accounting is to allocate equipment inputs to outputs.

Inputs of land and buildings are treated in essentially the same manner as inputs of equipment. They are somewhat more difficult to allocate to the output because of their longer life and because a single item, such as a building, may contribute simultaneously to a great many output items. Allocation is made with the aid of depreciation and cost accounting techniques and practices.

Allocation of inputs of indirect materials, equipment, buildings, and land rests finally upon estimates or judgments. Although this fact is often obscured by the complexities of and the necessary reliance upon accounting practices for day-to-day operations, it should not be lost sight of when life-cycle cost studies are to be made.

Capital in the form of money is an essential input, although it must ordinarily be exchanged for producer goods in order to make a contribution to output. Interest on money used is usually considered to be a cost and so may be considered an input. Its allocation to output will necessarily be related to the allocation of human effort, services, material, and equipment in which money has been invested.

Taxes are essentially the purchase of governmental service required by private enterprise. Since business activity cannot be carried on without the payment of taxes, they comprise a required input. There are many types of taxes, such as ad valorem, excise, sales, and income. The amounts may be known precisely and therefore are accurately called inputs. However, it is often difficult to allocate taxes to outputs, especially in the case of income taxes, which are levied after the profit is derived.

2.3 SOME CLASSIFICATIONS OF COST

A number of cost classifications have come into existence to serve as a basis for life-cycle cost and economic analysis. As concepts, these classifications are useful in calling to mind the source and effect of costs that will have a bearing on the end result of a project. In this section we define and discuss these cost classifications. In the next section, a cost breakdown structure classification of life-cycle cost is presented.[1]

First or Investment Cost

By definition, *first cost* is considered to involve the cost of getting an activity or project started. The main advantage in recognizing this classification is that it calls attention to investment costs associated with the initiation of a new activity that might not otherwise be given proper consideration. Ordinarily, this classification is limited to costs that occur only once for any given undertaking.

First cost ordinarily is made up of a number of cost elements that do not recur after a project is initiated. For purchased equipment, these include the purchase price plus shipping cost, installation cost, and training cost. For a fabricated structure, system, or item of equipment, they include engineering design and development costs, test and evaluation cost, and construction or production cost as well as shipping, installation, and training costs.

Many activities that otherwise may be profitable cannot be undertaken because their associated first cost represents too high a level of investment. Many proposals that are otherwise sound are not initiated because the first cost involved is beyond the reach of the controlling organization.

Operation and Maintenance Cost

Whereas first cost occurs only once in getting an activity started, operation and maintenance costs will be experienced continually over the useful life of the project. Included in this cost category are labor costs of operating and maintenance personnel, fuel and power costs, operating and maintenance supply costs, spare and repair part costs, costs for insurance and taxes, and a fair share of indirect costs called overhead or burden. These costs can be substantial, and often they exceed the first cost in total amount. The timing of their occurrence differs substantially, however, in that operating and maintenance costs occur over time until the structure, system, or equipment is retired from service.

Many complex systems and types of equipment require elaborate logistic support activities to sustain their operation. Operating and maintenance costs are incurred by these support systems themselves and are rightfully charged back to the primary activity or venture being supported. Included in the costs

[1] There are obvious costs identified with activities, which can be directly related to the expenditure of dollars. These costs are identified herein as "economic costs." On the other hand, there are noneconomic costs of a more intangible nature and difficult to convert into dollars i.e., psychological costs, political costs, social costs, etc. In this book only economic costs are considered.

of support systems are the usual labor, energy, material, and overhead costs as well as the often-overlooked cost of holding inventories of spare and repair parts, transportation and logistic costs, and the costs of communication and coordination. Only in recent years have support systems been separately considered as important adjuncts to the operation and maintenance of the complex systems and structures.

Fixed and Variable Cost

Fixed cost is ordinarily defined as that group of costs involved in a going activity whose total will remain relatively constant throughout the range of operational activity. The concept of fixed cost has a wide application. For example, certain losses in the operation of an engine are in some measure independent of its output of power. Among its fixed costs, in terms of energy for a given speed and load, are those for the power to drive the fan, the valve mechanism, and the oil and fuel pumps. Almost any task involves preparation independent of its extent. Thus, to paint a small area may require as much effort for the cleaning of a brush as to paint a large area. Similarly, manufacturing involves fixed costs that are independent of the volume of output.

Fixed costs arise from making preparations for the future. Equipment is purchased now in order that labor costs may be reduced in the future. Materials that may never be needed are purchased in large quantities and stored at much expense and with some risk in order that idleness of production facilities and people may be avoided. Research is carried on with no immediate benefit in view in the hope that it will pay in the long run. The investments that give rise to fixed cost are made in the present in the hope that they will be recovered with a profit as a result of reductions in variable costs or increases in income.

Fixed costs are made up of such cost items as depreciation, maintenance, taxes, insurance, lease rentals, interest on invested capital, sales programs, certain administrative expenses, and research. These costs arise from the decisions of the past and in general are not subject to rapid change. Volume of operational activity, on the other hand, may fluctuate widely and rapidly. As a result, fixed costs per unit may easily go out of control. This is probably the major cause of unsuccessful activity, for few people have the foresight or luck to make commitments in the present that will fit requirements of the future even reasonably well. Since fixed costs cannot be changed readily, consideration must be focused on maintaining a satisfactory volume and character of activity.

Variable cost is ordinarily defined as that group of costs which vary in some relationship to the level of operational activity. For example, the consumption of fuel by an engine may be expected to be proportional to its output of power, and the amount of paint used may be expected to be proportional to the area painted. In manufacturing, the amount of material needed per unit of product may be expected to remain constant, and therefore the material cost will vary directly with the number of units produced. In general, all costs, such as direct labor, direct material, direct power, and the like, which can readily be allocated to each unit of product are considered to constitute the variable costs, and the balance of the costs of the enterprise are regarded as fixed. The fixed and variable portions of total cost are illustrated in Figure 2.2.

Variable expense may be expected to increase in a stepped pattern. To increase production beyond a certain extent, another machine may be added. Even though its full capacity may not be utilized, a full crew may need to be employed to operate it. Also, an increase in production may be expected to result in the use of materials in greater quantities and thus in their purchase at a lower cost per unit due to quantity discounts and volume handling.

Incremental or Marginal Cost

The terms *incremental cost* and *marginal cost* refer to essentially the same concept. The word *incremental* means increase, and an *incremental cost* means an increase in cost. Usually, reference is made to an increase of cost in relation to some other factor, thus resulting is such expressions as incremental cost per ton, incremental cost per gallon, or incremental cost per unit of production. The term *marginal cost* refers specifically to an increment of output whose cost is barely covered by the monetary return derived from it. Figure 2.3 illustrates the nature of fixed and variable cost as a function of output in units. The incremental cost of producing 10 units between outputs of 60 and 70 units per day is illustrated to be $8. Thus the average incremental cost of these 10 units may be computed as Δ cost / Δ output = $8/10 = $0.80 per unit.

In actual situations it is ordinarily difficult to determine incremental cost. There is no general approach to the problem, but each case must be analyzed on the basis of the facts that apply to it at the time and the future period involved. Incremental costs can be overestimated or underestimated,

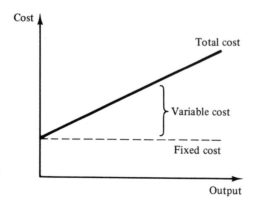

Figure 2.2 Fixed, variable, and total costs.

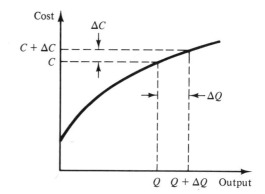

Figure 2.3 Incremental cost ΔC resulting from incremental output ΔQ.

and either error may be costly. Overestimation of incremental costs may obscure a profit possibility; underestimation, on the other hand, may lead to the undertaking of an activity that will result in a loss. Thus accurate information is necessary if sound decisions are to be made.

Direct and Indirect Cost

The cost of manufacturing an item or providing a service will consist of a direct cost and an indirect cost. Both of these categories can be subdivided further. Direct cost consists of three elements: direct material, direct labor, and direct expense. Indirect cost consists of indirect material, indirect labor, and indirect expense. These subdivisions form a costing system that is illustrated in Figure 2.4.

Materials are the basic substances that are required in the conversion of, or which are themselves converted to, useful products. The determination of direct material cost requires a bill of materials as well as the process involved in the fabrication of an item. The prefix *direct* refers to the fact that the materials used under this classification can be directly associated with the product, whereas indirect costs cannot.

Labor costs pertain to the wages paid for work performed. Wages usually cover two types of payments: those to the salaried workers and those to the hourly workers. Salaried workers include maintenance personnel, carpenters, and drafters. Hourly workers are usually classified as direct labor. Supervision, inspection, technical, and maintenance work are examples of work belonging to the classification of indirect labor.

Labor costs reflect remuneration for work performed. However, a very significant part of labor costs is the cost of providing fringe benefits. These benefits include worker's compensation, group insurance, pension plans, holidays and sick pay, profit-sharing payments, and social security payments. Benefits are an indirect cost.

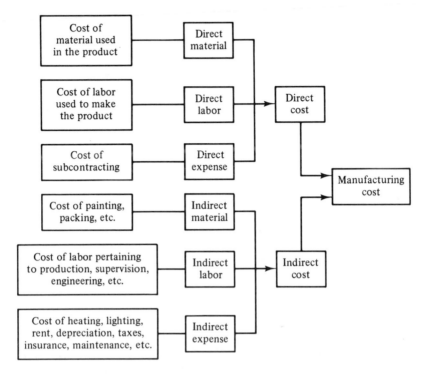

Figure 2.4   Cost categories for manufacturing.

Apart from labor and material costs, there are other expenses involved in the operation of any facility. Among these are the indirect expenses due to taxes, insurance, rent, power, interest, depreciation, and maintenance.

Total and Unit Cost

When dealing with cost, the *total cost* concept should serve as a starting point to ensure that *all* relevant cost factors are appropriately considered. The analyst can easily overlook a significant facet of cost unless he or she intuitively addresses the overall cost spectrum prior to selecting the specific elements of cost that are pertinent to the situation at hand. Total cost includes all life-cycle costs associated with the system or product, as defined in Chapter 1.

Unit cost, on the other hand, is the total cost divided by some related base and may be expressed in terms of cost per item produced, cost per person, cost per increment of effectiveness (e.g. reliability), cost per capacity output, cost per interval of time, and so on. Actually, unit costs should be expressed in measures that are the most meaningful for the purpose(s) at hand, and there must be a complete understanding as to what is included in both the numerator and denominator of the unit cost figure of merit used. Further, caution must be exercised since unit cost often represents an average that may change with the magnitude of the numerator, denominator, or both.

Recurring and Nonrecurring Cost

Another approach to classifying cost involves the concepts of *recurring* and *nonrecurring*. *Recurring cost* refers to those costs that occur again and again (from one period to the next) or at specified intervals. Examples include the cost of ongoing program management activities, continuing engineering support required throughout the production/construction phase of a program, repetitive activities associated with assembly labor and material in producing a given quantity of items, and sustaining customer service activity for a system or product throughout its programmed life cycle.

Nonrecurring cost, on the other hand, is usually a "one-time" cost not of a repetitive nature. Examples are engineering design and development, system/product qualification testing, the acquisition and installation of manufacturing tools and test equipment, the construction of a new facility, and so on.

When evaluating changes in program schedules, different quantities of products, alternative production schemes, and the like, it is often beneficial to classify costs as either recurring or nonrecurring. This classification adds insight despite its simplicity.

Life-cycle cost embraces all costs, nonrecurring and recurring, that occur over the life cycle. During the acquisition phase, nonrecurring costs are incurred. These constitute the first cost of the structure or system. During utilization, recurring costs are experienced. Life-cycle economic analysis considers all costs over the life cycle and seeks to minimize their sum with the time value of money included.

Sunk or Past Cost

When doing a life-cycle cost analysis, the decision maker seeks the course of action that is expected to result in the most favorable future benefits. Because only the future consequences of investment alternatives can be affected by current decisions, an important principle in economic studies is to disregard costs incurred in the past. A past cost or *sunk cost* is one that cannot be recovered or altered by future action and is therefore irrelevant.

Although the principle that sunk costs should be ignored seems reasonable, it is quite difficult for many people to apply. Sunk costs are significant when assessing the actual cost of some past activity or product, and when determining whether a function was accomplished efficiently. Sunk costs are also beneficial in serving as a basis for predicting future costs, even though they cannot be recovered in the process.

On the other hand, the day-to-day aspects of decision making affecting the future rely on all relevant costs from here on. Sunk costs are already expended, do not represent meaningful alternatives, and are no longer real costs. The important issue lies in the *future cost* of a given alternative. Life-cycle cost analyses, as discussed herein, deal only with future costs.

2.4 THE COST BREAKDOWN STRUCTURE

The cost breakdown structure (CBS) is another way of classifying cost, with the classification being life-cycle oriented. The CBS is used as a basis for assessing the life-cycle cost of each alternative being considered. An example of a top-level cost breakdown structure is presented in Figure 2.5.

The cost breakdown structure links objectives and activities with resources, and constitutes a logical subdivision of cost by functional activity area, major element of a system, and/or more discrete classes of common or like items. The CBS is usually tailored to meet the needs of each individual project or program. It should exhibit the following characteristics:

1. All life-cycle costs should be considered and identified in the cost breakdown structure. This includes research and development cost, production and construction cost, operation and system support cost, and retirement and disposal cost.
2. Cost categories are generally identified with a significant level of activity or with a major item of material. Cost categories in the CBS must be well defined, and managers, engineers, accountants, and others must have the same understanding of what is included in a given cost category and what is not included.
3. Costs must be broken down to the level necessary to provide management with the visibility required in evaluating various facets of system design and development, production, operational use, and support. Management must be able to identify high-cost areas and cause-and-effect relationships.
4. The CBS, and the categories defined, should be coded in a manner to facilitate the analysis of specific areas of interest while virtually ignoring other areas. For example, the analyst may wish to investigate supply support costs as a function of engineering design, or distribution costs as a function of manufacturing, independent of other aspects of the system.
5. The CBS and the categories defined should be coded in such a manner as to enable the separation of producer costs, supplier costs, and consumer costs in an expeditious manner.
6. When related to a particular program, the cost structure should be directly compatible (through cross-indexing, coding, etc.) with planning documentation, the work breakdown structure, work packages, the or-

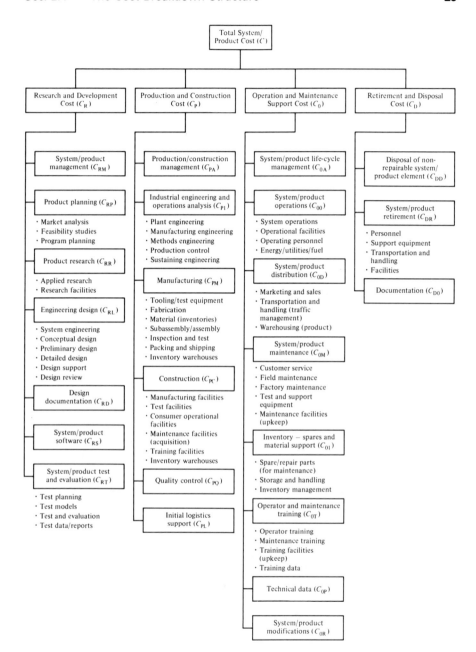

Figure 2.5   A general cost breakdown structure.

ganization structure, scheduling networks, Gantt charts, and so on. Costs that are reported through various management information systems must be compatible and consistent with those comparable cost factors in the CBS.

Referring to Figure 2.5, the cost categories identified are obviously too broad to ensure any degree of accountability and control. The analyst cannot readily determine what is and what is not included, nor can he or she validate that the proper relationships or parameters have been utilized in determining the specific cost factors that are inputted into the illustrated cost structure. The cost analyst requires much more information than is presented in Figure 2.5. In response, the CBS must be expanded to include a detail description of each cost category (in the order presented in the CBS), along with the symbology and quantitative relationships used to derive costs. Appendix B presents a general CBS broken down to reflect the various cost inputs in more detail.

2.5 THE TIME VALUE OF MONEY

The time value of money in the form of an interest rate is an important element in most decision situations involving money flow over time. Because money can earn at a certain interest rate, it is clear that a dollar in hand at present is worth more than a dollar to be received at a future time. A lender may consider interest received as a gain or profit, whereas a borrower usually considers interest to be a charge or cost.

Because money can earn at a certain interest rate through its investment for a period of time, a dollar to be received at some future date is not worth as much as a dollar in hand at present. This relationship between interest and time leads to the concept of the *time value of money*.

A dollar in hand now is worth more than a dollar received n years from now because having the dollar now gives the opportunity for investing that dollar for n years more than the dollar to be received n years hence. Since money has *earning power*, this opportunity will yield a return, so that after n years the original dollar plus its interest will be a larger amount than the $1 received at the time. Thus the fact that money has time value means that equal dollar amounts at different points in time have different value as long as the interest rate that can be earned exceeds zero.

Money also has a time value because the *purchasing power* of a dollar changes through time. During periods of inflation the amount of goods that can be bought for a particular amount of money decreases as the time of purchase occurs further out in the future. Therefore, when considering the time value of money it is important to recognize both the earning power of money and the purchasing power of money. Both of these effects are explicitly presented in Chapter 3.

2.6 THE EARNING POWER OF MONEY

Funds borrowed for the prospect of gain are commonly exchanged for goods, services, or instruments of production. This leads to consideration of the *earning power of money* they may make it profitable to borrow. Consider the example of Mr. Digg, who manually digs ditches for underground cable.[2] For this he is paid $0.40 per linear foot and averages 200 linear feet per day. Weather conditions limit this kind of work to 180 days per year. Thus he has an income of $80 per day worked, or $14,400 per year.

An advertisement brings to his attention a power ditcher than can be purchased for $8,000. He buys the ditcher after borrowing $8,000 at 14% interest. The machine will dig an average of 800 linear feet per day. By reducing the price to $0.30 per linear foot, Mr. Digg can get sufficient work to keep the machine busy when the weather will permit.

Estimated operating and maintenance costs for the ditching machine are $40 per working day. At the end of the year the machine is worthless because it is worn out. A summary of the venture is given in Table 2.1. An increase in net earnings for the year over the previous year of $26,880 − $14,400 = $12,480 is enjoyed by Mr. Digg.

TABLE 2.1 Summary of Power Ditcher Purchase and Operation

Transaction	Receipts	Disbursements
Amount of loan	$ 8,000	
Payment for ditches dug,		
180 days × 800 ft × $0.30 per foot	43,200	
Purchase of ditcher		$ 8,000
Operating and maintenance,		
180 days × $40 per day		7,200
Interest on loan, $8,000 × 0.14		1,120
Repayment of loan		8,000
Total	$51,200	$24,320
Receipts less disbursements	$26,880	

The example above is an illustration of what is known as the *earning power of money*. It was an instrument of production, the power ditcher, that enabled Mr. Digg to increase his earnings. Borrowed money made it possible for the instrument of production to be employed.

Others also gain when producer goods are profitably employed. The public gains by having ditches dug for $0.30 instead of $0.40 per foot. Also,

---

[2] This example was adapted from G. J. Thuesen, and W. J. Fabrycky, *Engineering Economy*, 7th ed. (Englewood Cliffs, NJ: Prentice-Hall, Inc., 1989).

tax revenue will increase, owing to the greater net earnings enjoyed by Mr. Digg. Increasing productivity through the employment of equipment makes these gains possible.

2.7 THE PURCHASING POWER OF MONEY

Inflation and deflation are terms that relate to changes in price levels in an economy. Without addressing the causes of the changes in price levels, the focus here will be on the methods needed to determine the rate of change of price levels and how these changes should be reflected in life-cycle costing studies.

The prices for goods and services are driven upward or downward because of numerous factors at work within the economy. The cumulative effect of these factors causes the price of goods and services to change. For example, increases in productivity and in the availability of goods tend to reduce prices, while government policies such as price supports and deficit financing tend to increase prices. When all such effects are taken together, the most common result has been that prices increase.

To account properly for the time value of money in equivalence calculations, it is important that both the earning power of money and its purchasing power be reflected properly. The concept of the purchasing power of money, along with the analytical techniques needed to incorporate this concept into life-cycle costing studies, is treated at appropriate points in this book.

QUESTIONS AND PROBLEMS

1. Describe the two classes of goods recognized by economists.
2. Contrast the meaning of value and utility.
3. Contrast the utility of consumer goods with the utility of producer goods.
4. Why is it that the utility of consumer goods is determined subjectively, whereas the utility of producer goods is usually determined objectively?
5. Explain how utilities are created.
6. Make a list of economic inputs and outputs for a commercial activity; a public project.
7. What elements combine to make up first cost?
8. How may first cost be a limiting factor in the success of an activity?
9. What elements combine to make up operation and maintenance cost?
10. Contrast nonrecurring and recurring costs associated with a venture.
11. Give an example of a situation where one should evaluate both the acquisition cost and cost of operation.
12. Discuss the difference between fixed cost and variable cost.

13. List some difficulties associated with classifying a cost as either fixed or variable.

14. What is an incremental or marginal cost?

15. Explain the difference between direct and indirect cost in manufacturing.

16. Define sunk cost and explain why it should not be considered in life-cycle costing studies.

17. What is the cost breakdown structure?

18. What purpose does the CBS serve?

19. What characteristics should be incorporated in the CBS?

20. Why is the CBS so important in life-cycle costing?

21. What is meant by the time value of money?

22. Why does money have earning power?

23. High interest rates can nullify the beneficial effect of the earning power of money. Explain.

3

Interest Formulas and Equivalence

Most alternatives arising from design and operational situations may be described in terms of their estimated inputs and outputs over the life cycle. Alternatives can be compared against each other on a fair basis only if their prospective benefits and costs are converted to an equivalent economic base, with the time value of money taken into consideration. Interest formulas are needed to perform this conversion process. In this chapter, interest formulas for both annual and continuous compounding assumptions are derived, the equivalence of money flows over time is explained, and the effect of inflation on economic equivalence is considered.

3.1 INTEREST AND ECONOMIC EQUIVALENCE

Before deriving interest formulas and illustrating their role in determining economic equivalence, it is important to examine some prerequisite topics. Primary among these is the concept of interest and the interest rate. Others are definitions of simple and compound interest, compounding frequency considerations, the meaning of economic equivalence, and a standard format for money flow diagrams.

Interest and Interest Rate

The term *interest* is used to designate a rental amount charged by financial institutions for the use of money. This concept of interest can be extended to earning assets, which "borrow" from their owner, repaying through generated earnings. The economic gain that may occur from the use of money gives money its time value. Because projects require the investment of money, it is essential that the time value of this money be properly reflected in their evaluation.

An *interest rate* is the rate of gain received from an investment. Usually, this rate of gain is stated on a per-year basis. It represents the percentage gain realized on the money committed to the undertaking. Thus a 10% interest rate indicates that for every dollar of money used, an additional $0.10 must be returned as payment for the use of that money. This interest rate is determined by market forces derived from supply and demand. The price of money (interest rate) is determined by mutual agreement between the borrower and lender and is known as the *market rate*.

From one perspective, interest is an amount of money *received* as a result of investing funds, either by loaning it or by using it in the purchase of materials, labor, or facilities. Interest received in this connection is gain or profit. From another perspective, interest is an amount of money *paid out* as a result of borrowing funds. Interest paid is a *cost*.

Inflation has an effect on the market rate of interest. In times of inflationary increase, it is generally advantageous to be a borrower. Conversely, borrowed funds are a burden in deflationary times, when the interest rate is likely to be greater than the deflation rate. The key concept here is the purchasing power of money in the future in relation to its time value.

Simple and Compound Interest

The interest rate is the ratio of the borrowed money to the fee charged for its use over a period of time, usually one year, expressed as a percentage. For example, if $120 is paid for the use of $1,000 for one year, the interest rate is 12%. Under simple interest, the interest due upon repayment of a borrowed amount is proportional to the length of time the money is borrowed. Under compound interest, the interest due at the end of the interest period is either paid at that time or earns interest upon itself.

For the case of simple interest, let I represent the interest earned, P the principal amount, n the interest period, and i the annual interest rate. Then

$$I = Pni \qquad (3.1)$$

Suppose that $1,000 is borrowed at a simple interest rate of 12% per annum.

At the end of three years, the amount of interest would be

$$I = \$1,000(3)(0.12) = \$360$$

The principal plus interest would be $1,360, due at the end of the three-year loan period.

When interest is permitted to compound, interest is calculated at the end of each interest period. There are a number of loan repayment plans, ranging from paying the interest when due to accumulating the interest until the loan is due. For example, the annual payments on a three-year loan of $1,000 at 12% interest per year, payable when due, would be as shown in Table 3.1.

If the borrower does not pay the interest earned at the end of each period and is charged interest on the *total* amount owed (principal plus interest), the interest is said to be *compounded*. The interest owed in the previous year becomes part of the total amount owed for this year. This year's interest charge includes interest that has been earned on previous interest charges. For example, a loan of $1,000 at 12% interest compounded annually for a three-year period will produce the results shown in Table 3.2.

Although the arrangements shown in Tables 3.1 and 3.2 require that the interest be calculated on the unpaid balance, the plans produce different effects because of the way payments are made. In the first arrangement, payment of interest at the time it is due avoids the payment of interest on interest. The reverse is true in the second payment plan. Thus the effect of compound interest depends on the size of the payments and when they are made.

TABLE 3.1 Calculation of Compound Interest When Interest Is Paid Annually

Year	Amount Owed at Beginning Year	Interest to Be Paid at End of Year	Amount Owed at End of Year	Amount to Be Paid by Borrower at End of Year
1	$1,000.00	$120.00	$1,120.00	$ 120.00
2	1,000.00	120.00	1,120.00	120.00
3	1,000.00	120.00	1,120.00	1,120.00

TABLE 3.2 Calculation of Compound Interest When Interest Is Permitted to Accumulate

Year	Amount Owed at Beginning of Year	Interest to Be Added to Loan at End of Year	Amount Owed at End of Year	Amount Paid by Borrower at End of Year
1	$1,000.00	$ $1,000 \times 0.12 = \$120.00$	$1,120.00	$ 0.00
2	1,120.00	$1,120 \times 0.12 =$ 134.40	1,254.40	0.00
3	1,254.40	$1,254.40 \times 0.12 =$ 150.53	1,404.93	1,404.93

A comparison can now be made between simple interest and compound interest using the example above: Under simple interest, $360 in interest was payable at the end of the third year. When interest was permitted to compound annually for three years, $404.93 was payable. The $44.93 difference is from interest earned on interest.

Compounding Frequency Considerations

Although the annual compounding assumption is the most common, financial arrangements may specify more frequent compounding of interest. The effective interest rate is desired. This is based on a nominal annual rate and the compounding frequency. Let

r = nominal interest rate per year
i = effective interest rate per compounding period
c = number of compounding periods per year

The *nominal* interest rate is[1]

$$r = c \times i$$

and the *effective* interest rate per compounding period is

$$i = \frac{r}{c} \tag{3.2}$$

Under more frequent compounding, the actual or effective interest rate per year is higher than the nominal interest rate. For example, consider a nominal interest rate of 12% compounded semiannually. The value of $1 at the end of one year when $1 is compounded at 6% for each half-period is

$$F = \$1(1.06)(1.06)$$

$$= \$1(1.06)^2 = \$1.1236$$

Since the actual interest on the dollar for one year is $0.1236, the effective annual interest rate is 12.36%.

An expression for the effective annual interest rate may be derived from the idea above. Let

$$i_a = \text{effective annual interest rate} = \left(1 + \frac{r}{c}\right)^c - 1 \tag{3.3}$$

where r and c are annual.

---

[1] The nominal interest rate is commonly referred to in financial arrangements as the *annual percentage rate*, APR. Note that when the number of compounding periods per year is one, the nominal and effective rates are the same.

In the limit, interest may be compounded an infinite number of times per year—that is, *continuously*. Under this assumption, the effective annual interest for continuous compounding is defined as

$$i_a = \lim_{c \to \infty} \left(1 + \frac{r}{c}\right)^c - 1$$

But since

$$\left(1 + \frac{r}{c}\right)^c = \left[\left(1 + \frac{r}{c}\right)^{c/r}\right]^r$$

and

$$\lim_{c \to \infty} \left(1 + \frac{r}{c}\right)^{c/r} = e = 2.7182$$

then

$$i_a = \lim_{c \to \infty} \left[\left(1 + \frac{r}{c}\right)^{c/r}\right]^r - 1 = e^r - 1 \qquad (3.4)$$

Economic Equivalence

If two or more situations are to be compared, their measures must be placed on an equivalent basis. Which is worth more, 4 ounces of compound *A* or 1,800 grains of compound *A*? To answer this question, it is necessary to place the two amounts on an equivalent basis by the use of the proper conversion factor. After conversion of ounces to grains, the question becomes: Which is worth more, 1,750 grains of compound *A* or 1,800 grains of compound *A*? The answer is now obvious.

Two things are said to be *equivalent* when they have the same effect. For example, the torques produced by applying forces of 100 pounds and 200 pounds 2 feet and 1 foot, respectively, from the fulcrum of a lever are equivalent, since each produces a torque of 200 foot-pounds.

Three factors are involved in the equivalence of sums of money: (1) the amounts of the sums, (2) the times of occurrence of the sums, and (3) the interest rate. Interest formulas consider time and the interest rate. They are useful conversion factors for calculating the equivalence of monetary amounts occurring at different points in time.

An example of economic equivalence is given in Tables 3.1 and 3.2. The payback plan of Table 3.1 is equivalent to the payback plan of Table 3.2. This is true even though the amount of interest differs. As long as the prevailing interest rate is 12%, a person should be indifferent to the receipt of $120 per year for three years or $404.93 at the end of three years. The equivalence of these amounts is calculated as

$$\$120(1.12)^2 + \$120(1.12)^1 + \$120(1.12)^0 = \$404.93$$

The illustration of equivalence above is trivial. Most design and operational alternatives are described by complex patterns of receipts and disbursements over time. Reducing these monetary amounts to a common base is essential in making comparisons equivalently.

Money Flow Diagrams

As a model for identifying and recording the economic effects of alternatives, a graphical description of each alternative's monetary flows may be used. This graphical descriptor, called a *money flow diagram*, will provide information necessary for analyzing a proposal.[2] A money flow diagram represents receipts during a period of time by an upward arrow (a monetary increase) located at the period's end. The arrow's height may be proportional to the magnitude of the receipts during that period. Similarly, disbursements during a period are represented by a downward arrow (a monetary decrease) located at the end of the period.[3] These arrows are then placed on a time line that spans all time periods covered by the proposal.

As an example, the money flow diagrams in Figure 3.1 pertain to the loan situation described in Table 3.1. In this illustration the borrower receives $1,000, and this amount appears as a positive flow in the borrower's money flow diagram. Each year the borrower pays $120 in interest; these amounts, plus repayment of the $1,000 borrowed, appear as negative flows. Also shown in Figure 3.1 is the lender's money flow diagram. The lender experiences a

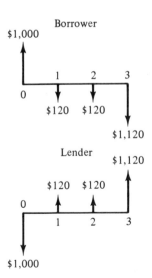

Figure 3.1 Money flow diagrams (Table 3.1 situation).

[2] In the literature, *cash flow diagram* is the phrase most often used.

[3] Positive money flows are receipts (revenues or cost savings), whereas disbursements are investments, costs, expenses, and so on.

negative flow of $1,000, followed by positive flows for interest received and for repayment of the original amount loaned. Note that the point of view taken determines the shape of any money flow diagram.

For the Table 3.2 situation, the money flow diagrams for the borrower and the lender are shown in Figure 3.2. As before, the borrower received $1,000 (a positive flow) and pays $1,404.93 as a negative flow three years hence. The lender's money flow diagram shows opposite directions for the flows. The money flows diagrammed in Figure 3.1 are equivalent to those shown in Figure 3.2.

When an activity has both receipts and disbursements occurring simultaneously, a net money flow may be calculated. The net flow is the arithmetic sum of the receipts (+) and the disbursements (−) that occur at the same point in time. Utilization of net money flows in decision making implies that the net dollars received or disbursed have the same effect on a decision as do total receipts and disbursements considered separately.

Disbursements made to initiate an activity are considered to take place at the beginning of the project. Receipts and disbursements occurring during the life of the project are usually assumed to occur at the end of the year or interest period in which they occur. This "year-end" convention is adopted for describing money flows over time and for developing the applicable money flow diagrams. In the next section we derive interest formulas to be used in dealing with money flows over time in accordance with the convention adopted.

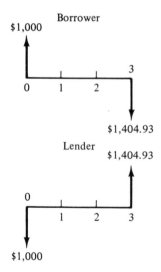

Figure 3.2 Money flow diagrams (Table 3.2 situation).

3.2 *INTEREST FORMULA DERIVATIONS*

A schematic model for money flow over time is shown in Figure 3.3. This money flow model is the basis for the derivation of interest formulas. It may be applied to all phases of the system life cycle for the purpose of life-cycle cost and economic analysis. Let

i = annual rate of interest

n = number of interest periods, usually annual

P = amount at a time assumed to be the present

A = single amount in a series of n equal amounts at the end of each interest period

F = amount, n interest periods hence, equal to the compound amount P, or the sum of the compound amounts of A, at the interest rate i

Annual Compounding Formulas

The most common assumption is that of discrete compounding interest. Normally, this compounding frequency is annual, but it may be any other finite period of shorter duration. The limit is an infinitesimally small compounding period leading to continuous compounding. The formulas derived in the paragraphs that follow are for the discrete compounding assumption.[4]

Single-payment compound-amount formula.   When interest is permitted to compound, the interest earned during each interest period is added to the principal amount at the beginning of the next interest period. Using the terms defined, the relationship among F, P, n, and i can be developed as shown in Table 3.3. The resulting factor, $(1 + i)^n$, is the *single-payment compound-amount factor* and is designated

$$\begin{pmatrix} F/P, i, n \\ \quad \end{pmatrix}$$

This factor may be used to express the equivalence between a present amount,

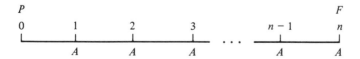

Figure 3.3   The general money flow model.

[4]Tables for annual compounding interest are given in Appendix D for a wide range of interest rates.

TABLE 3.3 Single-Payment Compound-Amount Formula

Year	Amount at Beginning of Year	Interest Earned during Year	Compound Amount at End of Year
1	P	Pi	$P + Pi = P(1+i)$
2	$P(1+i)$	$P(1+i)i$	$P(1+i) + P(1+i)i = P(1+i)^2$
3	$P(1+i)^2$	$P(1+i)^2 i$	$P(1+i)^2 + P(1+i)^2 i = P(1+i)^3$
n	$P(1+i)^{n-1}$	$P(1+i)^{n-1} i$	$P(1+i)^{n-1} + P(1+i)^{n-1} i = P(1+i)^n = F$

P, and a future amount, F, at an interest rate i for n years. The formula is

$$F = P(1+i)^n$$

or

$$F = P(\overset{F/P,\,i,\,n}{\qquad}) \tag{3.5}$$

The compound amount of $1,000 in three years at 12% interest compounded annually may be found from Equation 3.5 as

$$F = \$1,000(1 + 0.12)^3$$

$$= \$1,000(1.405) = \$1,405$$

or by the use of the factor designation and its tabular value from Appendix D, Table D.8,

$$F = \$1,000(\overset{F/P,\,12,\,3}{1.405}) = \$1,405$$

This is the same result (except for rounding) as that found in the compound interest example of Table 3.2 (see also Figure 3.2).

Single-payment present-amount formula. The single-payment compound-amount formula may be solved for P and expressed as

$$P = F\left[\frac{1}{(1+i)^n}\right]$$

The resulting factor, $1/(1+i)^n$, is the *single-payment present-amount factor* and is designated

$$(\overset{P/F,\,i,\,n}{\qquad})$$

This factor may be used to express the equivalence between a future amount, F, and a present amount, P, at an interest rate i for n years. The formula is

$$P = F(\overset{P/F,\,i,\,n}{\qquad}) \tag{3.6}$$

As an example, assume that it is desired to find the amount in the present that is equivalent to $1,405 three years hence if the interest rate is 12%. This amount is found from Equation 3.6 as

$$P/F, 12, 3$$
$$P = \$1,405(\ 0.7118\ ) = \$1,000$$

This is an example verifying the equivalence of $1,000 now and $1,405 in three years, as illustrated in Table 3.2 (see also Figure 3.2).

Equal-payment-series compound-amount formula.   In some situations, a series of receipts or disbursements occurring uniformly at the end of each year may be encountered. The sum of the compound amount of this series may be determined by reference to Figure 3.3.

The A dollars flowing at the end of the nth year will earn no interest and will contribute exactly A dollars to F. The A dollars flowing at the end of period $n - 1$ will earn interest in the amount of Ai, and $A(1 + i)$ will be contributed to the sum. The amount at the end of period $n - 2$ will contribute $A(1 + i)^2$. The sum of this series will be

$$F = A(1) + A(1 + i)^1 + A(1 + i)^2 + \cdots + A(1 + i)^{n-2} + A(1 + i)^{n-1}$$

Multiplying by $(1 + i)$ gives

$$F(1 + i) = A[(1 + i)^1 + (1 + i)^2 + (1 + i)^3 + \cdots + (1 + i)^{n-1} + (1 + i)^n]$$

Subtracting the first expression from the second gives

$$F(1 + i) - F = A[(1 + i)^n - 1]$$

$$Fi = A[(1 + i)^n - 1]$$

$$F = A \left[\frac{(1 + i)^n - 1}{i} \right]$$

The resulting factor, $[(1 + i)^n - 1]/i$, is the *equal-payment-series compound-amount factor* and is designated

$$F/A, i, n$$
$$(\qquad)$$

This factor may be used to express the equivalence between an equal-payment series, A, and a future amount F, at an interest rate i for n years. The formula is

$$F/A, i, n$$
$$F = A(\qquad) \qquad\qquad (3.7)$$

Consider an example where $120 is received at the end of each year for three years at 12% interest. The total that will be accumulated at the end of the three-year period is

$$F/A, 12, 3$$
$$F = \$120(\ 3.374\ ) = \$405$$

Referring again to the example of Tables 3.1 and 3.2, the calculation above illustrates the equivalence of paying interest annually versus allowing interest to earn interest upon itself.

Equal-payment-series sinking-fund formula.   The equal-payment-series compound-amount formula may be solved for A and expressed as

$$A = F\left[\frac{i}{(1 + i)^n - 1}\right]$$

The resulting factor, $i/[1 + i)^n - 1]$, is the *equal-payment-series sinking-fund factor* and is designated

$$(\overset{A/F,i,n}{\quad})$$

This factor may be used to express the equivalence between a future amount, F, and an equal-payment series, A, at an interest rate i for n years. The formula is

$$A = F(\overset{A/F,i,n}{\quad}) \tag{3.8}$$

As an example, suppose that it is desired to find the annual payments needed to accumulate \$405 over three years. The annual amounts needed at an interest rate of 12% is

$$A = \$405(\overset{A/F,12,3}{0.2964}) = \$120$$

This verifies again the equivalence of the plans presented in Tables 3.1 and 3.2.

Equal-payment-series capital-recovery formula.   The substitution of $P(1 + i)^n$ for F in the equal-payment-series sinking-fund formula results in

$$A = P(1 + i)^n\left[\frac{i}{(1 + i)^n - 1}\right]$$

$$= P\left[\frac{i(1 + i)^n}{(1 + i)^n - 1}\right]$$

The resulting factor, $i(1 + i)^n/[(1 + i)^n - 1]$, is the *equal-payment-series capital-recovery factor* and is designated

$$(\overset{A/P,i,n}{\quad})$$

This factor may be used to express the equivalence between future equal-payment series, A, and a present amount, P, at an interest rate i for n years. The formula is

$$A = P(\overset{A/P,i,n}{\quad}) \tag{3.9}$$

As an example of the application of this formula, assume that the loan of $1,000 is to be repaid by a plan different from that in Table 3.1 or 3.2. If the repayment is to be in three equal amounts embracing both principal and interest at 12%, the annual payments are

$$A = \$1,000(\overset{A/P,\,12,\,3}{0.4164}) = \$416.40$$

Equal-payment-series present-amount formula.   The equal-payment-series capital-recovery formula can be solved for P and expressed as

$$P = A\left[\frac{(1+i)^n - 1}{i(1+i)^n}\right]$$

The resulting factor, $[(1+i)^n - 1]/i(1+i)^n$, is the *equal-payment-series present-amount factor* and is designated

$$\overset{P/A,\,i,\,n}{(\qquad)}$$

This factor may be used to express the equivalence between future equal-payment series, A, and a present amount, P, at an interest rate i for n years. The formula is

$$P = A(\overset{P/A,\,i,\,n}{\qquad}) \tag{3.10}$$

As an example of the application of this formula, the three equal payments of $416.40 are equivalent to

$$P = \$416.40(\overset{P/A,\,12,\,3}{2.4018}) = \$1,000$$

Uniform-gradient-series formula.   Periodic money flows do not always occur in an equal series. They may increase or decrease by a constant amount. In general, a uniformly increasing series of flows for n interest periods may be expressed as $A_1, A_1 + G, A_1 + 2G, \ldots, A_1 + (n-1)G$, as shown in Figure 3.4, where A_1 denotes the first year-end flow in the series and G the annual change in the magnitude of the flows.

Individual money flows in a uniform-gradient series may be treated by applying the derived interest formulas to each flow in the series. This method will yield good results but will be time consuming. Another approach is to reduce the uniformly increasing series of flows to an equivalent equal-flow series so that the equal-flow-series factor can be used. Let

$A_1 = $ flow at the end of the first year
$G = $ annual change or gradient
$n = $ number of years
$A = $ annual equivalent equal amount

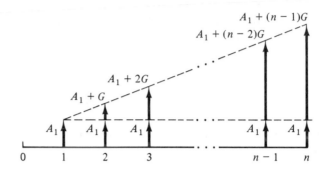

Figure 3.4 A uniformly increasing gradient series.

A uniform-gradient series may be considered to be made up of two separate series, and equal-flow series "base" A_1, and a gradient series 0, G, $2G, \ldots, (n-1)G$ at the end of successive years. Each flow in the equal-flow series equivalent to this series can be represented as

$$A = A_1 + A_2$$

where

$$A_2 = F(\overset{A/F,i,n}{}) = F\left[\frac{i}{(1+i)^n - 1}\right] \tag{3.11}$$

and F is the future equivalent amount of the gradient series.

The future equivalent amount can be found by recognizing that the gradient series can be separated into $(n-1)$ distinct series with equal annual flows of G. This amount can be stated as

$$F = G(\overset{F/A,i,n-1}{}) + G(\overset{F/A,i,n-2}{}) + \cdots + G(\overset{F/A,i,2}{}) + G(\overset{F/A,i,1}{})$$

or

$$= G\left[\frac{(1+i)^{n-1} - 1}{i}\right] + G\left[\frac{(1+i)^{n-2} - 1}{i}\right] + \cdots$$

$$+ G\left[\frac{(1+i)^2 - 1}{i}\right] + G\left[\frac{(1+i)^1 - 1}{i}\right]$$

$$= \frac{G}{i}[(1+i)^{n-1} + (1+i)^{n-2} + \cdots + (1+i)^2 + (1+i) + 1] - \frac{nG}{i}$$

The terms in the brackets constitute the equal-payment-series compound-amount factor for n years. Therefore,

$$F = \frac{G}{i}\left[\frac{(1+i)^n - 1}{i}\right] - \frac{nG}{i} \tag{3.12}$$

Substituting Equation 3.12 into Equation 3.11 gives

$$A_2 = \frac{G}{i}\left[\frac{(1+i)^n - 1}{i}\right]\left[\frac{i}{(1+i)^n - 1}\right] - \frac{nG}{i}\left[\frac{i}{(1+i)^n - 1}\right]$$

$$= \frac{G}{i} - \frac{nG}{i}\left[\frac{i}{(1+i)^n - 1}\right]$$

or

$$A_2 = \frac{G}{i} - \frac{nG}{i}(\overset{A/F,i,n}{\quad})$$

$$= G\left[\frac{1}{i} - \frac{n}{i}(\overset{A/F,i,n}{\quad})\right]$$

The resulting factor,

$$\left[\frac{1}{i} - \frac{n}{(1+i)^n - 1}\right]$$

is the *uniform-gradient-series factor* and is designated

$$\overset{A/G,i,n}{(\quad)}$$

This factor may be used to express the equivalence between a uniform gradient amount, G, and an equal-flow series, A_2, at an interest rate i for n years. The formula is

$$A_2 = G(\overset{A/G,i,n}{\quad}) \tag{3.13}$$

As an example of the use of the gradient factor, assume that an initial positive money flow of $1,000 is to increase by $100, with the last flow occurring at the end of the tenth year. At an interest rate of 8% compounded annually, the annual equivalent amount is

$$A = \$1,000 + \$100(\overset{A/G,8,10}{3.8713}) = \$1,387$$

The gradient conversion factor may also be used for a linearly decreasing series of money flows. If the series above is decreasing by $100 per year, the annual equivalent amount is

$$A = \$1,000 - \$100(\overset{A/G,8,10}{3.8713}) = \$613$$

Geometric-gradient-series formula. In many situations, annual money flows increase or decrease over time by a constant percentage. If g is used to designate the percentage change in the magnitude of the money flows from one period to the next, the magnitude of the tth flow is related to flow F_1 as

$$F_t = F_1(1+g)^{t-1} \qquad t = 1, 2, \ldots, n$$

When g is positive, the series will increase as illustrated in Figure 3.5. When g is negative, the series will decrease.

To derive an expression for the present amount, P, the relationship between F_1 and F_t can be used, together with the single-payment present-amount factor, as

$$P = F_1\left[\frac{(1+g)^0}{(1+i)^1}\right] + F_1\left[\frac{(1+g)^1}{(1+i)^2}\right] + F_1\left[\frac{(1+g)^2}{(1+i)^3}\right] + \cdots + F_1\left[\frac{(1+g)^{n-1}}{(1+i)^n}\right]$$

Multiply each term by $(1+g)/(1+g)$ and simplify

$$P = \frac{F_1}{1+g}\left[\frac{(1+g)^1}{(1+i)^1} + \frac{(1+g)^2}{(1+i)^2} + \frac{(1+g)^3}{(1+i)^3} + \cdots + \frac{(1+g)^n}{(1+i)^n}\right]$$

Let

$$\frac{1}{1+g'} = \frac{1+g}{1+i}$$

where g' is the *growth-free rate*. Substituting for each item gives

$$P = \frac{F_1}{1+g}\left[\frac{1}{(1+g')^1} + \frac{1}{(1+g')^2} + \frac{1}{(1+g')^3} + \cdots + \frac{1}{(1+g')^n}\right]$$

The terms within the brackets constitute the equal-payment-series present-amount factor for n years. Therefore,

$$P = \frac{F_1}{1+g}\left[\frac{(1+g')^n - 1}{g'(1+g')^n}\right]$$

or

$$P = F_1\left[\frac{\overset{P/A,g',n}{(\qquad)}}{1+g}\right] \tag{3.14}$$

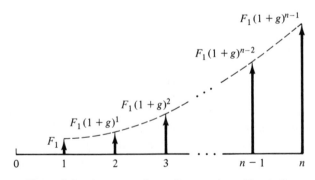

Figure 3.5   A geometric gradient series with $g > 0$.

The factor within brackets is the *geometric-gradient-series factor*. Its use requires finding g' from

$$g' = \frac{1+i}{1+g} - 1 \tag{3.15}$$

The geometric-gradient-series factor may also be used for decreasing-gradient evaluations. In this case g will be negative and will result in a positive value for g' for all positive values of i. As an example, suppose that a revenue flow of $250,000 during the first year is expected to decrease by 10% per year. The present equivalent of the anticipated gross revenue at an interest rate of 17% over eight years may be found as follows:

$$g' = \frac{1+0.17}{1-0.10} - 1 = 0.30 \quad \text{or} \quad 30\%$$

$$P = \$250,000 \frac{\overset{P/A,\,30,\,8}{(\,2.9247\,)}}{1-0.10} = \$812,417$$

In this example, the value for the *P/A* factor was available directly from the 30% interest table in Appendix D.[5]

More-Frequent Compounding

The annual compounding formulas were derived on the basis of an interest rate for an interest period; for an annual interest rate compounded annually. These formulas may be used for compounding frequencies less than one year. It is only necessary for both i and n to be consistent in terms of time units.

Consider the following example. It is desired to find the compound amount of $1,000 four years from now at a nominal annual interest rate of 18% compounded semiannually. Finding the effective *annual* rate from Equation 3.3 gives

$$i_a = \left(1 + \frac{0.18}{2}\right)^2 - 1 = 0.1881 \text{ per year}$$

and the compound amount is

$$F = \$1,000(1 + 0.1881)^4$$

$$= \$1,000(\overset{F/P,\,18.81,\,4}{1.9926}) = \$1,992.60$$

---

[5]Equation 3.15 may yield a g' which is a decimal fraction, or is negative. In these cases, it is necessary to calculate the value of the *P/A* factor from its algebraic form since the tables are based on whole percentages.

Alternatively, since the nominal rate is 18% compounded semiannually, the effective rate for an interest period of one-half year is

$$i = \frac{0.18}{2} = 0.09 \text{ per six months}$$

Over a four-year period there are eight half-year periods. Accordingly, $n = 8$ six-month periods. The compound amount is

$$F = \$1,000(1 + 0.09)^8$$

$$\overset{F/P,9,8}{= \$1,000(1.9926) = \$1,992.60}$$

The compounding frequency adopted may be specified by a financial agreement. However, in economic decision applications the choice of a compounding frequency should be that which best "models" the way in which money flows during use.

Continuous Compounding Formulas

In many economic evaluations, it is reasonable to assume that continuous compounding of interest more nearly represents reality than does annual compounding. Also, the assumption of continuous compounding may be more convenient computationally. This assumption can be used to derive a set of continuous compounding formulas where r is defined as the nominal annual interest rate.

Single-payment compound-amount formula.   The single-payment compounding-amount formula may be expressed to reflect the number of compounding periods as

$$F = P\left(1 + \frac{r}{c}\right)^{cn}$$

When interest is assumed to compound continuously, the interest earned is instantaneously added to the principal at the end of each infinitesimal interest period.

For continuous compounding, the number of compounding periods per year is considered to be infinite. Therefore,

$$F = P\left[\lim_{c \to \infty}\left(1 + \frac{r}{c}\right)^{cn}\right]$$

Rearranging terms yields

$$F = P\left\{\lim_{c \to \infty}\left[\left(1 + \frac{r}{c}\right)^{c/r}\right]^{rn}\right\}$$

where

$$\lim_{c \to \infty}\left(1 + \frac{r}{c}\right)^{c/r} = e = 2.7182$$

Therefore,

$$F = Pe^{rn}$$

The resulting factor, e^{rn}, is the *single-payment compound-amount factor*[6] for continuous compounding interest and is designated

$$\overset{F/P,r,n}{[\qquad]} \tag{3.16}$$

Single-payment present-amount formula.   The single-payment compound amount formula may be solved for P and expressed as

$$P = F\left[\frac{1}{e^{rn}}\right]$$

The resulting factor, e^{-rn}, is the *single-payment present-amount factor* for continuous compounding interest and is designated

$$\overset{P/F,r,n}{[\qquad]} \tag{3.17}$$

Equal-payment-series present-amount formula.   By considering each amount in the series individually, the total present amount of the series is a sum of the individual present amounts as

$$P = A(e^{-r}) + A(e^{-r2}) + \cdots + A(e^{-rn})$$
$$= Ae^{-r}(1 + e^{-r} + e^{-r2} + \cdots + e^{-r(n-1)})$$

This is Ae^{-r} times the geometric series

$$\sum_{j=0}^{n-1}\left(\frac{1}{e^r}\right)^j$$

Therefore,

$$P = Ae^{-r}\left[\frac{1 - e^{-rn}}{1 - e^{-r}}\right]$$
$$= A\left[\frac{1 - e^{-rn}}{e^r - 1}\right]$$

The resulting factor, $(1 - e^{-rn})/(e^r - 1)$, is the *equal-payment-series present-amount factor* for continuous compounding interest and is designated

$$\overset{P/A,r,n}{[\qquad]} \tag{3.18}$$

---

[6] Also note that any continuous compounding formula may be derived from its annual compounding counterpart by substituting the effective continuous interest rate for i. For the factor just developed, substitute $i = e^r - 1$ into $(1 + i)^n$, giving e^{rn}.

Equal-payment-series capital-recovery formula. The equal-payment-series present-amount formula may be solved for A as

$$A = P\left[\frac{e^r - 1}{1 - e^{-rn}}\right]$$

The resulting factor, $(e^r - 1)/(1 - e^{-rn})$, is the *equal-payment-series capital-recovery factor* for continuous compounding interest and is designated

$$\left[\begin{array}{c} A/P,r,n \\ \end{array}\right] \tag{3.19}$$

Equal-payment-series sinking-fund formula. The substitution of Fe^{-rn} for P in the equal-payment-series capital-recovery formula gives

$$A = Fe^{-rn}\left[\frac{e^r - 1}{1 - e^{-rn}}\right]$$

$$= F\left[\frac{e^r - 1}{e^{rn} - 1}\right]$$

The resulting factor, $(e^r - 1)/(e^{rn} - 1)$, is the *equal-payment-series sinking-fund factor* for continuous compounding interest and is designated

$$\left[\begin{array}{c} A/F,r,n \\ \end{array}\right] \tag{3.20}$$

Equal-payment-series compound-amount formula. The equal-payment-series sinking-fund formula may be solved for F as

$$F = A\left[\frac{e^{rn} - 1}{e^r - 1}\right]$$

The resulting factor, $(e^{rn} - 1)/(e^r - 1)$, is the *equal-payment-series compound-amount factor* for continuous compounding interest and is designated

$$\left[\begin{array}{c} F/A,r,n \\ \end{array}\right] \tag{3.21}$$

Uniform-gradient-series formula. The equivalent annual payment, A, corresponding to an initial payment, A_1, linear gradient, G, number of years, n and interest rate, r, may be found in a similar manner as for annual compounding. It can be shown that

$$A = A_1 + G\left[\frac{1}{e^r - 1} - \frac{n}{e^{rn} - 1}\right]$$

The resulting factor,

$$\left[\frac{1}{e^r - 1} - \frac{n}{e^{rn} - 1}\right]$$

is the *uniform-gradient-series factor* for continuous compounding interest and is designated

$$A/G, r, n$$
$$[\qquad] \tag{3.22}$$

Geometric-gradient-series formula.   As before, substitution of the effective continuous compounding interest rate $(e^r - 1)$ for i, the effective interest rate in the comparable discrete compounding interest formula, will yield the continuous compounding formula desired. Using the relationship in Equation 3.15

$$g' = \frac{1+i}{1+g} - 1$$

for the money flow in Figure 3.5 gives the g' value for continuous compounding as

$$g' = \frac{1 + e^r - 1}{1+g} - 1 = \frac{e^r}{1+g} - 1$$

Now the present equivalent of a series of discrete flows growing at a rate of g percent per period when compounding is continuous is

$$P/A, g', n$$
$$P = F_1 \left[\frac{[\qquad]}{1+g} \right] \tag{3.23}$$

Summary of Interest Formulas

The two groups of interest formulas derived in this section are summarized in Table 3.4. Each group is based on assumptions about the compounding frequency of interest and the underlying money flow model.

3.3 EQUIVALENCE OF MONEY FLOWS

Two monetary amounts are economically equivalent when they have the same value in exchange. In this section, several approaches to the determination of economic equivalence will be presented symbolically. These general approaches are then followed by numerical examples based on the money flow diagram of Figure 3.6 representing an unspecified project or venture with both receipts and disbursements.

Present Equivalent Amount

The present equivalent approach is based on finding a present equivalent amount, PE, that represents the difference between present equivalent re-

$F = $ feature, $A = $ account

TABLE 3.4 Summary of Interest Formulas and Designations

Factor	Find	Given	Discrete Compounding	Continuous Compounding
Single payment				
Compound amount	F	P	$F = P(1+i)^n = P(\overset{F/P,i,n}{\;})$	$F = Pe^{rn} = P[\overset{F/P,r,n}{\;}]$
Present amount	P	F	$P = F\dfrac{1}{(1+i)^n} = F(\overset{P/F,i,n}{\;})$	$P = F\dfrac{1}{e^{rn}} = F[\overset{P/F,r,n}{\;}]$
Equal-payment series				
Compound amount	F	A	$F = A\left[\dfrac{(1+i)^n-1}{i}\right] = A(\overset{F/A,i,n}{\;})$	$F = A\left[\dfrac{e^{rn}-1}{e^r-1}\right] = A[\overset{F/A,r,n}{\;}]$
Sinking fund	A	F	$A = F\left[\dfrac{i}{(1+i)^n-1}\right] = F(\overset{A/F,i,n}{\;})$	$A = F\left[\dfrac{e^r-1}{e^{rn}-1}\right] = F[\overset{A/F,r,n}{\;}]$
Present amount	P	A	$P = A\left[\dfrac{(1+i)^n-1}{i(1+i)^n}\right] = A(\overset{P/A,i,n}{\;})$	$P = A\left[\dfrac{1-e^{-rn}}{e^r-1}\right] = A[\overset{P/A,r,n}{\;}]$
Capital recovery	A	P	$A = P\left[\dfrac{i(1+i)^n}{(1+i)^n-1}\right] = P(\overset{A/P,i,n}{\;})$	$A = P\left[\dfrac{e^r-1}{1-e^{-rn}}\right] = P[\overset{A/P,r,n}{\;}]$
Gradient series				
Uniform gradient series	A	G	$A = G\left[\dfrac{1}{i} - \dfrac{n}{(1+i)^n-1}\right] = G(\overset{A/G,i,n}{\;})$	$A = G\left[\dfrac{1}{e^r-1} - \dfrac{n}{e^{rn}-1}\right] = G[\overset{A/G,r,n}{\;}]$
Geometric gradient series	P	F_1	$P = \dfrac{F_1}{1+g}\left[\dfrac{(1+g')^n-1}{g'(1+g')^n}\right] = F_1\left(\dfrac{\overset{P/A,g',n}{\;}}{1+g}\right)$	$P = \dfrac{F_1}{1+g}\left[\dfrac{(1+g')^n-1}{g'(1+g')^n}\right] = F_1\left[\dfrac{\overset{P/A,g',n}{\;}}{1+g}\right]$

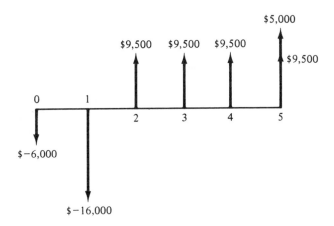

Figure 3.6   A money flow example.

ceipts and present equivalent disbursements for an alternative at a given
interest rate. Thus the present equivalent amount at an interest rate i over n
years is found by applying Equation 3.6 as

$$\text{PE}(i) = F_0(\overset{P/F,i,0}{\quad}) + F_1(\overset{P/F,i,1}{\quad}) + F_2(\overset{P/F,i,2}{\quad}) + \cdots + F_n(\overset{P/F,i,n}{\quad})$$

$$= \sum_{t=0}^{n} F_t(\overset{P/F,i,t}{\quad}) \qquad (3.24)$$

But since $(\overset{P/F,i,t}{\quad}) = (1+i)^{-t}$,

$$\text{PE}(i) = \sum_{t=0}^{n} F_t(1+i)^{-t} \qquad (3.25)$$

For the Figure 3.6 example, the present equivalent amount at 12% using
Equation 3.24 is

$$\text{PE}(12) = -\$6{,}000(\overset{P/F,12,0}{1.0000}) - \$16{,}000(\overset{P/F,12,1}{0.8929}) + \$9{,}500(\overset{P/F,12,2}{0.7972})$$

$$+ \$9{,}500(\overset{P/F,12,3}{0.7118}) + \$9{,}500(\overset{P/F,12,4}{0.6355}) + \$14{,}500(\overset{P/F,12,5}{0.5674})$$

$$= \$8{,}314$$

or by using Equation 3.25,

$$\text{PE}(12) = -\$6{,}000(1.12)^0 - \$16{,}000(1.12)^{-1} + \$9{,}500(1.12)^{-2}$$

$$+ \$9{,}500(1.12)^{-3} + \$9{,}500(1.12)^{-4} + \$14{,}500(1.12)^{-5}$$

$$= \$8{,}314$$

Since the present equivalent amount is greater than zero, this is a desirable venture at 12%.

Annual Equivalent Amount

The annual equivalent approach is similar to the present equivalent approach except that the difference between receipts and costs is now expressed as an annual equivalent amount, AE, at a given interest rate as

$$AE(i) = PE(i)(\overset{A/P,i,n}{}) \tag{3.26}$$

But since

$$PE(i) = \sum_{t=0}^{n} F_t (1 + i)^{-t}$$

and

$$(\overset{A/P,i,n}{}) = \left[\frac{i(1+i)^n}{(1+i)^n - 1} \right]$$

$$AE(i) = \left[\sum_{t=0}^{n} F_t (1 + i)^{-t} \right] \left[\frac{i(1+i)^n}{(1+i)^n - 1} \right] \tag{3.27}$$

For the Figure 3.6 example, the annual equivalent amount using Equation 3.26 is

$$AE(12) = \$8,314(\overset{A/P,12,5}{0.2774}) = \$2,306$$

or, by using Equation 3.27,

$$AE(12) = [-\$6,000(1.12)^0 - \$16,000(1.12)^{-1} + \$9,500(1.12)^{-2}$$
$$+ \$9,500(1.12)^{-3} + \$9,500(1.12)^{-4} + \$14,500(1.12)^{-5}]$$
$$\left[\frac{0.12(1.12)^5}{(1.12)^5 - 1} \right] = \$2,306$$

These results mean that the money invested at $t = 0$ and $t = 1$ will yield a 12% return plus an equivalent of $2,306 at the end of years 1 through 5.

Future Equivalent Amount

The future equivalent approach is based on finding an equivalent amount, FE, that represents the difference between the future equivalent receipts and future equivalent disbursements for an alternative at a given interest rate. Thus the future equivalent amount at an interest rate i over n years is found by applying Equation 3.5 as

$$\text{FE}(i) = F_0(\overset{F/P,i,n}{}) + F_1(\overset{F/P,i,n-1}{}) + \cdots + F_{n-1}(\overset{F/P,i,1}{}) + F_n(\overset{F/P,i,0}{})$$

$$= \sum_{t=0}^{n} F_t(\overset{F/P,i,n-t}{}) \tag{3.28}$$

and

$$(\overset{F/P,i,n-t}{}) = (1+i)^{n-t}$$

$$\text{FE}(i) = \sum_{t-0}^{n} F_t(1+i)^{n-t} \tag{3.29}$$

or

$$\text{FE}(i) = \text{PE}(i)(\overset{F/P,i,n}{}) \tag{3.30}$$

For the Figure 3.6 example, the future equivalent approach using Equation 3.28 gives

$$\text{FE}(12) = -\$6,000(\overset{F/P,12,5}{1.762}) - \$16,000(\overset{F/P,12,4}{1.574}) + \$9,500(\overset{F/P,12,3}{1.405})$$

$$+ \$9,500(\overset{F/P,12,2}{1.254}) + \$9,500(\overset{F/P,12,1}{1.1208}) + \$14,500(\overset{F/P,12,0}{1.000})$$

$$= \$14,649$$

or, by the use of Equation 3.30,

$$\text{FE}(12) = \$8,314(\overset{F/P,12,5}{1.762}) = \$14,649$$

Since the future equivalent amount is greater than zero, this is a desirable venture at 12%.

Internal Rate of Return

The rate-of-return approach is usually the best method for comparing a specific proposal with other opportunities believed to exist but not delineated. The rate of return is a universal measure of economic success since the return from different classes of opportunities are usually well established and generally known. This permits comparison of an alternative against accepted norms.

Rate of return is a widely accepted index of profitability. It is defined as the interest rate that causes the equivalent receipts of a money flow to be equal to the equivalent disbursements of that money flow. The interest rate that reduces the $\text{PE}(i)$, $\text{AE}(i)$, or $\text{FE}(i)$ of a series of receipts and disbursements to zero is a formal definition of rate of return. Mathematically, the rate of return for a proposal is the interest rate i^* that satisfies the equation

$$0 = \text{PW}(i^*) = \sum_{t=0}^{n} F_t(1 + i^*)^{-t} \tag{3.31}$$

where the proposal has a life of n years.

As an example of the rate-of-return approach, the Figure 3.6 example can be evaluated on the basis of the rate of return that would be secured from invested funds. This can be done either by equating the present equivalent, annual equivalent, or future equivalent amounts.

Equating the present equivalent amount of receipts and disbursement at $i = 25\%$ gives

$$\overset{P/F, 25, 1}{\$6{,}000 + \$16{,}000(\,0.8000\,)} \ne \overset{P/F, 25, 2}{\$9{,}500(\,0.6400\,)} + \overset{P/F, 25, 3}{\$9{,}500(\,0.5120\,)}$$

$$\overset{P/F, 25, 4}{+ \$9{,}500(\,0.4096\,)} + \overset{P/F, 25, 5}{\$14{,}500(\,0.3277\,)}$$

$$\$18{,}800 \ne \$19{,}586.85$$

At $i = 30\%$,

$$\overset{P/F, 30, 1}{\$6{,}000 + \$16{,}000(\,0.7692\,)} \ne \overset{P/F, 30, 2}{\$9{,}500(\,0.5917\,)} + \overset{P/F, 30, 3}{\$9{,}500(\,0.4552\,)}$$

$$\overset{P/F, 30, 4}{+ \$9{,}500(\,0.3501\,)} + \overset{P/F, 30, 5}{\$14{,}500(\,0.2693\,)}$$

$$\$18{,}307 \ne \$17{,}176$$

Interpolating gives

$$i = 25\% + 5\left[\frac{(\$19{,}587 - \$18{,}800) - 0}{(\$19{,}587 - \$18{,}800) - (\$17{,}176 - \$18{,}307)}\right] = 27.05\%$$

From these results a present equivalent graph can be developed as shown in Figure 3.7. From the graph it is evident that the rate of return on the venture is just over 27%. This means that the investment of $6,000 and $16,000 at the beginning of years 1 and 2, respectively, should yield a 27.05% rate of return over the five-year period.

Payback or Payout Period

Often a proposed system can be evaluated in terms of how long it will take an investment to pay for itself from benefits, revenues, or savings. Projects that tend to pay for themselves quickly are desirable because there is less uncertainty with estimates of short duration.

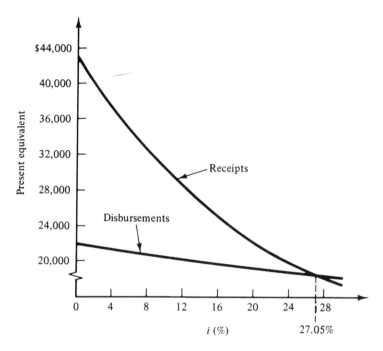

Figure 3.7 Solution for the rate of return.

The payback period is the amount of time required for the present equivalent of receipts (savings) to equal the present equivalent of the disbursements (costs); the annual equivalent receipts and disbursements may also be equated. For the present equivalent approach,

$$0 \le \sum_{t=0}^{n^*} F_t(1+i)^{-t} \tag{3.32}$$

The smallest value of n^* that satisfied the expression above is the payback duration.[7]

Considering a duration of four years, the equation for present equivalent of receipts and disbursements is

$$\overset{P/F, 12, 1}{\$6,000 + \$16,000(\,0.8929\,)} = \overset{P/F, 12, 2}{\$9,500(\,0.7972\,)} + \overset{P/F, 12, 3}{\$9,500(\,0.7118\,)}$$

$$+ \overset{P/F, 12, 4}{\$9,500(\,0.6355\,)}$$

$$\$20,286 \ne \$20,373$$

[7]Payback analysis can be done for situations where "receipts" are costs avoided. Receipts need not be revenues or profits.

For a duration of three years, the equation for present equivalent of receipts and disbursements is

$$\underset{P/F, 12, 1}{\$6,000 + \$16,000(\ 0.8929\ )} = \underset{P/F, 12, 2}{\$9,500(\ 0.7972\ )} + \underset{P/F, 12, 3}{\$9,500(\ 0.7118\ )}$$

$$\$20,286 \neq \$14,336$$

Interpolating yields

$$n = 3 + 1\left[\frac{(\$20,286 - \$14,336) - 0}{(\$20,286 - \$14,336) - (\$20,286 - \$20,373)}\right] = 3.99 \text{ years}$$

From these results a present equivalent graph can be developed as shown in Figure 3.8. From the graph it is evident that the payout period for the project is approximately four years.

Annual Equivalent Asset Cost

A very useful application of the annual equivalent approach pertains to the cost of an asset. The cost of any asset is made up of two components, the cost of depreciation and the cost of interest on the undepreciated balance. It can be shown that the annual equivalent cost of an asset is independent of the depreciation function chosen to represent the value of the asset over time.

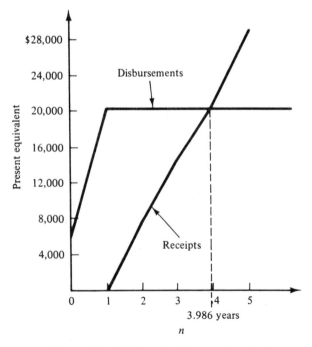

Figure 3.8   Solution for the payout period.

As an example of the cost of depreciation plus the cost of interest on the undepreciated balance, consider the following example based on straight-line depreciation. An asset has a first cost of $5,000, a salvage value of $1,000, a service life of five years, and the interest rate is 10%. The annual costs are shown in Figure 3.9.

The present equivalent cost of depreciation plus interest on the undepreciated balance from Equation 3.24 is

$$\overset{P/F,10,1}{\$1,300(\ 0.9091\ )} + \overset{P/F,10,2}{\$1,220(\ 0.8265\ )} + \overset{P/F,10,3}{\$1,140(\ 0.7513\ )}$$

$$+ \overset{P/F,10,4}{\$1,060(\ 0.6830\ )} + \overset{P/F,10,5}{\$980(\ 0.6209\ )} = \$4,379$$

and the annual equivalent cost of the asset is

$$\overset{A/P,10,5}{\$4,379(\ 0.2638\ )} = \$1,155$$

Regardless of the depreciation function that describes the reduction in value of a physical asset over time, the annual equivalent cost of an asset may be expressed as the annual equivalent first cost minus the annual equivalent salvage value. This annual equivalent cost is the amount an asset must earn each year if the invested capital is to be recovered along with a return on the investment.

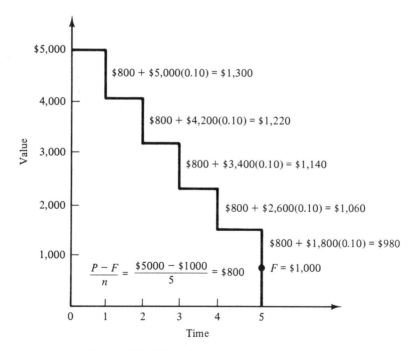

Figure 3.9   Value-time function for an asset.

The annual equivalent cost is derived as

$$A = P(\overset{A/P,i,n}{\quad}) - F(\overset{A/F,i,n}{\quad})$$

But since

$$(\overset{A/F,i,n}{\quad}) = (\overset{A/P,i,n}{\quad}) - i$$

$$A = P(\overset{A/P,i,n}{\quad}) - F[(\overset{A/P,i,n}{\quad}) - i]$$

$$A = (P - F)(\overset{A/P,i,n}{\quad}) + F(i) \qquad (3.33)$$

The annual equivalent cost of any asset may be found from knowledge of its first cost, P, its anticipated service life, n, its estimated salvage value, F, and the interest rate, i. For example, an asset with a first cost of \$5,000, a service life of five years, and a salvage value of \$1,000 will lead to an annual equivalent cost of

$$(\$5,000 - \$1,000)(\overset{A/P,10,5}{\ 0.2638\ }) + \$1,000(0.10) = \$1,155$$

if the interest rate is 10%. This agrees with the first method.

3.4 INFLATION AND EQUIVALENCE

The prices that must be paid for goods and services are continually fluctuating. Historically, the most common movement of prices has been up (inflation). Downward price movements (deflation) have been less frequent. As prices increase, the purchasing power of money declines, while decreasing prices have the opposite effect on the purchasing power of money. Figure 3.10 exhibits more than a half century of inflationary and deflationary experience.[8]

Measures of Inflation and Deflation

To measure and extend price-level changes for consumer and producer goods, it is necessary to calculate price indexes. The applicable inflation rate can be derived from these price indices. This inflation rate can then be used to estimate the purchasing power of money in the future.

Consumer and producer price indices.   A *price index* is a ratio of the price at some point in time to the price at some earlier point in time. This earlier point is usually a selected base year so that the index being calculated, as well as other indexes, can be related to the same base.

---

[8]Because inflation in recent history has been much more common than deflation, the examples presented will deal primarily with inflation. However, the method is general and will apply equally to situations where prices are decreasing.

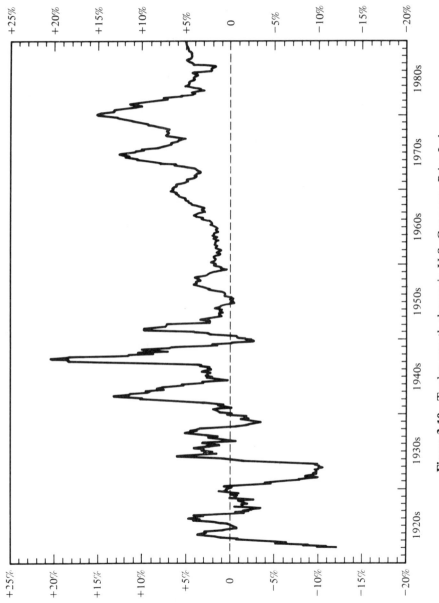

Figure 3.10 Twelve-month change in U.S. Consumer Price Index.

63

Data for the development of price indexes are collected and analyzed by the Department of Commerce (Bureau of Economic Analysis) and the Department of Labor (Bureau of Labor Statistics). These price indices are prepared for individual commodities and classes of products as well for consumer and producer prices as broad aggregations. Table 3.5 gives the Producer Price Index (PPI) and the Consumer Price Index (CPI) for a number of years with 1967 as the base.

To reflect changes in price levels accurately for a life-cycle costing study, the index used should be pertinent to the situation. For consumer goods, the CPI should be used. However, for producer goods, the PPI should be used, although these aggregate indices do not distinguish between the individual goods making up the index. Accordingly, it is often necessary to utilize indices for the specific commodity or service.

Finding the inflation rate.   An annual percentage rate representing the increase (or decrease) in prices over a one-year period is known as the

TABLE 3.5   Producer and Consumer
Price Indices

Year	PPI	CPI
1967	100.0	100.0
1968	102.5	104.2
1969	106.2	109.8
1970	103.3	116.3
1971	106.7	121.3
1972	110.5	125.3
1973	121.9	133.1
1974	144.4	147.7
1975	160.4	161.2
1976	167.7	170.5
1977	178.2	181.5
1978	191.4	195.4
1979	214.4	217.4
1980	245.0	246.8
1981	268.0	272.4
1982	274.3	289.1
1983	277.1	298.4
1984	283.9	311.1
1985	285.2	322.2
1986	278.9	328.4
1987	286.4	340.4
1988	299.3	354.3
1989	324.6	371.5
1990[a]	340.8	390.1

[a] Estimated.

inflation rate. The rate for a given year is generally based on the price in the preceding year. Thus the inflation rate has a compounding effect.

The annual inflation rate may be calculated from any of the available indexes. For the PPI indexes in Table 3.5, the inflation rate, f, for year $t + 1$ is

$$f_{t+1} = \frac{\text{PPI year} (t + 1) - \text{PPI year} (t)}{\text{PPI year} (t)} \tag{3.34}$$

Thus the annual inflation rate for 1980 based on the PPI was

$$\frac{245.0 - 214.4}{214.4} = 0.143 \quad \text{or} \quad 14.3\% \text{ per year}$$

Often an average annual inflation rate is needed in an economic analysis. This requires the determination of a single average rate, $\bar{f}$, that represents a composite of the individual yearly rates. For example, the average inflation rate for producer prices from the end of 1970 to the end of 1980 (10 years) can be calculated as[9]

$$103.3(1 + \bar{f})^{10} = 245.0$$

$$\bar{f} = 9.02\% \text{ per year}$$

The concept of the average annual inflation rate facilitates calculations. In most instances, the estimation of individual yearly inflation rates is time consuming and usually is no more accurate than using a single composite rate. However, where the individual rate approach seems best, the procedure involves $(1 + f_1)(1 + f_2) \cdots (1 + f_n)$. For example, if prices are inflating at a rate of 9% per year the first year and 8% per year in the next year, the price at the end of the second year will be

$$(1 + 0.09)(1 + 0.08)(\text{price at beginning of first year})$$

Most life-cycle costing studies depend on estimates of future inflation rates. These future rates should be based on trends from the past, predicted economic conditions, and judgment.

The purchasing power of money.   As prices increase or decrease, the amount of goods and services that can be purchased for a fixed number of dollars decreases or increases accordingly. Under inflationary conditions, the purchasing power of the dollar is decreasing. The amount of this loss of purchasing power for the dollar is shown in Table 3.6 (with 1967 as the base).

Suppose that a person can invest $100 at the present with the expectation of earning 6% annually for the next eight years. At the end of eight years the

[9] In this chapter reference to the average annual inflation rate means the geometric average rather than the arithmetic average.

TABLE 3.6   The Purchasing Power of Money

Year	Producer Prices	Consumer Prices
1967	1.000	1.000
1968	0.976	0.960
1969	0.942	0.915
1970	0.968	0.860
1971	0.938	0.824
1972	0.905	0.798
1973	0.820	0.751
1974	0.693	0.677
1975	0.623	0.620
1976	0.596	0.587
1977	0.561	0.551
1978	0.523	0.512
1979	0.466	0.460
1980	0.408	0.405
1981	0.373	0.367
1982	0.365	0.346
1983	0.361	0.335
1984	0.352	0.321
1985	0.351	0.310
1986	0.359	0.305
1987	0.349	0.294
1988	0.334	0.282
1989	0.308	0.269
1990[a]	0.293	0.256

[a] Estimated.

accumulated amount would be

$$\overset{F/P,6,8}{\$100(\ 1.594\ )} = \$159.40$$

Also suppose that this person can purchase two automobile tires for the $100.
If these tires are increasing in price at an annual rate of 9%, at the end of eight
years the tires will cost

$$\overset{F/P,9,8}{\$100(\ 1.993\ )} = \$199.30$$

Under this differential in the interest rate and the inflation rate, the person
would be disappointed if she ignored the loss in purchasing power accom-
panying the decision.

Actual and Constant Dollar Analysis

Time value of money considerations in life-cycle costing studies require
separate treatment of the earning power and the purchasing power of money.
Two approaches are presented that allow for the simultaneous treatment of

these influences. The first approach assumes that cash flows are measured in terms of actual dollars and the second is based on the concept of constant dollars.

Money flows in actual or constant dollars.   Money flows can be represented in terms of either actual dollars or constant dollars. These are:

1. *Actual dollars* represent the dollars received or disbursed at any point in time. This amount is measured by totaling the denominations of the currency paid or received. The money flows presented thus far were in terms of actual dollars. Other names for actual dollars are: then-current dollars, current dollars, future dollars, escalated dollars, and inflated dollars.[10]

2. *Constant dollars* represent the hypothetical purchasing power of future monetary amounts in terms of the purchasing power of dollars at some base year. This base year can be arbitrarily selected, although it is usually assumed to be time zero, the beginning of the project. Other names for constant dollars are: real dollars, deflated dollars, today's dollars, and zero-date dollars.

A money flow can be expressed in terms of actual dollars either by direct assessment in actual dollars or by conversion of a constant-dollar estimates to actual dollars. Similarly, if it is desired to express the flow in terms of constant dollars, these dollars can be directly estimated, or the estimate can be made in actual dollars and then converted to constant dollars. The most effective approach depends on the nature of the data regarding future money flows and on whether the analysis is to be in actual or constant dollars.

The conversion of actual dollars at a particular point in time to constant dollars (based on purchasing power n years earlier) at the *same* point in time is often required. When inflation has occurred at an annual percentage, this conversion is

$$\text{constant dollars} = \frac{1}{(1 + \bar{f})^n}(\text{actual dollars}) \qquad (3.35)$$

Conversion of constant dollars to actual dollars for the same set of circumstances is accomplished by solving Equation 3.35 for actual dollars as

$$\text{actual dollars} = (1 + f)^n(\text{constant dollars}) \qquad (3.36)$$

As an example of this calculation when historical data are used, consider the conversion of 1985 actual dollars to 1985 constant dollars with a base year

[10] In this chapter actual dollars omit cost growth due to program or project modification. Only inflationary pressures from economic factors are included. Cost growth is discussed in Part II.

of 1967. Using the CPI index in Table 3.5,

$$\text{constant dollars}_{1985} = \frac{100}{322.2}(\$1) = \$0.310$$

The constant-dollar value of $0.310 can be verified by Table 3.6, which gives, for the base year of 1967, the constant-dollar values for a number of years, including 1985.

In this example, the relationship $3.222 = (1 + \bar{f})^{18}$ is noted, where $\bar{f}$ is the geometric average of the inflation rate over the 18 years from 1967 to 1985. Actually, there are different inflation rates for each year, and their product over the 18 years gives

$$(1 + f_{1968})(1 + f_{1969})(1 + f_{1970}) \cdots (1 + f_{1985}) = (1 + \bar{f})^{18}$$

As an example, assume that a $1,000, 10% bond has five years remaining until maturity. Its money flow in actual dollars will be as shown in Table 3.7. The constant-dollar money flow based on the purchasing power of money at the present $(t = 0)$ is shown in the last column. This money flow assumes an inflation rate of 8% per year over the five years.

By examining the constant-dollar money flow, the owner of the bond observes what the bond is providing in terms of today's purchasing power. Five years from the present the $1,100 will purchase only what $748.66 will purchase at present. That is, five years from the present a dollar received is worth only $0.681 in purchasing power.

Where the level of activity remains the same over time, it is often easier to determine costs by estimating in terms of constant dollars. For example, if an aircraft is to be utilized the same number of hours per year, it is reasonable to expect that the same amount of fuel will be consumed per year. Thus this year's fuel cost will be identical to next year's fuel cost, and so on. If it is necessary to convert these constant-dollar costs to actual dollars, the conversion factor $(1 + f)^n$ can be applied.

TABLE 3.7 Conversion of Actual-Dollar Money Flows to Constant-Dollar Flows

Time	Money Flow (actual dollars)	Conversion Factor	Money Flow (constant dollars)
1	$ 100	$\dfrac{1}{(1.08)^1}$	$ 92.59
2	100	$\dfrac{1}{(1.08)^2}$	85.73
3	100	$\dfrac{1}{(1.08)^3}$	79.38
4	100	$\dfrac{1}{(1.08)^4}$	73.50
5	1,100	$\dfrac{1}{(1.08)^5}$	748.66

Definitions of _i_, _i'_, and _f_.   To develop the relationships between actual-dollar analysis and constant-dollar analysis, precise definitions for the various interest rates are needed. The following definitions are presented to distinguish the market rate of interest, the inflation-free rate, and the inflation rate.

1. _Market interest rate (i)_ represents the opportunity to earn as reflected by the actual rates of interest available in the economy. This rate is a function of the activities of investors operating within the market. Since astute individuals are well aware of the power of money to earn and the detrimental effects of inflation, the interest rates quoted include the effects of both the earning power and the purchasing power of money. When the rate of inflation increases, there is usually a corresponding upward movement in quoted interest rates.[11] Other names are: current-dollar interest rate, actual interest rate, and inflated interest rate.

2. _Inflation-free interest rate (i')_ is the inflation-free interest rate that represents the earning power of money with the effects of inflation removed. This interest rate is an abstraction; it must be calculated, since it is not generally used in financial transactions. The inflation-free interest rate is not quoted by bankers or investors and is therefore not generally known to the public. If there is no inflation in an economy, the inflation-free interest rate and the market interest rate are identical. Other names are: real interest rate and constant-dollar interest rate.

Relationship among _i_, _i'_, and _f_.   It is desirable to compute equivalents in either the actual-dollar or the constant-dollar domain. Therefore, it is important to understand the relationships between these domains. Figure 3.11 presents a single cash receipt at a point in time n years from the base year, the present. This receipt is shown as F in the actual-dollar domain and as F' in the constant-dollar domain.

If the expected inflation rate is f per year, it has previously been shown that the factor $(1 + f)^n$ reverses this process. Thus the inflation rate f is required to transform dollars from one domain to the same point in time in the other domain. If the base year had not been selected at the present (say that it occurred two years prior to the present), the factor to convert actual dollars to constant dollars n years from the present would be $1/(1 + f)^{n+2}$.

To transform dollars to their equivalences at different points in time within the actual-dollar domain, the market interest rate (i) is used. The factor $1/(1 + i)^n$ converts actual dollars at $t = n$ to actual dollars at $t = 0$. The factor $(1 + i)^n$ converts actual dollars at an earlier time to their equivalents in future periods.

---

[11]Subsequent chapters assume that cash flows are in terms of actual dollars with the rate used in the calculations being the market interest rate denoted by i.

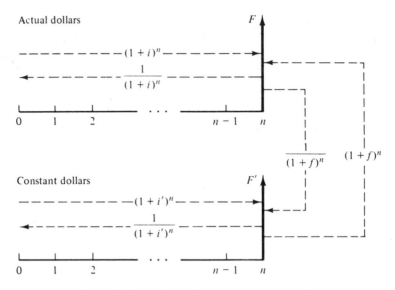

Figure 3.11   Relationships among i, i', and f.

As shown in Figure 3.11, the inflation-free rate is the basis for computing equivalences in the constant-dollar domain. The factor $1/(1 + i')^n$ gives the constant-dollar equivalence at $t = 0$ of the constant cash flow at $t = n$. Accordingly, computing equivalences in the constant-dollar domain, the inflation-free rate is the appropriate rate to apply. The reason for this approach should be evident, since the inflationary effects have been removed from the money flows in the constant-dollar domain. Thus earning-power-of-money calculations should apply an interest rate that is free of inflationary effects.

If the constant-dollar base year is time zero, then at $t = 0$ in Figure 3.11 actual dollars and constant dollars have identical purchasing power—that is, actual dollars at the base year will purchase the same goods or services as constant dollars. At no other point in time does this one-for-one relationship between actual and constant dollars exist.

For analysis in either the actual-dollar or the constant-dollar domain to be consistent, the equivalent amount at time zero in either domain must be equal. Starting at $t = n$ with F in the actual-dollar domain, computing its equivalence at $t = 0$ can be accomplished in two ways. The first approach utilizes actual dollars and converts them to their equivalence at $t = 0$ using

$$P = F\frac{1}{(1 + i)^n}$$

The second approach converts the actual dollars to constant dollars and then finds the equivalence of that constant-dollar amount at $t = 0$ using

$$Mkt = 8\% \quad \frac{1.08}{1.05} = 1.0286$$
$$inflat = 5\% \qquad \text{or} \quad 2.86\%$$

$$F' = F\frac{1}{(1+f)^n}$$

$$P = F'\frac{1}{(1+i')^n} = F\frac{1}{(1+f)^n}\frac{1}{(1+i')^n}$$

Since the P values must be equal at the base year, equating the results of the two methods of computing equivalence gives

$$F\frac{1}{(1+i)^n} = F\frac{1}{(1+f)^n(1+i')^n}$$

$$(1+i)^n = (1+f)^n(1+i')^n$$

$$i = (1+f)(1+i') - 1$$

Solving for i' yields

$$i' = \frac{1+i}{1+f} - 1 \tag{3.37}$$

As an example, suppose that the inflation rate is 10% per year, while the market interest rate is known to be 15% per year. Finding i' gives

$$i' = \frac{1.15}{1.10} - 1 = 4.55\%$$

If a single amount of $1,000 is received 12 years from the present, what is the equivalent amount at $t = 0$? It is

$$\overset{P/F,15,12}{P = \$1,000(\ 0.1869\ ) = \$186.90}$$

or

$$\overset{P/F,10,12\quad P/F,4.55,12}{P = \$1,000(\ 0.3186\ )(\ 0.5866\ ) = \$186.90}$$

The preferred approach will usually depend on whether the result is to be presented in actual or constant dollars and whether the cash flow estimates are in actual or constant dollars.

Geometric Gradient Inflation Analysis

When a dollar amount, F_1, beginning at $t = 1$ is increasing at a constant rate, the geometric gradient factor may be applied. Often the increase described is due to inflationary effects. The dollar amount may be costs or revenues.

Consider a situation where fuel costs $2,000 this year. The organization expects these costs to increase at a rate of 9% per year: 7% because of inflation and 1.869% $[(1.01869)(1.07) = (1.09)]$ because of an increase in the amount of fuel consumed. If the interest rate available for investment is 12%, what is the present equivalent of the next eight years of fuel costs? This equivalent cost is found using the geometric gradient, where the first-year cost of $2,000 is increasing at the annual rate of 9%. With $g' = (1.12)/(1.09) - 1 = 0.0275$, the expression is

$$P = \frac{\$2,000(\overset{P/A,2.75,8}{7.0943})}{1.09} = \$13,017$$

Suppose that the organization wants to compute a single amount at $t = 8$ equivalent to these 8 years of fuel costs. This amount in actual dollars is

$$F = \$13,017(\overset{F/P,12,8}{2.476}) = \$32,230$$

If the equivalent amount just determined is needed in terms of constant dollars (base $t = 0$), convert from actual dollars at $t = 8$ to constant dollars at $t = 8$ using the inflation rate of 7% as

$$F' = \$32,230(\overset{P/F,7,8}{0.5820}) = \$18,758$$

The geometric gradient may also be applied to constant-dollar money flows. Assume that a geometrically growing constant-dollar series is increasing at the rate of 5% per year over 15 years. If $i = 14\%$ and $f = 6\%$ over the time interval of the series and F_1 (in constant dollars) is $3,000, what is the present equivalent of this series?

Equation 3.15 is based on i being the interest rate at which money is moved through time, and g, the rate of growth of the series. It is

$$g' = \frac{1+i}{1+g} - 1$$

In the situation just stated, the geometric series is in constant dollars. Therefore, the inflation-free rate must be applied in place of i when finding g' as

$$i' = \frac{1+i}{1+f} - 1 = \frac{1.14}{1.06} - 1 = 0.0755$$

This gives

$$g' = \frac{1.0755}{1.05} - 1 = 0.0243$$

from which

$$P = \frac{\$3,000(\overset{P/A,2.43,15}{12.4492})}{1.05} = \$35,569$$

Thus $35,569 is the present equivalent of the series of constant-dollar amounts growing at 5% per year with an inflation rate of 6% and a market interest rate of 14%.

QUESTIONS AND PROBLEMS

1. Compare the interest earned by $1,000 for 10 years at 10% simple interest with the interest earned by the same amount for 10 years at 10% compounded annually.

2. For what period of time will $600 have to be invested to amount to $1,200 if it earns 12% simple interest per annum?

3. What effective interest rate per compounding period corresponds to the following nominal interest rates?
   (a) $r = 8\%$ compounded quarterly.
   (b) $r = 14\%$ compounded semiannually.
   (c) $r = 9\%$ compounded continuously.

4. Draw the money flow diagram for the F/A factor from the viewpoint of a person making annual deposits.

5. Draw the money flow diagram for the A/P factor from the viewpoint of a person spending from a cash gift received in the present.

6. What will be the amount accumulated by each of the following present investments?
   (a) $600 in 10 years at 12% compounded annually.
   (b) $20,000 in 18 years at 16% compounded continuously.
   (c) $5,000 in 30 years at 11.5% compounded annually.

7. What is the present value of the following future receipts?
   (a) $8,000 12 years from now at 18% compounded annually.
   (b) $6,200 53 years from now at 12% compounded annually.
   (c) $13,000 18 years from now at 9% compounded continuously.

8. What is the accumulated value of each of the following series of payments?
   (a) $1,400 at the end of each year for 10 years at 8% compounded annually.
   (b) $100 at the end of each year for 40 years at 10% compounded continuously.
   (c) $250 at the end of each year for 25 years at 9.6% compounded annually.

9. What equal annual series of payments must be paid into a sinking fund to accumulate the following amounts?
   (a) $60,000 in 12 years at 12% compounded annually.
   (b) $18,000 in 50 years at 13% compounded continuously.
   (c) $5,400 in 9 years at 8% compounded annually.

10. What is the present value of the following series of prospective payments?
    (a) $1,500 a year for 10 years at 14% compounded annually.
    (b) $1,000 a year for 9 years at 8% compounded continuously.
    (c) $900 a year for 40 years at 17.6% compounded annually.

11. What series of equal annual payments is necessary to repay the following present amounts?
    (a) $4,000 in 5 years at 15% compounded annually.

(b) $10,000 in 12 years at 11% compounded annually.

(c) $100,000 in 30 years at 9.6% compounded annually.

12. What equal annual payment series is necessary to repay the following increasing or decreasing series of payments?

   (a) A series of 6 end-of-year payments that begins at $2,000 and increases at the rate of $100 a year with 10% interest compounded annually.

   (b) A series of 25 end-of-year payments that begins at $400 and increases at the rate of $200 a year with 12.5% interest compounded annually.

   (c) A series of 10 end-of-year payments that begins at $6,000 and decreases at the rate of $200 a year with 12% interest compounded annually.

13. What is the present equivalent value of the following geometrically increasing series of payments?

   (a) A first-year base of $2,000 increasing at 5% per year until year 10 at an interest rate of 12%.

   (b) A first-year base of $15,000 increasing at 8% per year until year 8 with an interest rate of 13%.

   (c) A first-year base of $80,000 increasing at 15% per year until year 7 with an interest rate of 12%.

14. What is the present equivalent value of the following geometrically decreasing series of payments?

   (a) A first-year base of $9,000 decreasing by 10% per year to year 8 with an interest rate of 17%.

   (b) A first-year base of $1,000,000 decreasing by 25% per year to year 4 with an interest rate of 15%.

   (c) A first-year base of $50,000 decreasing by 5% per year to year 30 with an interest rate of 14% compounded continuously.

15. What interest rate is necessary for an amount of money to double in eight years?

16. Plot i as a function of n to illustrate the range of combinations of these variables that result in the doubling of an initial invested amount P.

17. What value for i compounded annually will make a P of $1,000 equivalent to an F of $4,000 if n is 12 years?

18. An interest rate of 10% compounded continuously is desired on an investment of $30,000. How many years will be required to recover the investment with the desired return if $8,000 is received each year?

19. What is the effective interest rate if a nominal rate of 14% is compounded continuously? If an effective interest rate of 8% is desired, what must the nominal rate be if compounding is continuous?

20. A series of payments—$10,000, first year; $9,000, second year; $8,000, third year; $7,000, fourth year; and $6,000, fifth year—is equivalent to what present equivalent amount at 10% interest compounded annually; compounded continuously? Solve using the gradient factor and then by using only the single-payment present-amount factor.

21. A construction firm is considering the purchase of an air compressor. The compressor has the following estimated end-of-year maintenance costs:

Year	1	2	3	4	5	6
Maintenance Costs	$800	$800	$900	$1,000	$1,100	$1,200

What is the present equivalent maintenance cost if the interest rate is 12%?

22. A laboratory can be air conditioned by piping chilled water from a central refrigeration plant. Two competing proposals are being considered for the piping system, as outlined in the table. On the basis of a 10-year life, find the number of hours of operation per year for which the cost of the two systems will be equal if the interest rate is 9%.

	3-Inch System	4-Inch System
Motor size (horsepower)	12	8
Installed cost of pump and pipe	$3,200	$4,400
Installed cost of motor	450	300
Salvage value of system	500	600
Energy cost per hour of operation	0.32	0.18

23. For interest at 14% compounded semiannually:
   (a) What payment can be made now to prevent an expense of $2,000 every six months for the next seven years?
   (b) What semiannual deposit into a fund is required to total $16,000 in eight years?

24. The operating and maintenance expenses of a machine are expected to increase $\frac{1}{2}$% per month. This month's expenses are $2,000. Find the equal annual series that is equivalent to the monthly expenses over five years for an interest of 1% compounded monthly.

25. An asset was purchased for $5,200 with the anticipation that it would serve for 12 years and be worth $600 as scrap. After five years of operation the asset was sold for $1,800. The interest rate is 14%.
   (a) What was the anticipated annual equivalent cost of capital recovery plus return?
   (b) What was the actual annual equivalent cost of capital recovery plus return?

26. A cement mixer purchased for $3,300 has an estimated salvage value of $500 and an expected life of three years. An average of 25 cubic yards of concrete per month will be produced by the mixer.
   (a) Calculate the annual equivalent cost of capital recovery plus return with an interest rate of 8%.
   (b) Calculate the annual equivalent cost of capital recovery plus return per cubic yard of concrete with an interest rate of 12%.

27. Calculate the annual rate of inflation from the Consumer Price Index for the following years.
   (a) 1977.
   (b) 1986.
   (c) 1990.

28. Calculate the average annual rate of inflation based on the CPI from the end of:
    (a) 1967 through 1990.
    (b) 1975 through 1984.
    (c) 1980 through 1985.

29. Find the constant-dollar equivalent of a $3,000 receipt n years from the present if the annual inflation rate is f. The constant-dollar base year is the present.
    (a) $n = 20, f = 4\%$.
    (b) $n = 15, f = 10\%$.
    (c) $n = 40, f = 8\%$.

30. A series of four end-of-year receipts of $4,000 has been promised. If over the next four years the market interest rate is 12% per year and the annual inflation rate is 7%, find the present equivalent of this series using:
    (a) Actual-dollar analysis.
    (b) Constant-dollar analysis. ~ gradient

31. $20,000 is to be received 10 years hence, followed by a $40,000 receipt 17 years from the present. If over this time span the annual inflation rate is 5% while the expected annual market rate is 9%, calculate the present equivalent of these money flows using:
    (a) Actual-dollar analysis.
    (b) Constant-dollar analysis.

32. A project is anticipated to incur a $100,000 constant-dollar cost each year for a six-year period.
    (a) If the rate of inflation is 6% and the market rate is 10%, what is the present equivalent of this series?
    (b) What is the equal-annual series of payments equivalent to this series in actual dollars?

33. The annual energy cost for a refrigeration unit is estimated to be $18,000 in the coming year and then increase by 9% per year due to inflation. If the unit is to be operated for 10 years, find the present equivalent energy cost if the interest rate is 12%. Solve using:
    (a) Geometric gradient approach.
    (b) Constant dollar analysis.

4

Alternatives and Decision Making

An alternative is a proposed course of action to be chosen from a finite set of alternatives. However, not all alternatives are attainable or economically feasible. Some are proposed for consideration even though there is little likelihood that they will prove to be desirable. Bases for determining the economic desirability of alternatives were set forth in Chapter 3. In this chapter a systematic procedure for decision making among mutually exclusive alternatives in accordance with established criteria is presented.

4.1 ELEMENTS OF DECISION CRITERIA

Three elements of decision criteria for comparing mutually exclusive alternatives require special consideration: (1) the differences between alternatives, (2) the minimum attractive rate of return (MARR), and (3) the do-nothing alternative (A_0).

Differences between Alternatives

It is the *difference* between mutually exclusive alternatives that is relevant for decision making. As an example, the money flow difference between two alternatives is shown in Table 4.1. Alternatives A_1 and A_2 can be compared by examining the money flow difference. The following decision rules can be used to choose the most desirable alternative:

1. If money flow $(A_2 - A_1)$ is economically desirable, alternative A_2 is preferred to alternative A_1.

2. If money flow $(A_2 - A_1)$ is economically undesirable, alternative A_1 is preferred to alternative A_2.

In the example of Table 4.1, a decision to pursue alternative A_2 rather than A_1 requires an additional or incremental investment of $50,000. Extra receipts in the amount of $10,000 per year for 10 years and an extra $5,000 at the end of year 10 are anticipated. Do the extra receipts justify the extra investment? This question must be answered to determine which alternative is best.

Minimum Attractive Rate of Return

An investment alternative that does not yield a return that exceeds some *minimum attractive rate of return* (MARR) should not be pursued. This cutoff rate is usually established by a policy decision within the organization.

The minimum attractive rate of return may be viewed as the rate at which a firm can always invest if it has a large number of opportunities yielding such a return. When money is committed to a project, an opportunity to invest that money at the MARR has been forgone. Accordingly, the minimum attractive rate of return is considered to be an "opportunity" cost.

If the MARR selected is too high, many projects that have good returns may be rejected. On the other hand, a MARR that is too low may allow the acceptance of proposals that are marginally productive or result in economic loss. Accordingly, a trade-off must be made between being too selective and not being selective enough.

The minimum attractive rate of return is not the cost of capital. Normally, the MARR is substantially higher than the cost of money. If a firm's cost of money is 11%, its minimum attractive rate of return may be 20%. This

TABLE 4.1   Money Flow Difference between Two Alternatives (Thousands)

End of Year	Alternative		Money Flow Difference $(A_2 - A_1)$
	*A*1	*A*2	
0	$-30	$-80	$-50
1–10	10	20	10
10	5	10	5

difference arises because few firms are willing to invest in projects that are expected to earn only slightly more than the cost of capital. This is due to the risk element in most projects and because of uncertainty about future outcomes.

The Do-Nothing Alternative

In addition to the alternatives formally selected for evaluation, another alternative is almost always present; that of making no decision, designated A_0. The decision not to decide may be either a result of active consideration or passive failure to act. Such a decision is usually motivated by the belief that there will be opportunities in the future that may prove more profitable than those known at present.

In life-cycle economic analysis it is assumed that available money not committed to projects being considered will be invested in the do-nothing alternative. Under this assumption, the available money is not idle. Rather it is assumed to be invested in unrelated instruments yielding a rate of return equal to the MARR.

When an alternative is being evaluated, it is essential that the option to invest at the MARR be considered as an option. This option is often ignored, leading to the selection of an alternative less desirable than doing nothing.

4.2 TYPES OF PROPOSALS

A proposal is a single project or undertaking being considered as an investment opportunity. An all-inclusive and complete proposal rarely emerges in its final state. It begins as a hazy but interesting idea. Attention is then directed to analysis and synthesis, and the result is a definite proposal. In its final form, a proposal should consist of a complete description of its objectives and economic elements in terms of benefits and cost.

It is important to distinguish a proposal from an investment alternative (or decision option). In accordance with these distinctions, every proposal could be considered to be an investment alternative. However, an investment alternative can consist of a group of proposals.

Independent Proposals

When the acceptance of a proposal from a set has no effect on the acceptance of any of the other proposals in the set, the proposal is said to be *independent.* Even though few proposals are truly independent, it is reasonable to treat certain proposals as though they are independent. For example, the decision to renovate a facility would normally be considered independent of the decision to undertake an advertising program, since each has a different objective.

It is usually possible to recognize some relationship between proposals that are functionally different. For example, it might be expected that the proposal to renovate a facility will lead to a lower product cost through increased productivity. This cost saving may have an effect on the selling price of the product, which in turn may affect market demand. Advertising is also intended to influence consumer demand. Unless such relationships are rather direct, they can be ignored. In addition, if the amounts of money available for investment in the production or marketing operations are not immediately transferable, it is reasonable to disregard any financial dependency between the proposals.

If proposals are functionally different and there are no other obvious dependencies between them, it is reasonable to consider the proposals to be independent. For example, proposals concerning the purchase of a numerically controlled machine, a security system, and automated test equipment would usually be considered independent.

Dependent Proposals

In many decision situations, a group of proposals will be related to one another in such a way that the acceptance of one of them will influence the acceptance of others. Such interdependencies among proposals occur for a variety of reasons. First, if the proposals contained in the set being considered are related so that the acceptance of one proposal from the set precludes the acceptance of any of the others, the proposals are said to be *mutually exclusive*. Mutually exclusive proposals usually exist when a decision has been made to fulfill a need and there are a number of proposals, each of which will satisfy that need.

Another type of relationship between proposals arises from the fact that once some initial project is undertaken, a number of other auxiliary activities become necessary or feasible as a result of the initial action. Such auxiliary activities are called *contingent* proposals. For example, the purchase of computer software is contingent on the purchase of computer hardware. The construction of a building is contingent on the construction of the foundation. A contingent relationship is a one-way dependency between proposals. That is, the acceptance of a contingent proposal is dependent on the acceptance of some prerequisite proposal, but the acceptance of the prerequisite proposal is independent of the contingent proposals.

When there are limitations on the amount of money available for investment and the first cost of all the proposals exceeds the money available, *financial interdependencies* are introduced. These interdependencies are usually complex and they will occur whether the proposals are independent, mutually exclusive, or contingent.

Essential Proposals

Certain activities or projects may be mandated by circumstances beyond control of the organization. Others may be within control of the firm, but are to be funded due to their extraordinary attractiveness. In either case, proposals in the essential category must be funded. Accordingly, such proposals are to be included among the final decision options.

4.3 FORMING MUTUALLY EXCLUSIVE ALTERNATIVES  either, or

Proposals can be independent, mutually exclusive, contingent, or essential, and additional interdependencies between them can exist if there is a limited amount of investment capital. To devise special rules to include each of these different relationships in a decision situation would lead to a complicated procedure that is difficult to apply.

To provide a simple method of handling various types of proposals, and insight into formulations of the decision problem, a general approach will be presented. This approach requires that all proposals be arranged so that the selection decision involves only the consideration of cash flows for mutually exclusive alternatives.

A general procedure for forming exclusive alternatives from a given set of proposals is based on an enumeration of all possible combinations of the proposals. For example, if two proposals (P_1 and P_2) are being considered, four mutually exclusive investment alternatives exist, as shown in Table 4.2.[1]

Generalization of the foregoing procedure for k proposals, $k = 1, 2, 3, \ldots$, leads to a number of alternatives, A, given by

$$A = 2^k$$

A 0–1 matrix exhibiting all possible alternatives can now be developed. Let $1, 2, 3, \ldots, k-1, k$ designate columns (proposals) from left to right. Start with all zeros for do nothing in row A_0. Then, alternate zeros and ones in each column at every 2^{k-1} rows as shown in Table 4.3.

TABLE 4.2 Forming Investment Alternatives from Proposals

Alternative	Proposal		Decision
	P_1	P_2	
A_0	0	0	Do nothing
A_1	1	0	Accept P_1
A_2	0	1	Accept P_2
A_3	1	1	Accept P_1 and P_2

[1] A binary variable, $X_j = 0$ or 1, is used to indicate proposal acceptance or rejection.

TABLE 4.3 General 0–1 Matrix of Investment Alternatives

Investment Alternative	Proposal					
	P_1	P_2	P_3	$\cdots$	P_{k-1}	P_k
A_0	0	0	0	$\cdots$	0	0
A_1	1	0	0		0	0
A_2	0	1	0		0	0
A_3	1	1	0		0	0
A_4	0	0	1		0	0
A_5	1	0	1		0	0
$\vdots$	$\vdots$					$\vdots$
$A_2{}^k - 2$	0	1	1		1	1
$A_2{}^k - 1$	1	1	1	$\cdots$	1	1

The approach just presented makes possible the consideration of a variety of proposal relationships in a single form: the mutually exclusive alternative. Accordingly, any decision criteria used to make decisions about mutually exclusive alternatives can also accommodate proposals that are independent, mutually exclusive, contingent, or essential if the proposals are arranged into mutually exclusive alternatives. In addition, the imposition of a budget constraint can easily be incorporated into the decision process.

As an example application, suppose that four proposals are being considered with money flows over a 10-year planning horizon as shown in Table 4.4. Proposals P_1 and P_3 are mutually exclusive, proposal P_4 is contingent on proposal P_1, and proposal P_2 is contingent on proposal P_3. The budget limit is $100,000.

With four proposals in Table 4.4, it is clear that there are 2^4 or 16 possible mutually exclusive investment alternatives to consider. These alternatives are enumerated by following the procedure in Table 4.2. Table 4.5 is the result.

Next, the feasibility of each mutually exclusive alternative must be tested. The tests to be applied derive from dependencies among the proposals. First, composite money flows are calculated for each alternative from the

TABLE 4.4 Money Flows for Four Proposals (Thousands)

Money Flow	Proposal			
	P_1	P_2	P_3	P_4
Initial investment	$-30	$-25	$-85	$-70
Net annual savings	9	7	21	14
Salvage value	4	3	10	6

TABLE 4.5   Matrix of Investment Alternatives for Four Proposals

Investment Alternative	Proposal			
	P_1	P_2	P_3	P_4
A_0	0	0	0	0
A_1	1	0	0	0
A_2	0	1	0	0
A_3	1	1	0	0
A_4	0	0	1	0
A_5	1	0	1	0
A_6	0	1	1	0
A_7	1	1	1	0
A_8	0	0	0	1
A_9	1	0	0	1
A_{10}	0	1	0	1
A_{11}	1	1	0	1
A_{12}	0	0	1	1
A_{13}	1	0	1	1
A_{14}	0	1	1	1
A_{15}	1	1	1	1

TABLE 4.6   Composite Money Flows (Thousands)

Investment Alternative	Initial Investment	Net Annual Benefit	Salvage Value
A_0	$ 0	$ 0	$ 0
A_1	30	9	4
A_2	25	7	3
A_3	55	16	7
A_4	85	21	10
A_5	115	30	14
A_6	110	28	13
A_7	140	37	17
A_8	70	14	6
A_9	100	23	10
A_{10}	95	21	9
A_{11}	125	30	13
A_{12}	155	35	16
A_{13}	185	44	20
A_{14}	180	42	19
A_{15}	210	51	23

money flows in Table 4.4 and the involved proposals exhibited in Table 4.5. These composite money flows are shown in Table 4.6.

Infeasible alternatives are identified and eliminated from further consideration. Table 4.7 summarizes the results from a search for infeasible alternatives. Remaining are investment alternatives A_0, A_1, A_4, and A_9, all of which

TABLE 4.7 Identifying Infeasible Alternatives

Investment Alternative	Alternative Feasible?	Reasons for Infeasibility
A_0	Yes	
A_1	Yes	
A_2	No	P_2 contingent on P_3
A_3	No	P_2 contingent on P_3
A_4	Yes	
A_5	No	Budget constraint and P_1 and P_3 mutually exclusive
A_6	No	Budget constraint
A_7	No	Budget constraint and P_1 and P_3 mutually exclusive
A_8	No	P_4 contingent on P_1
A_9	Yes	
A_{10}	No	P_2 contingent on P_3 and P_4 contingent on P_1
A_{11}	No	Budget constraint and P_2 contingent on P_3
A_{12}	No	Budget constraint and P_4 contingent on P_1
A_{13}	No	Budget constraint and P_1 and P_3 mutually exclusive
A_{14}	No	Budget constraint and P_4 contingent on P_1
A_{15}	No	Budget constraint and P_1 and P_3 mutually exclusive

TABLE 4.8 Money Flows Representing Four Mutually Exclusive Alternatives (Thousands)

End of Year	Alternative			
	A_0	A_1	A_4	A_9
0	0	$-30	$-85	$-100
1–10	0	9	21	23
10	0	4	10	10

are feasible and mutually exclusive. These are summarized in Table 4.8 in terms of their money flows. Methods for selecting the best from among these are presented in subsequent sections.

4.4 COMPARISONS BASED ON TOTAL INVESTMENT

Comparisons based on present equivalent, annual equivalent, and future equivalent on total investment approaches are presented in this section. Although computationally different, comparisons based on total investment will select the most desirable mutually exclusive alternative. The mutually exclusive alternatives given in Table 4.8 will be compared as an illustration of the total investment approach using a MARR = 15%.

Present Equivalent on Total Investment[2]

The present equivalent on total investment criterion is one of the most frequently used methods for selecting an investment alternative from a set of mutually exclusive alternatives. The stated objective is to choose the alternative with the maximum present equivalent amount.

Calculation of the present equivalent amount follows the form given in Equation 3.24 or Equation 3.25. For each alternative, the present equivalent amount is found as follows:

$$PE(15)_{A_0} = \$0$$

$$PE(15)_{A_1} = \$-30 + \$9(\overset{P/A,\,15,\,10}{5.0188}) + \$4(\overset{P/F,\,15,\,10}{0.2472}) = \$16.16$$

$$PE(15)_{A_4} = \$-85 + \$21(\overset{P/A,\,15,\,10}{5.0188}) + \$10(\overset{P/F,\,15,\,10}{0.2472}) = \$22.87$$

$$PE(15)_{A_9} = \$-100 + \$23(\overset{P/A,\,15,\,10}{5.0188}) + \$10(\overset{P/F,\,15,\,10}{0.2472}) = \$17.90$$

The maximum value of the present equivalent amounts for these four alternatives is $22,870, occurring for alternative A_4. It is possible for alternatives with smaller first costs to have present equivalent amounts greater than those with a larger first cost. For example, alternative A_4 has a larger present amount than A_9 even though it requires less initial outlay.

Annual and Future Equivalent on Total Investment

Chapter 3 demonstrated that the present equivalent, annual equivalent, and future equivalent amounts are consistent approaches for comparing alternatives. If either the annual equivalent amount or the future equivalent amount is substituted for the present equivalent amount as the basis for comparison under this criterion, the same conclusion will be reached. By applying the annual equivalent on total investment criterion or the future equivalent on total investment criterion to the alternatives in Table 4.8, alternative A_4 is selected. This is shown by the following computations based on Equation 3.26 or Equation 3.27:

$$AE(15)_{A_0} = \$0$$

---

[2] It may appear that the present equivalent on total investment approach violates the basic decision rule that considers the differences between alternatives (see Section 4.1). The fact that such differences are reflected in the comparison of the present equivalent amounts on total investment is demonstrated in G. J. Thuesen and W. J. Fabrycky, *Engineering Economy,* 7th ed. (Englewood Cliffs, NJ: Prentice-Hall, Inc., 1989).

$$\text{AE}(15)_{A_1} = \$-30(\ \overset{A/P,\,15,\,10}{0.1993}\ ) + \$9 + \$4(\ \overset{A/F,\,15,\,10}{0.0493}\ ) = \$3.22$$

$$\text{AE}(15)_{A_4} = \$-85(\ \overset{A/P,\,15,\,10}{0.1993}\ ) + \$21 + \$10(\ \overset{A/F,\,15,\,10}{0.0493}\ ) = \$4.55$$

$$\text{AE}(15)_{A_9} = \$-100(\ \overset{A/P,\,15,\,10}{0.1993}\ ) + \$23 + \$10(\ \overset{A/F,\,15,\,10}{0.0493}\ ) = \$3.56$$

For the future equivalent approach, Equation (3.28) or Equation (3.30) is used as follows:

$$\text{FE}(15)_{A_0} = \$0$$

$$\text{FE}(15)_{A_1} = \$-30(\ \overset{F/P,\,15,\,10}{4.046}\ ) + \$9(\ \overset{F/A,\,15,\,10}{20.304}\ ) + \$4 = \$65.36$$

$$\text{FE}(15)_{A_4} = \$-85(\ \overset{F/P,\,15,\,10}{4.046}\ ) + \$21(\ \overset{F/A,\,15,\,10}{20.304}\ ) + \$10 = \$92.47$$

$$\text{FE}(15)_{A_9} = \$-100(\ \overset{F/P,\,15,\,10}{4.046}\ ) + \$23(\ \overset{F/A,\,15,\,10}{20.304}\ ) + \$10 = \$72.39$$

An examination of the calculations for the future equivalent amounts indicates that the receipts from the activity are actually invested at the minimum attractive rate of return from the time they are received to the end of the life of the project. Thus future equivalent calculations explicitly consider the investment or *reinvestment* of the future receipts generated by investment alternatives. The three decision criteria presented (PE, AE, or FE) are consistent and lead to the same selection of alternatives. It follows that use of the present equivalent amount and the annual equivalent amount implicitly assumes the investment or reinvestment of receipts at the MARR.

4.5 PRESENT EQUIVALENT ON INCREMENTAL INVESTMENT

Differences between mutually exclusive alternatives are the basis for decision making. The present equivalent on incremental investment approach provides an example, since it requires that the incremental differences between alternative money flows actually be calculated.

To compare one alternative to another, first determine the money flow representing the difference between the alternatives. Then the decision to select a particular alternative rests on the determination of the economic desirability of the additional increment of investment required by one alternative over the other. The incremental investment is considered to be desirable if it yields a return that exceeds the MARR. If

$$\text{PE}(i)_{A_2 - A_1} > 0: \quad \text{accept } A_2$$

$$PE(i)_{A_2 - A_1} < 0: \quad \text{reject } A_2 \text{ and retain } A_1$$

To apply this decision criterion to a set of mutually exclusive alternatives, such as shown in Table 4.8, proceed as follows:

1. List the alternatives in ascending order based on their initial investments. This is already done in Table 4.8.
2. Select as the initial *current best* the alternative that requires the smallest investment. In most cases, the initial current best will be the do-nothing alternative, as in this example.
3. Compare the initial current best alternative and the first *challenger*. The challenger is always the alternative with the next higher initial investment that has not been compared previously. The comparison is made by examining the differences between the two money flows. If the present equivalent amount of the incremental flow evaluated at the MARR is greater than zero, the challenger becomes the new current best. If the present equivalent is less than or equal to zero, the current best alternative remains unchanged and the challenger is eliminated from consideration. The new challenger is the next alternative in order of ascending first cost that has not been a challenger previously. Then the next comparison is made between the alternative that is the current best and the alternative that is currently the challenger.
4. Repeat the comparisons of the challengers to the current best alternative as described in step 3. These comparisons are continued until all alternatives are exhausted. The alternative that emerges as the final current best will be the alternative that maximizes the present equivalent amount and provides a rate of return exceeding the MARR.

Steps 3 and 4 lead to the following calculations for the alternatives being considered in Table 4.8. Assume that the MARR is 15%.

The first comparison to be made in this example is between alternative A_1 (the first challenger) and the do-nothing alternative (the initial current best alternative). The subscript notation in $PE(15)_{A_1 - A_0}$ indicates that the present equivalent amount is for the money flow representing the difference between alternative A_1 and do nothing.[3]

$$PE(15)_{A_1 - A_0} = \$-30 + \$9(\overset{P/A, 15, 10}{5.0188}) + \$4(\overset{P/F, 15, 10}{0.2472}) = \$16.16$$

Because the present equivalent amount of the differences between the cash flows is greater than zero (it is \$16.16), alternative A_1 becomes the cur-

---

[3] When comparing an alternative to the do-nothing alternative, the money flow representing the incremental investment is the same as the money flow on the total investment.

rent best. The second challenger is A_4. Next, alternative A_4 (second challenger) is compared to A_1 on an incremental basis as follows:

$$\text{PE}(15)_{A_4 - A_1} = \$-55 + \$12(\overset{P/A,\,15,\,10}{5.0188}) + \$6(\overset{P/F,\,15,\,10}{0.2472}) = \$6.71$$

Since this value is positive (\$6.71), alternative A_4 becomes the new current best. The third challenger is alternative A_9. Comparing the current best with alternative A_9 yields

$$\text{PE}(15)_{A_9 - A_4} = \$-15 + \$2(\overset{P/A,\,15,\,10}{5.0188}) + \$0(\overset{P/F,\,15,\,10}{0.2472}) = \$-4.96$$

The present equivalent on the additional investment required by alternative A_9 over A_4 is negative. Therefore, that increment is economically undesirable. Thus A_4 remains the current best alternative. The list of alternatives has been exhausted so that there is no new challenger. Therefore, according to step 4, when all challengers have been considered, the current best alternative is the one that maximizes the present equivalent amount and provides a return greater than the MARR. It follows that alternative A_4 is the best selection from the set of alternatives in Table 4.8.

Substitution of the annual equivalent amount or the future equivalent amount for the present equivalent amount as the basis for comparison by incremental decision making will give consistent results. This consistency is expected in accordance with the presentation in Chapter 3.

4.6 RATE OF RETURN ON INCREMENTAL INVESTMENT

Rate of return on incremental investment is a procedure based on the same concept of incremental analysis as was applied in Section 4.5. After the alternatives are arranged in order of increasing first cost, the incremental money flows are determined by the procedure described for present equivalent on incremental investment. The only difference in the decision rules for these two criteria is in step 3, which determines whether an increment of investment is economically desirable. The decision rule for the rate of return on incremental investment approach is

$$i^*_{A_2 - A_1} > \text{MARR:} \quad \text{accept } A_2$$

$$i^*_{A_2 - A_1} \leq \text{MARR:} \quad \text{reject } A_2 \text{ and retain } A_1$$

To apply rate-of-return analysis on an incremental basis, it is first necessary to rank the alternatives by increasing first cost and then to select the initial current best alternative. For the set of alternatives in Table 4.8, steps 3 and 4 of the incremental analysis procedure require the following calculations. Find the value i^* so that the equation representing the present equivalent of the incremental money flow is set equal to zero. For increment A_1-A_0 and MARR $= 15\%$,

$$0 = \$ - 30 + \$9(\overset{P/A,\, i,\, 10}{\quad}) + \$4(\overset{P/F,\, i,\, 10}{\quad})$$

$$i^*_{A_1 - A_0} = 27.88\%$$

Since the rate of return on the increment is greater than the MARR, alternative A_1 becomes the initial "current best" and the do-nothing alternative is dropped from further consideration. Next, compare alternative A_4 to alternative A_1. For the increment A_4-A_1 and MARR $= 15\%$,

$$0 = \$ - 55 + \$12(\overset{P/A,\, i,\, 10}{\quad}) + \$6(\overset{P/F,\, i,\, 10}{\quad})$$

$$i^*_{A_4 - A_1} = 18.04\%$$

Again, the rate of return of this increment is greater than the MARR. Alternative A_4 becomes the current best and A_1 is rejected. Next, compare A_9 to A_4, the current best alternative. For increment A_9-A_4 and MARR $= 15\%$,

$$0 = \$ - 15 + \$2(\overset{P/A,\, i,\, 10}{\quad}) + 0$$

$$i^*_{A_9 - A_4} = 5.61\%$$

Since i^* is less than the MARR, alternative A_4 remains the current best and A_9 is removed from consideration. All the alternatives have now been compared, and A_4 (the last current best alternative) is the best choice. This is the same as found by the present equivalent on incremental investment approach in Section 4.5.

4.7 ALTERNATIVES WITH UNEQUAL LIVES

Prior examples have demonstrated the application of various decision criteria for alternatives that have equal lives. It is often required that alternatives having unequal service lives be compared. In these situations it is necessary to make certain assumptions about the service life cycle so that the techniques of decision making just discussed can be applied.

The principle that all alternatives under consideration must be compared over the same time interval is basic to sound decision making. Despite the existence of unequal lives, the time spans over which alternatives are considered must be equal. The effect of undertaking one alternative can be considered identical to the effect of undertaking any of the others when the same time interval is used.

The time interval over which alternatives are to be compared is usually referred to as the *study period* or planning horizon. This study period, denoted by n^*, may be set by policy, or it may be determined by the time span over which reasonably accurate money flow estimates can be made. Also, the life cycles of the alternatives being studied can be a basis for determining the study period. For example, the study period might be the life of the shortest-lived alternative or perhaps the life of the longest-lived alternative.

An alternative may have a life shorter than, equal to, or greater than the study period selected. Differing assumptions can be imposed to deal with each situation. These are:

1. *Alternative's life equal to study period.* No adjustment to the money flow is required. When all alternatives being compared have equal lives, the analysis follows the examples presented in Sections 4.4 through 4.6.
2. *Alternative's life longer than study period.* When the life of an alternative extends beyond the study period, there is some remaining value at the end of the study period and adjustments must be made.
3. *Alternative's life shorter than study period.* When the life of an alternative is shorter than the study period, some assumptions must be made about what is to occur during the "gap" in service.

No problems exist in dealing with situation 1 above. For situations 2 and 3, several approaches are available. Foremost among these are adjustments to salvage values and the assumption that short-lived assets can be replicated so as to achieve a least common multiple of lives.[4]

QUESTIONS AND PROBLEMS

1. A firm is considering proposals 1, 2, and 3, one of which must be adopted. Proposal 1 is contingent on proposal 2, and proposals 2 and 3 are mutually exclusive.
   (a) List all mutually exclusive investment alternatives.
   (b) Designate alternatives as feasible or infeasible, giving all reasons for infeasibility.
2. Engineering projects 1, 2, and 3 with lives of six years are being considered with money flows (in thousands) estimated to be

	Project 1	Project 2	Project 3
Investment	$500	$600	$700
Annual revenue	$300	$400	$450
Annual cost	$150	$180	$200
Salvage value	$60	$80	$100

---

[4] A complete treatment of the unequal life problem may be found in G. J. Thuesen and W. J. Fabrycky, *Engineering Economy*, 7th ed. (Englewood Cliffs, NJ: Prentice-Hall, Inc., 1989).

Projects 1 and 2 are mutually exclusive and project 3 is contingent on project 2.
The budget limit is $1,100,000.
(a) Develop the matrix of investment alternatives.
(b) Indicate which alternatives are not feasible and give reasons for infeasibility.
(c) Develop the composite money flows for feasible investment alternatives.

3. A company is considering engineering proposals 1, 2, and 3, with eight year lives
and money flows estimated to be

	Proposal		
	P1	P2	P3
Investment	$800,000	$600,000	$400,000
Annual revenue	$450,000	$400,000	$300,000
Annual cost	$200,000	$180,000	$150,000
Salvage value	$100,000	$80,000	$60,000

Proposals 1 and 2 are mutually exclusive and proposal 3 is contingent on proposal
2. The budget limit is $1,200,000.
(a) Develop the matrix of investment alternatives, indicate which ones are not
feasible, and give reasons for the infeasibility.
(b) Develop the composite money flows for feasible alternatives.
(c) Use the present equivalent on total investment approach to find the best
alternative if the interest rate is 15%.

4. Two mutually exclusive alternatives have money flows described as follows:

	Year			
Alternative	0	1	2	3
A	$−10,000	$5,000	$5,000	$5,000
B	−12,000	6,000	6,000	6,000

For a MARR of 20%:
(a) Determine the present equivalent on incremental investment.
(b) Determine the rate of return on incremental investment.

5. Of the three investment alternative that follow, only one can be selected. Find the
range of values of the MARR for which each of the alternatives is best. Use the
incremental rate-of-return method.

	Year				
Alternative	0	1	2	3	4
A_1	$−1,500	$ 900	$ 900	$ 900	$ 900
A_2	−3,400	1,550	1,550	1,550	1,550
A_3	−9,800	3,500	3,500	3,500	3,500

6. The following mutually exclusive alternatives were found to be feasible from a set of proposals. All money flows are in thousands.

| | End of Year: | | |
Alternative	0	1–6	6
A_0	$ 0	$ 0	$ 0
A_1	−600	220	80
A_2	−500	150	60

For a MARR of 13%, find:
(a) PE on total investment.
(b) AE on total investment.
(c) FE on total investment.

7. Five improvement alternatives are being considered for a highway. Listed below are the estimated construction costs, maintenance costs, and the user cost associated with each improvement alternative.

Alternative	Construction Costs per Mile	Annual Maintenance Costs per Mile	Annual Users Cost per Mile
A_1	$1,500,000	$9,800	$450,000
A_2	1,875,000	8,700	427,000
A_3	2,100,000	8,000	400,000
A_4	2,250,000	6,600	370,500
A_5	2,437,500	6,400	356,000

The life of the improvement is expected to be 25 years with no salvage value. If the cost of money is 10%, which highway improvement is most desirable?
(a) Solve using incremental analysis.
(b) Solve using total investment analysis.
(c) If the estimated costs are in constant dollars and the annual inflation rate is 8%, which improvement is favored?

8. A firm has identified three mutually exclusive investment alternatives. The life of all three is estimated to be five years with negligible salvage value. The MARR is 8%.

| | Alternative | | |
	A_1	A_2	A_3
Investment	$10,000	$14,000	$17,000
Annual net income	2,600	3,880	4,600
Return on total investment	10%	12%	11%

Find the alternative that should be selected by:
(a) Rate of return on incremental investment.
(b) Present equivalent on incremental investment.

9. A company is considering the purchase of one of two new systems. The data on each are given below.

	Machine A	Machine B
Initial cost	$3,400,000	$6,500,000
Service life	3 years	6 years
Salvage value	$100,000	$500,000
Net annual operating cost	$2,000,000	$1,800,000

If the MARR is 12%, which alternative should be selected using:
(a) Present equivalent comparison.
(b) Annual equivalent comparison.
(c) Incremental rate-of-return comparison.

10. The following table gives the receipts and disbursements for a project. Determine the desirability of the project for a 14% interest rate based on the present equivalent comparison and the annual equivalent comparison.

End of Year:	Receipts	Disbursements
0	$ 0	$1,500
1	600	0
2	500	400
3	500	0
4	1,200	100

11. A new automatic controller can be installed for $30,000 and will have a $3,000 salvage value after 10 years. This controller is expected to decrease operating cost by $4,000 per year.
(a) What rate of return is expected if the controller is used for 10 years?
(b) For what life will the controller give a return of 15%?

12. An office building and its equipment are insured to $7,000,000. The present annual insurance premium is $0.85 per $100 of coverage. A sprinkler system with an estimated life of 20 years and no salvage value can be installed for $180,000. Annual maintenance and operating cost is estimated to be $3,800. The premium will be reduced to $0.40 per $100 coverage if the sprinkler system is installed.
(a) Find the rate of return if the sprinkler system is installed.
(b) With a MARR of 12%, find the payout period for the sprinkler system.

13. Engineering proposals A, B, C, and D are being considered with money flows (in thousands) over 10 years as follows:

	Proposal			
	A	B	C	D
Investment	$46	$6	$82	$64
Net Annual Benefit	8	6	18	16
Salvage Value	3	2	7	6

Proposals B and D are mutually exclusive, proposal C depends on D, and proposal A depends on B. The budget limit is $100,000. Which proposals should be pursued? Use the incremental present equivalent approach and the incremental rate of return approach. The MARR is 12%.

$$5$$

Decision Evaluation Theory

In this final chapter of Part I (Concepts and Theory), a formal structure for decision evaluation is developed. This structure originates with the life-cycle concepts and process presented in Chapter 1, incorporates the cost concepts discussed in Chapter 2, integrates equivalence of money flows as derived in Chapter 3, and explicitly recognizes mutually exclusive alternatives as defined in Chapter 4. Specific topics presented are the general economic equivalence function, the economic optimization function, the decision evaluation matrix, decisions under certainty, risk, and uncertainty, and evaluating multiple criteria. These topics provide a foundation for the methodology and applications to be covered in Parts II and III.[1]

5.1 EVALUATION BY ECONOMIC EQUIVALENCE

Section 3.3 presented algebraic expressions for the present equivalent, annual equivalent, and the future equivalent amounts as well as expressions for the internal rate of return and the payback period. A general economic equivalence function subsuming each of these equivalence approaches may be

---

[1] Specific examples to help with a complete understanding of the theoretical aspects of this chapter are presented in Part II. More comprehensive examples are presented as case studies in Part III.

stated as

$$\text{PE, AE, or FE} = f(F_t, i, n) \tag{5.1}$$

where $t = 0, 1, 2, \ldots, n$ and where

> F_t = positive or negative money flow at the end of year t
> i = annual rate of interest
> n = number of years

The product life cycle is the underlying money flow generator over its acquisition and utilization phases as shown for a hypothetical situation in Figure 5.1 (also refer to Figure 1.2). For acquisition by purchase (Figure 5.1a), the mapping of the general equivalence function over the life cycle is simple. Here acquisition occurs instantaneously, with F_0 as the first cost or initial investment (designated P in Chapter 3). Net benefits or revenues in this example occur at the end of each year for eight years; F_1 through F_8. Salvage value or cost, if any, is included in F_8.

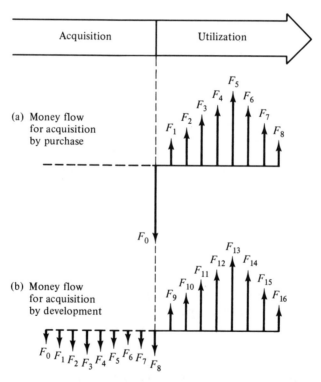

Figure 5.1   Money flows for two modes of acquisition/utilization.

When acquisition requires expenditures for design and development (Figure 5.1b), mapping of the general equivalence function over the life cycle is more complex. Here acquisition spans a number of years, with expenditures composed of F_0 through F_8 (F_1 through F_3 for conceptual and preliminary design, F_4 through F_6 for detail design and development, and F_7 through F_8 for production and/or construction). Net benefits or revenues occur at the end of each year for eight years; F_9 through F_{16}. Salvage value or cost, if any, is included in F_{16}.

The present equivalent, annual equivalent, and future equivalent amounts were shown to be consistent bases for the evaluation of a single alternative, or for the comparison of mutually exclusive alternatives. Any one of these may be used in accordance with the general economic equivalence function of Equation 5.1. Additionally, Equation 5.1 provides a general structure for evaluation by the internal rate of return or payout period approaches. Chapters 3 and 4 provided the needed analytical foundation for decision evaluation in accordance with Equation 5.1.

5.2 THE ECONOMIC OPTIMIZATION FUNCTION

Decision evaluation often requires the determination of both economic equivalence and economic optimization. When investment cost, periodic costs, and/or project life is a function of one or more decision variables, it is important to optimize over these variables as a prerequisite to the determination of economic equivalence. This optimization is linked to decision evaluation through one or more money flows, which, in turn, are used in calculating a measure of economic equivalence. Optimization requires that an evaluation measure be derived from an economic optimization function.

An economic optimization function is a mathematical model formally linking an evaluation measure, E, with controllable decision variables, X, and system parameters, Y, which cannot be controlled by the decision maker. It provides a means for testing decision variables in the presence of system parameters. This test is an indirect experiment performed mathematically, which results in an optimized value for E. The functional relationship, in its unconstrained form, may be expressed as[2]

$$E = f(X, Y) \tag{5.2}$$

As an example of the optimization function structure for an unconstrained decision situation, consider the determination of an optimal procurement quantity for inventory operations. Here the evaluation measure is cost,

---

[2] Only unconstrained forms of the optimization function are presented in this book. For the theory and applications of the constrained function, see B. S. Blanchard and W. J. Fabrycky, *Systems Engineering and Analysis*, 2nd ed. (Englewood Cliffs, NJ: Prentice-Hall, Inc., 1990).

and the objective is to choose a procurement quantity in the face of demand, procurement cost, and holding cost, so that total cost is minimized. The procurement quantity is the variable directly under the control of the decision maker. Demand, procurement cost, and holding cost are not directly under his or her control. Use of the optimization function allows the decision maker to arrive at a value for the variable under his or her control that trades-off conflicting cost elements.

The optimization function may be extended to operational and design decisions involving alternatives. This extension involves the identification and isolation of decision-dependent system parameters, Y_d, from decision-independent system parameters, Y_i. Accordingly, Equation 5.2 can be restated in unconstrained form as

$$E = f(X, Y_d, Y_i) \qquad (5.3)$$

As an example of the application of this version of the decision evaluation function, consider the establishment of a procurement and inventory system to meet the demand for an item that is available from one of several sources. Decision variables are the procurement level and the procurement quantity. For each source under consideration there exists a set of source-dependent parameters. These are the item cost per unit, the procurement cost per procurement, the replenishment rate, and the procurement lead time. Uncontrollable (source independent) system parameters include the demand rate, the holding cost per unit per period, and the shortage penalty cost. The objective is to determine the procurement level, and procurement quantity, and the procurement source so that total system cost will be minimized.

In design decision making, consider the deployment of a population of repairable equipment units to meet a demand. Three decision variables may be identified: the number of units to deploy, the number of maintenance channels to provide, and the age at which units should be retired. Controllable system parameters include the reliability, maintainability, energy efficiency, and design life. Uncontrollable system parameters include the cost of energy, the time value of money, and the penalty cost incurred when there are insufficient units operational to meet demand. Since the controllable parameters are design dependent, the objective is to develop design alternatives in the face of decision variables so that the design alternative that will minimize total system cost can be identified.

5.3 THE DECISION EVALUATION MATRIX

A particular decision can result in one of several outcomes, depending on which of several future events takes place. For example, a decision to go sailing can result in a high degree of satisfaction if the day turns out to be sunny, or in a low degree of satisfaction if it rains. These levels of satisfaction would be reversed if the decision were made to stay home. Thus for the two states of nature, sun and rain, there are different payoffs depending on the alternative chosen.

A decision evaluation matrix is a formal way of exhibiting the interaction of a finite set of alternatives and a finite set of possible futures (or states of nature). In this usage, alternatives are different courses of action from which a decision maker expects to choose. The states of nature are normally not natural events such as sun, rain, or snow, but are a wide variety of future outcomes over which the decision maker has no direct control.

The general decision evaluation matrix is a model depicting the positive and negative results that will occur for each alternative under each possible future. In abstract form, this model is structured as shown in Figure 5.2. Its symbols are defined as follows:

A_i = alternative available for selection by the decision maker, where $i = 1, 2, \ldots, m$

F_j = a future not under control of the decision maker, where $j = 1, 2, \ldots, n$

P_j = probability that the jth future will occur, where $j = 1, 2, \ldots, n$

E_{ij} = evaluation measure (positive or negative) associated with the ith alternative and the jth future.[3]

Several assumptions underlie the application of this decision evaluation matrix to decision making under assumed certainty, risk, and uncertainty. Foremost among these is the presumption that all feasible alternatives have been considered and all possible futures have been identified. Alternatives not considered cannot be adopted, no matter how desirable they may prove to be. Possible futures not identified can significantly affect the actual outcome relative to the planned outcome.

A_i \ F_j	F_1	F_2	$\cdots$	F_n
A_1	E_{11}	E_{12}	$\cdots$	E_{1n}
A_2	E_{21}	E_{22}	$\cdots$	E_{2n}
.	.	.		.
.	.	.		.
.	.	.		.
A_m	E_{m1}	E_{m2}	$\cdots$	E_{mn}

Figure 5.2 Decision evaluation matrix.

[3]The evaluation measure placed in each cell of the decision evaluation matrix may be a present equivalent, annual equivalent, or future equivalent amount determined from Equation 5.1 or it may be an optimized evaluation measure determined from Equation 5.3.

Evaluation measures in the matrix model are associated with outcomes that may be either objective or subjective. The most common case is one in which the outcome values are objective and therefore subject to quantitative expression in cardinal form. For example, the payoffs may be profits expressed in dollars, yield expressed in pounds, costs (negative payoffs) expressed in dollars, or other desirable or undesirable measures. Subjective outcomes, on the other hand, are those that are valued on an ordinal or ranking scale. Examples are expressions of preference, such as a good corporate image being preferred to a poor image, higher-quality outputs being preferred to those of lower quality, and so on.

Other assumptions of importance in the evaluation matrix representation of decisions are:

1. The occurrence of one future precludes the occurrence of any other future (futures are mutually exclusive).
2. The occurrence of a specific future is not influenced by the alternative selected.
3. The occurrence of a specific future is not known with certainty, even though certainty is often assumed for analysis purposes.

5.4 DECISIONS UNDER CERTAINTY[4]

In dealing with physical aspects of the environment, physical scientists and engineers have a body of systematic knowledge and physical laws on which to base their reasoning. Such laws as Boyle's law, Ohm's law, and Newton's law of motion were developed primarily by collecting and comparing many comparable instances and by the use of an inductive process. These laws may then be applied with a high degree of certainty to specific instances. They are supplemented by many models for physical phenomena that enable conclusions to be reached about the physical environment that match the facts with narrow limits. Much is known with certainty about the physical environment.

Much less, particularly of a quantitative nature, is known about the environment within which operational decisions are made. Nonetheless, the primary aim of life-cycle economic analysis is to bring a rational approach to bear to the maximum feasible extent. This is done with the aid of conceptual simplifications and models of reality, the most common being the assumption of a single known future. It is not claimed that knowledge about the future is in hand. Rather, the suppression of risk and uncertainty is one of the ways in which the scientific approach simplifies reality in order to gain insight. Such

[4] Certainty is often assumed in decision making as a simplification of reality. The treatment of risk and uncertainty is usually required.

insight can assist greatly in decision making, provided that its shortcomings are recognized and accommodated.

The evaluation matrix for decision making under assumed certainty is not a matrix at all. It is a vector with as many evaluations as there are alternatives, with the outcomes constituting a single column. This decision vector is a special case of the matrix of Figure 5.2. It appears as in Figure 5.3, with the payoffs represented by E_i, where $i = 1, 2, \ldots, m$. The single future, which is assumed to occur with certainty, actually carries a probability of unity $(P = 1.0)$ in the matrix. All other futures are suppressed by carrying probabilities of zero $(P = 0.0)$.

When the outcomes, E_i, are stated in monetary terms (cost or profit), the decision rule or principle of choice is quite simple. If the alternatives are equal in all other respects, one would choose the alternative that minimizes cost or maximizes profit. In the case of cost, choose

$$\min_{i}\{E_i\} \qquad \text{for } i = 1, 2, \ldots, m \qquad (5.4)$$

For profit, choose

$$\max_{i}\{E_i\} \qquad \text{for } i = 1, 2, \ldots, m \qquad (5.5)$$

It is often not possible to accept the premise that only the cost or the profit differences are important, with intangibles and irreducibles have little or no effect. Unquantifiable nonmonetary factors may be significant enough to outweigh calculated costs of profit differences among alternatives. In other cases, the outcome is not easily expressed in monetary terms, or even in quantitative terms of some other evaluation measure, such as time, percent of market, and so on. Valid qualitative comparisons may be made when the quantitative outcomes cannot stand alone and/or when the outcomes are nonquantitative.

The use of outcomes scales often makes possible a somewhat rational choice from among a number of nonquantifiable alternatives, each with an outcome rating determined by expert opinion, estimation, history, or other means. Foremost among these are ordinal comparisons. Where intangibles and irreducibles are significant, ranking each outcome above or below every other outcome leads to a preferred choice. To do this, each outcome can be

A_i	F_j	F
A_1		E_1
A_2		E_2
.		.
.		.
A_m		E_m

Figure 5.3 Decision evaluation vector.

compared to a common standard, or the outcome can be paired and compared. As an example of the paired approach, suppose that four alternatives
are assumed to lead (with certainty) to four outcomes E_1, E_2, E_3, E_4. Suppose
further that the six possible pairs are arranged according to preference as
follows:[5]

$$E_1 > E_3 \qquad E_2 > E_3 \qquad E_2 > E_1$$
$$E_2 > E_4 \qquad E_3 > E_4 \qquad E_1 > E_4$$

In these comparisons, E_2 is preferred three times: E_1 twice; E_3 once; and E_4
not at all. Accordingly, the preference ranking is

$$E_2 > E_1 > E_3 > E_4$$

5.5 DECISIONS UNDER RISK

There is usually little assurance that predicted futures will coincide with actual
futures. The physical and economic elements on which a course of action depends may vary from their estimated values because of chance causes. Not
only are the estimates of future cost problematical, but, in addition, the
anticipated future worth of most ventures is known only with a degree of
assurance. This lack of certainty about the future makes decision making one
of the most challenging tasks faced by individuals, industry, and government.

Decision making under risk occurs when the decision maker does not
suppress acknowledged ignorance about the future, but makes it explicit
through the assignment of probabilities. Such probabilities may be based on
experimental evidence, expert opinion, subjective judgment, or a combination of these.

Consider the following example. A computer and information systems
firm has the opportunity to bid on two related contracts being advertised by
a municipality. The first pertains to the selection and installation of hardware
for a central computing facility together with required software. The second
involves the development of a distributed computing network involving the
selection and installation of hardware and software. The firm may be awarded
either contract C_1 or contract C_2, or both contract C_1 and C_2. Thus there are
three possible futures.

Careful consideration of the possible approaches leads to the identification of five alternatives. The first is for the firm to subcontract the hardware
selection and installation, but to develop the software itself. The second is for
the firm to subcontract the software development, but to select and install the

---

[5]The symbol > is used to indicate that the outcome identified first is preferred to its
counterpart.

hardware itself. The third is for the firm to handle both the hardware and software tasks itself. The fourth is for the firm to bid jointly with a partner firm on both the hardware and software projects. The fifth alternative is for the firm to serve only as project manager, subcontracting all hardware and software tasks.

With the possible futures and various alternatives identified, the next step is to determine profit values. Also to be determined are the probabilities for each of the three futures, where the sum of these probabilities must be unity. Suppose that these determinations lead to the profits and probabilities given in Table 5.1.

Table 5.1 is structured in accordance with the format of the decision evaluation matrix model exhibited in Figure 5.2. It is observed that the firm anticipates a profit of $100,000 if alternative A_1 is chosen and contract C_1 is secured. If contract C_2 is secured, the profit would also be $100,000. However, if both contract C_1 and C_2 are secured, the profit anticipated is $400,000. Similar information is exhibited for the other alternatives, with each row of the matrix representing the outcome expected for each future (column) for a particular alternative.

Before proceeding to the application of criteria for the choice from among alternatives, the decision evaluation matrix should be examined for dominance. Any alternatives that are clearly not preferred, regardless of the future which occurs, may be dropped from consideration. If the outcomes for alternative x are better than the outcomes for alternative y for all possible futures, alternative x is said to *dominate* alternative y, and y can be eliminated as a possible choice.

The computer systems firm, facing the evaluation matrix of Table 5.1, may eliminate A_5 from consideration since it is dominated by all other alternatives. This means that the possible choice of serving only as project manager is inferior to each and every one of the other alternatives, regardless of the way in which the projects are awarded. Therefore, the matrix can be reduced to that given in Table 5.2. The decision criteria in the selections that follow may be used to assist in the selection from among alternatives A_1 through A_4.

TABLE 5.1   Decision Evaluation Matrix (Profit in Thousands)

	Probability: Future:	(0.3) C_1	(0.2) C_2	(0.5) $C_1 + C_2$
	A_1	$ 100	$100	$400
	A_2	− 200	150	600
Alternative	A_3	0	200	500
	A_4	100	300	200
	A_5	− 400	100	200

Aspiration-Level Criterion

Some form of aspiration level exists in most personal and professional decision making. An aspiration level is some desired level of achievement such as profit, or some undesirable result level to be avoided, such as loss. In decision making under risk, the aspiration-level criterion involves selecting some level of achievement that is to be met, followed by a selection of that alternative which maximizes the probability of achieving the stated aspiration level.

The computer systems firm is now at the point of selecting from among alternatives A_1 through A_4, as presented in the reduced matrix of Table 5.2. Under the aspiration level criterion, management must set a minimum aspiration level for profit and possibly a maximum aspiration level of loss. Suppose that the profit level is set to be at least \$400,000 and the loss level is set to be no more than \$100,000. Under these aspiration-level choices, alternatives A_1, A_2, and A_3 qualify as to profit potential, but alternative A_2 fails the loss test and must be eliminated. The choice could now be made between A_1 and A_3 by some other criterion, even though both satisfy the aspiration-level criterion.

Most-Probable-Future Criterion

A basic human tendency is to focus on the most probable outcome from among several that could occur. This approach to decision making suggests that all except the most probable future be disregarded. Although somewhat equivalent to decision making under certainty, this criterion works well when the most probable future has a significantly high probability so as to partially dominate.

Under the most-probable-future criterion, the computer systems firm would focus its selection process from among the four alternatives on the profits associated with the future designated $C_1 + C_2$ (both contracts awarded). This is because the probability of this future occurring is 0.5, the most probable possibility. Alternative A_2 is preferred by this approach.

The most-probable-future criterion could be applied to select between

TABLE 5.2   Reduced Decision Evaluation Matrix (Profit in Thousands)

	Probability: Future:	(0.3) C_1	(0.2) C_2	(0.5) $C_1 + C_2$
Alternative	A_1	\$ 100	\$100	\$400
	A_2	− 200	150	600
	A_3	0	200	500
	A_4	100	300	200

A_1 and A_3, as identified under the aspiration-level criterion. If this is done, the firm would choose alternative A_3.

Expected-Value Criterion

Many decision makers strive to make choices that will maximize expected profit or minimize expected loss. This is ordinarily justified in repetitive situations where the choice is to be made over and over again with increasing confidence that the calculated expected outcome will be achieved. This criterion is viewed with caution only when the payoff consequences of possible outcomes are disproportionately large, making a result that deviates from the expected outcome a distinct possibility.

The calculation of the expected value requires weighting all payoffs by their probabilities of occurrence. These weighted payoffs are then summed across all futures for each alternative. For the computer systems firm, alternatives A_1 through A_4 yield the expected profits (in thousands) shown in Table 5.3. From this analysis it is clear that alternative A_3 would be selected. Further, if this criterion were to be used to resolve the choice of either A_1 or A_3 under the aspiration level approach, the choice would be alternative A_3.

Comparison of Decisions

It is evident that there is no one best selection when these criteria are utilized for decision making under risk. The decision made is dependent on the decision criterion adopted by the decision maker. For the example of this selection, the alternatives selected under each criterion were:

Aspiration-level criterion:	A_1 or A_3
Most-probable-future criterion:	A_2
Expected-value criterion:	A_3

If the application of the latter two criteria to the resolution of A_1 or A_3 chosen under the aspiration-level criterion is accepted as valid, then A_3 is

TABLE 5.3 Computation of Expected Profit (Thousands)

Alternative	Expected Profit
A_1	$\$\ 100(0.3) + \$100(0.2) + \$400(0.5) = \$250$
A_2	$\$-200(0.3) + \$150(0.2) + \$600(0.5) = \$270$
A_3	$\$\quad 0(0.3) + \$200(0.2) + \$500(0.5) = \$290$
A_4	$\$\ 100(0.3) + \$300(0.2) + \$200(0.5) = \$190$

preferred twice and A_2 once. From this it might be appropriate to suggest that A_3 is the best alternative arising from the use of these three criteria.

5.6 DECISIONS UNDER UNCERTAINTY

It may be inappropriate or impossible to assign probabilities to the several futures identified for a given decision situation. Often, no meaningful data are available from which probabilities may be developed. In other instances the decision maker may be unwilling to assign a subjective probability, as is often the case when the future could prove to be unpleasant. When probabilities are not available for assignment to future events, the situation is classified as decision making under uncertainty.

As compared with decision making under certainty and under risk, decisions under uncertainty are made in a more abstract environment. In this section several decision criteria will be applied to the example of Section 5.5 to illustrate the formal approaches that are available.

Laplace Criterion

Suppose that the computer systems firm is unwilling to assess the futures in terms of probabilities. Specifically, the firm is unwilling to differentiate between the likelihood at acquiring contract C_1, contract C_2, and contract C_1 and contract C_2. In the absence of these probabilities one might reason that each possible state of nature is as likely to occur as any other. The rationale of this assumption is that there is no stated basis for one state of nature to be more likely than any other. This is called the *Laplace principle* or the principle of insufficient reason based on the philosophy that nature is assumed to be indifferent.

Under the Laplace principle, the probability of the occurrence of each future state of nature is assumed to be $1/n$, where n is the number of possible future states. To select the best alternative, one would compute the arithmetic average for each. For the decision matrix of Table 5.3, this is accomplished as shown in Table 5.4. Alternative A_3 results in a maximum profit of $233,000 and would be selected.

TABLE 5.4   Computation of Average Profit (Thousands)

Alternative	Average Profit
A_1	($\ \ 100 + \$100 + \$400) \div 3 = \$200$
A_2	($-200 + \$150 + \$600) \div 3 = \$183$
A_3	($\ \ \ \ \ 0 + \$200 + \$500) \div 3 = \$233$
A_4	($\ \ 100 + \$300 + \$200) \div 3 = \$200$

Maximin and Maximax Criteria

Two simple decision rules are available for dealing with decisions under uncertainty. The first is the *maximin rule*, based on an extremely pessimistic view of the outcome of nature. The use of this rule would be justified if it is judged that nature will do its worst. The second is the *maximax rule*, based on an extremely optimistic view of the future. Use of this rule is justified if it is judged that nature will do its best.

Because of the pessimism embraced by the maximin rule, its application will lead to the alternative that assures the best of the worst possible outcomes. If E_{ij} is used to represent the payoff for the ith alternative and the jth state of nature, the required computation is

$$\max_i \{\min_j E_{ij}\} \qquad (5.6)$$

Consider the decision situation described by the decision matrix of Table 5.3. The application of the maximin rule requires that the minimum value in each row be selected. Then the maximum value is identified from these and associated with the alternative that would produce it. This procedure is illustrated in Table 5.5. Selection of either alternative A_1 or A_4 assures the firm of a profit of at least $100,000, regardless of the future.

TABLE 5.5 Profit by the Maximin Rule (Thousands)

Alternative	$\min_i E_{ij}$
A_1	$ 100
A_2	−200
A_3	0
A_4	100

The optimism of the maximax rule is in sharp contrast to the pessimism of the maximin rule. Its application will choose the alternative that assures the best of the best possible outcomes. As before, if E_{ij} represents the payoff for the ith alternative and the jth state of nature, the required computation is

$$\max_i \{\max_j E_{ij}\} \qquad (5.7)$$

Consider the decision situation of Table 5.3 again. The application of the maximax rule requires that the maximum value in each row be selected. Then the maximum value is identified from these and associated with the alternative that would produce it. This procedure is illustrated in Table 5.6. Selection of alternative A_2 is indicated. Thus the decision maker may receive a profit of $600,000 if the future is benevolent.

TABLE 5.6 Profit by the Maximax Rule (Thousands)

Alternative	$\max_i E_{ij}$
A_1	$400
A_2	600
A_3	500
A_4	300

A decision maker who chooses the maximin rule considers only the worst possible occurrence for each alternative and selects that alternative which promises the best of the worst possible outcome. In the example where A_1 was chosen, the firm would be assured of a profit of at least $100,000, but it could not receive a profit any greater than $400,000. Or, if A_4 were chosen, the firm could not receive a profit of any greater than $300,000. Conversely, the firm that chooses the maximax rule is optimistic and decides solely on the basis of the highest profit offered for each alternative. Accordingly, in the example in which A_2 was chosen, the firm faces the possibility of a loss of $200,000 while seeking a profit of $600,000.

Hurwicz Criterion

Because the decision rules presented above are extreme, they are shunned by many decision makers. Most people have a degree of optimism or pessimism somewhere between the extremes. A third approach to decision making under uncertainty involves an index of relative optimism and pessimism. It is called the *Hurwicz rule*.

A compromise between optimism and pessimism is embraced in the Hurwicz rule by allowing the decision maker to select an index of optimism, α, such that $0 \le \alpha \le 1$. When $\alpha = 0$ the decision maker is pessimistic about nature, while an $\alpha = 1$ indicates optimism about nature. Once α is selected, the Hurwicz rule requires the computation of

$$\max_i \{\alpha[\max_j E_{ij}] + (1 - \alpha)[\min_j E_{ij}]\} \tag{5.8}$$

where E_{ij} is the payoff for the ith alternative and the jth state of nature. As an example of the Hurwicz rule, consider the payoff matrix of Table 5.3 with $\alpha = 0.2$. The required computations are shown in Table 5.7 and alternative A_1 would be chosen by the firm.

TABLE 5.7 Profit by the Hurwicz Rule with $\alpha = 0.2$ (Thousands)

Alternative	$\alpha[\max E_{ij}] + (1 - \alpha)[\min E_{ij}]$
A_1	$0.2(\$400) + 0.8(\$\ 100) = \$\ \ 160$
A_2	$0.2(\$600) + 0.8(\$-200) = \$\ -40$
A_3	$0.2(\$500) + 0.8(\ \ \ \ 0) = \$\ \ 100$
A_4	$0.2(\$300) + 0.8(\$\ 100) = \$\ \ 140$

Additional insight into the Hurwicz rule can be obtained by graphing each alternative for all values of α between zero and one. This makes it possible to identify the value of α for which each alternative would be favored. Such a graph is shown in Figure 5.4. It may be observed that alternative A_1 yields a maximum expected profit for all values of $\alpha \leq \frac{1}{2}$. Alternative A_3 exhibits a maximum for $\frac{1}{2} \leq \alpha \leq \frac{2}{3}$ and alternative A_2 gives a maximum for $\frac{2}{3} \leq \alpha \leq 1$. There is no value of α for which alternative A_4 would be best except at $\alpha = 0$, where it is as good an alternative as A_1.

When $\alpha = 0$, the Hurwicz rule gives the same result as the maximin rule, and when $\alpha = 1$, it is the same as the maximax rule. This may be shown for the case where $\alpha = 0$ as

$$\max_i \{0 \, [\max_j E_{ij}] + (1 - 0)[\min_j E_{ij}]\} = \max_i [\min_j E_{ij}]$$

For the case where $\alpha = 1$,

$$\max_i \{1 \, [\max_j E_{ij}] + (1 - 1)[\min_j E_{ij}]\} = \max_i [\min_j E_{ij}]$$

Thus the maximin rule and the maximax rule are special cases of the Hurwicz rule.

The philosophy behind the Hurwicz rule is that focus on the most extreme outcomes or consequences bounds or brackets the decision. By use of this rule, the decision maker may weight the extremes in such a manner as to reflect their alternative importance.

Minimax Regret Criterion

A decision maker will "regret" the selection of an alternative if a state of nature occurs such that he or she could have done better by having selected

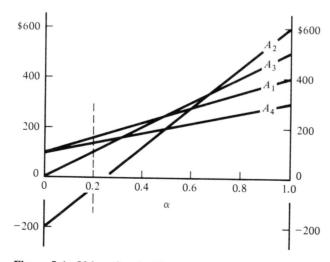

Figure 5.4   Values for the Hurwicz rule for four alternatives.

another alternative. This regret is the difference between the payoff that could have been achieved with perfect knowledge of the future and the payoff that was actually received from the alternative chosen. The regret rule is based on the premise that a decision maker wishes to avoid any regret, or at least to minimize the maximum regret resulting from a decision.

Application of the regret rule requires the formulation of a regret matrix. This is accomplished by identifying the maximum profit for each state (column). Next, each in the column is subtracted from the maximum profit identified. This is repeated for each column. For the profit matrix of Table 5.2 the maximum are \$100, \$300, and \$600 for C_1, C_2, and C_1 and C_2, respectively. Thus the regrets for C_1, applicable to alternatives A_1 through A_4, are \$100 − \$100 = 0; \$100 − (\$−200) = \$300; \$100 − \$0 = \$100; \$100 − \$100 = \$0. Repeating this computation for each state results in the regret matrix shown in Table 5.8.

If the regret values are designated R_{ij} for the ith alternative and the jth state, the regret rule requires the computation of

$$\min_{i} \{\max_{j} R_{ij}\} \qquad (5.9)$$

This computation is shown in Table 5.9. Selection of alternative A_3 assures the firm of a maximum regret of \$100,000.

A decision maker who uses the regret rule as a decision criterion will make that decision which will result in the least possible opportunity loss. People who have a strong aversion to criticism would be tempted to apply this rule since it puts them in a relatively safe position with respect to the future

TABLE 5.8   Regret Matrix (Thousands)

Alternative	C_1	C_2	$C_1 + C_2$
		State of Nature	
A_1	\$ 0	\$200	\$200
A_2	300	150	0
A_3	100	100	100
A_4	0	0	400

TABLE 5.9   Profit by the Regret Rule (Thousands)

Alternative	Max R_{ij}
A_1	\$200
A_2	300
A_3	100
A_4	400

states of nature that might occur. Thus this criterion has a conservative under-lying bias.

Comparisons of Decisions

As was the case for the decision criteria applied for decision making under risk, it is evident that there is no one best criterion for decision making under uncertainty. The decision made is dependent on the decision criterion adopted by the decision maker. For the examples of this section, the alternatives selected were

Laplace criterion:	A_3
Maximin criterion:	A_1 or A_4
Maximax criterion:	A_2
Hurwicz criterion ($\alpha = 0.2$):	A_1
Regret criterion:	A_3

Examination of the selections recommended by the five decision rules indicates that each has its own merit. Several factors may influence a decision maker's choice of a rule in a given decision situation. The decision maker's attitude toward uncertainty (pessimistic or optimistic) and his or her personal utility function are important influences. Thus the choice of a particular decision rule for a given decision must be based on subjective judgment.

5.7 DECISIONS INVOLVING MULTIPLE CRITERIA

Multiple criteria considerations in life-cycle economic analyses arise when both economic and noneconomic elements are present in the evaluation. In these situations, decision evaluation is facilitated by the use of a decision evaluation display exhibiting both cost and effectiveness measures. In this section both the decision evaluation display and cost-effectiveness analysis are presented as approaches to dealing with multiple criteria.

Decision Evaluation Display

Effectiveness is a measure of mission fulfillment for a product or system in terms of a stated need. Mission fulfillment may be expressed by one or more figures of merit, depending on the type of product or system and the objectives to be achieved. Some common effectiveness measures are shown on the right side of Figure 5.5.

Life-cycle cost, shown on the left side of Figure 5.5, and one or more effectiveness measures may be displayed simultaneously as an aid in decision

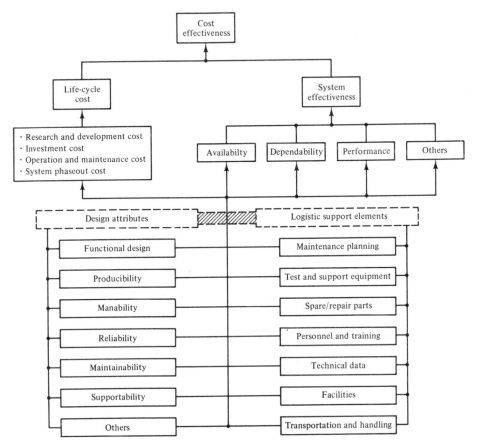

Figure 5.5 Elements for consideration in cost-effectiveness evaluation.

making. A decision evaluation display, as shown in Figure 5.6, is one way of doing this. Note that effectiveness requirements or thresholds are shown on the display. These are useful to the decision maker in assessing subjectively the degree to which each alternative satisfies effectiveness criteria. Life-cycle cost, shown on the horizontal axis, is an objective measure. The goal is to select the alternative with the lowest life-cycle cost that satisfies most of the effectiveness measures.

In the next section, cost-effectiveness is presented as an evaluation methodology for multiple criteria. It incorporates the decision evaluation display.

Cost-Effectiveness Analysis

Cost-effectiveness analysis originated in the economic evaluation of complex defense and space systems. Its predecessor, benefit-cost analysis, had

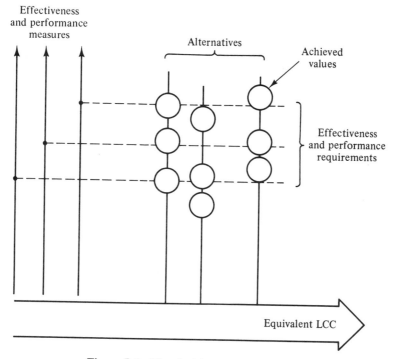

Figure 5.6   The decision evaluation display.

its origin in the civilian sector of the economy, and may be traced back to the Flood Control Act of 1936. Much of the philosophy and methodology of the cost-effectiveness approach was derived from benefit-cost analysis. As a result, there are many similarities in the techniques. The basic concepts inherent in cost-effectiveness analysis are now being applied to a broad range of problems in both the defense and the civilian sectors of public activities.

In applying cost-effectiveness analysis to complex systems, three requirements must be satisfied. First, the systems being evaluated must have common goals or purposes. The comparison of cargo aircraft with fighter aircraft would not be valid, but comparison with cargo ships would if both the aircraft and ships were to be utilized in military logistics. Second, alternative means for meeting the goal must exist. This is the case with cargo ships being compared with the cargo aircraft. Most details of the systems being evaluated must be available or estimated so that the cost and effectiveness of each system can be estimated.

Certain steps constitute a standardized approach to cost-effectiveness evaluations.[6] These steps are useful in that they define a systematic method-

---

[6]A. D. Kazanowski, "A Standardized Approach to Cost-Effectiveness Evaluations," Chapter 7 in J. Morley English, ed., *Cost Effectiveness* (New York: John Wiley & Sons, Inc., 1968).

ology for the evaluation of complex systems in economic terms. The following paragraphs summarize these steps.

First, it is essential that the desired goal or goals of the system be defined. In the case of military logistics mentioned above, the goal may be to move a certain number of tons of personnel and supporting equipment from one point to another in a specified interval of time. This may be accomplished by a few relatively slow cargo ships or a number of fast cargo aircraft. Care must be exercised in this step to be sure that the goals defined will satisfy mission requirements. Each delivery system must have the capability of delivering a mix of personnel and equipment that will meet the requirements of the mission. Comparison of aircraft that can deliver only personnel against ships that can deliver both personnel and equipment would not be valid in a cost-effectiveness study.

Once mission requirements have been identified, alternative system concepts and designs must be developed. If only one system can be conceived, a cost-effectiveness evaluation cannot be used as a basis for selection. Also, selection must be made on the basis of an optimum configuration for each system utilizing the economic optimization approach in Section 5.2.

System evaluation criteria must be established next for both the life-cycle and the effectiveness aspects of the system under study. Ordinarily, less difficulty exists in establishing cost criteria than in establishing criteria for effectiveness. This does not mean that cost estimation is easy; it simply means that the classifications and basis for summarizing cost are more commonly understood. Among the categories of cost are those arising throughout the system life cycle, which include costs associated with research and development, engineering, testing, production, operation, and maintenance.

System evaluation criteria on the effectiveness side of a cost-effectiveness study are quite difficult to establish. Also, many systems have multiple purposes that complicate the problem further. Some general effectiveness categories are utility, merit, worth, benefit, and gain. These are difficult to quantify, so such criteria as mobility, availability, maintainability, reliability, and others are normally used. Although precise quantitative measures are not available for all of them, these criteria are useful as a basis for describing system effectiveness.

The next step in a cost-effectiveness study is to select the fixed-cost or fixed-effectiveness approach. In the *fixed-cost approach* the basis for selection is the amount of effectiveness obtained at a given cost; in the *fixed-effectiveness* approach it is the cost incurred to obtain a given level of effectiveness. When multiple alternatives that provide the same service are compared on the basis of cost, the fixed-effectiveness approach is being used.

Candidate systems in a cost-effectiveness study must be analyzed on the basis of their merits. This may be accomplished by ranking the systems in order of their ability to satisfy the most important criterion. For example, if the criterion in military logistics is the number of tons of personnel and equipment moved from one point to another in a specified interval of time, this criterion becomes the primary one. Other criteria, such as maintainability, would be ranked in a secondary position. Often this procedure will eliminate the least promising candidates. The remaining candidates can then be subjected to a detailed cost and effectiveness analysis. If the cost and the effectiveness for the top contender are both superior to the respective values for other candidates, the choice is obvious. If criteria values for the top two contenders are identical, or nearly identical, and no significant cost difference exists, either may be selected based on irreducibles. Finally, if system costs differ significantly, and effectiveness differs significantly, the selection must be made on the basis of intuition and judgment. The decision evaluation display of Figure 5.6 can aid this process.

The final step in a cost-effectiveness study involves documentation of the purpose, assumptions, methodology, and conclusions. This is the communication step and it should not be treated lightly.

A Cost-Effectiveness Example

As an example of some aspects of cost-effectiveness analysis, consider the goal of moving personnel and equipment from one point to another, as outlined above. Suppose that only the cargo aircraft mode and the ship mode are feasible. Also suppose that some design flexibility exists within each mode, so that effectiveness in tons per day and availability may be established through design effort.

Assume that the Department of Defense has convinced Congress that such a military logistic system should be developed and that Congress has authorized a research and development program for a system whose present equivalent life-cycle cost is not to exceed $1.2 billion. The Department of Defense, in conjunction with a nonprofit research and engineering firm, has decided that three candidate systems should be conceived and costed. Table 5.10 shows the resulting present life-cycle cost and corresponding capacity (in tons per day) and anticipated system availability. These system effectiveness and cost characteristics are shown on a decision evaluation display in Figure 5.7.

TABLE 5.10   Life-Cycle Cost and Effectiveness for Three Logistic Systems

System	Capacity	Availability	Present Equivalent Life-Cycle Cost
Aircraft I	1,380	0.70	$1,000,000,000
Aircraft II	1,600	0.80	1,200,000,000
Ship	1,500	0.96	1,100,000,000

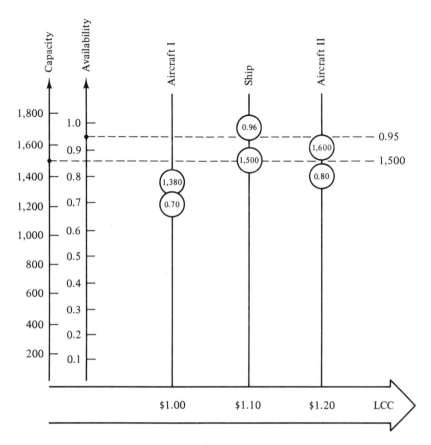

Figure 5.7 Decision evaluation display for three logistic systems.

The candidate systems may now be examined and evaluated. Note, first, that all three fall within the life-cycle cost, constraint of $1.2 billion. Note, also, that only the ship system meets the requirements of 1,500 tons per day and an availability of 0.95. Aircraft system I meets neither requirement and would be dropped from further consideration. However, aircraft system II might be examined more closely as an alternative to the ship system since it offers the highest capacity within budget. Of concern is its relatively low availability.

This example is simplified in its assumptions and analysis. Nothing has been said about how the study team was able to determine that a certain effectiveness and availability would result from a system with a present life-cycle cost of $1.2 billion. Also, the example pointed out only one secondary measure of effectiveness (availability), when there are likely to be many.

QUESTIONS AND PROBLEMS

1. Relate Equation 5.1 to the model for the equivalence of money flows as presented in Section 3.3.

2. Write the general form of the decision evaluation function and define its symbols.

3. Identify a decision situation and indicate the variables under the control of the decision maker and those not directly under his or her control.

4. Link Equation 5.3 and the decision evaluation matrix of Figure 5.2 for a hypothetical situation of your choice.

5. Develop an example to illustrate the application of paired outcomes in decision making among a number of nonquantifiable alternatives.

6. What approaches may be used to assign probabilities to future outcomes?

7. What is the role of dominance in decision making among alternatives?

8. Give an example of an aspiration level in decision making.

9. When would one follow the most probable future criterion in decision making?

10. What drawback exists in using the most probable future criterion?

11. How does the Laplace criterion for decision making under uncertainty actually convert the situation to decision making under risk?

12. Discuss the maximin and the maximax rules as special cases of the Hurwicz rule.

13. The cost of developing an internal training program for field maintenance is unknown, but described by the following probability distribution:

Cost	Probability of Occurrence
$ 80,000	0.20
95,000	0.30
105,000	0.25
115,000	0.20
130,000	0.05

(a) What is the expected cost of the program?
(b) What is the most probable cost?
(c) What is the maximum cost that will occur with a 95% assurance?

14. Net profit has been calculated for five investment opportunities under three possible futures. Which alternative should be selected under the most probable future criterion; the expected value criterion?

Alternative	(0.3) F_1	(0.2) F_2	(0.5) F_3
A_1	$ 100,000	$100,000	$380,000
A_2	- 200,000	160,000	590,000
A_3	0	180,000	500,000
A_4	110,000	280,000	200,000
A_5	400,000	90,000	180,000

15. Daily positive and negative payoffs are given for five alternatives and five futures in the matrix below. Which alternative should be chosen to maximize the probability of receiving a payoff of at least 9? What choice would be made by using the most probable future criterion?

Alternative	(0.15) F_1	(0.20) F_2	(0.30) F_3	(0.20) F_4	(0.15) F_5
A_1	12	8	−4	0	9
A_2	10	0	5	10	16
A_3	6	5	10	15	−4
A_4	4	14	20	6	12
A_5	−8	22	12	4	9

16. The following matrix gives the payoffs in utiles (a measure of utility) for three alternatives and three possible states of nature.

	State of Nature		
Alternative	S_1	S_2	S_3
A_1	50	80	80
A_2	60	70	20
A_3	90	30	60

Which alternative would be chosen under the Laplace principle? The maximin rule? The maximax rule? The Hurwicz rule with $\alpha = 0.75$?

17. The following payoff matrix indicates the costs associated with three decision options and four states of nature.

	State of Nature			
Option	S_1	S_2	S_3	S_4
T_1	20	25	30	35
T_2	40	30	40	20
T_3	10	60	30	25

Select the decision option that should be selected for the maximin rule; the maximax rule; the Laplace rule; the minimax regret rule; the Hurwicz rule with $\alpha = 0.2$; and the minimax regret rule. How do the rules applied to the cost matrix differ from those that are applied to a payoff matrix of profits?

18. The following matrix gives the expected profit in thousands of dollars for five marketing strategies and five potential levels of sales.

Strategy	Level of Sales				
	L_1	L_2	L_3	L_4	L_5
M_1	10	20	30	40	50
M_2	20	25	25	30	35
M_3	50	40	5	15	20
M_4	40	35	30	25	25
M_5	10	20	25	30	20

Which marketing strategy would be chosen under the maximin rule? The maximax rule? The Hurwicz rule with $\alpha = 0.4$?

19. Graph the Hurwicz rule for all values of α using the payoff matrix of Problem 18.

20. The following decision evaluation matrix gives the expected savings in maintenance costs (in thousands of dollars) for three policies of preventive maintenance and three levels of operation of equipment. Given the probabilities of each level of operation, $P_1 = 0.3$, $P_2 = 0.2$, determine the best policy based on the most probable future criterion. Also, determine the best policy under uncertainty, using the Laplace rule, the Maximax rule, and the Hurwicz rule with $\alpha = 0.2$.

Policy	Level of Operation		
	L_1	L_2	L_3
M_1	10	20	30
M_2	22	26	26
M_3	40	30	15

21. The design of a system is to be pursued from one of two available alternatives. Each alternative has a life-cycle cost associated with an expected future. The costs for the corresponding futures are given in the following table (in millions of dollars). If the probabilities of occurrence of the futures are 30%, 50%, and 20%, respectively, which alternative is most desirable from an expected cost viewpoint?

Design 1

Future	Year											
	1	2	3	4	5	6	7	8	9	10	11	12
Optimistic	0.4	0.6	5.0	7.0	0.8	0.8	0.8	0.8	0.8	0.8	0.8	0.8
Expected	0.8	0.9	1.0	7.0	10.0	1.2	1.2	1.2	1.2	1.2	1.2	1.2
Pessimistic	0.6	0.8	1.0	3.0	6.0	3.0	3.0	3.0	3.0	3.0	3.0	3.0

Design 2

Future	\multicolumn{12}{c}{Year}
	1	2	3	4	5	6	7	8	9	10	11	12
Optimistic	0.4	0.4	0.4	1.0	3.0	2.5	2.5	2.5	2.5	2.5	2.5	2.5
Expected	0.6	0.8	1.0	5.0	10.0	1.0	1.0	1.0	1.0	1.0	1.0	1.0
Pessimistic	0.6	0.8	1.0	5.0	6.0	3.1	3.1	3.1	3.1	3.1	3.1	3.1

22. Prepare a decision evaluation matrix for the design alternatives in Problem 21 and then choose the alternative that is best under the following decision rules: Laplace, maximax, maximin, and Hurwicz with $\alpha = 0.6$. Assume that the choice is under uncertainty.

23. A company wishes to develop a new type of coated ceramic insert for machining 4047 high-carbon steel which has a machinability rating of 55%. Company engineers have developed specifications for the insert. They are: ability to take a 0.25-in. depth of cut (total of 0.5 in. removed from the diameter) at 2,000 rpm with a feed rate of 0.003 in. per revolution on stock with a 3-in. diameter. The new tools should last 3 hours when making uninterrupted cuts at these feeds and speeds on 3-in.-diameter stock (total of 2,332.8 cubic inches of stock removed). The inserts should cost no more than $0.09 per unit to manufacture over the product life cycle, which will span 10 years (inception to phaseout). Minimum expected profit per unit over the life cycle is $0.50 per unit sold. The MARR is 15%.

The company has two alternatives: Alternative A provides for a tool that has a maximum life of 3.5 hours when machining high-speed steel with a 0.3125-in. depth of cut at 1,800 rpm with a feed rate of 0.0025 in. per revolution when machining stock with a 3-in. diameter. 2,500,000 of these inserts are expected to be sold per year. The selling price in year 3 will be $1.10, and increase by $0.05 per year until the end of year 10 ($1.45 in year 10). Design and development costs for this alternative are $250,000 in the first year. Costs to implement this alternative (e.g., salaries, facilities, training, etc.) incurred in year 2 are expected to be $600,000. Marketing costs incurred in year 3 are expected to be $200,000. Marketing costs are expected to be $50,000 per year starting in year 4 and continue through year 10. Actual manufacturing costs (starting in year 3 and ending in year 10) are expected to be: maintenance and operating costs, $25,000 per year; power costs, $7,500 per year; and direct labor costs, $100,000 per year. Product phaseout will occur at the end of year 10, and will result in a cost of $30,000.

Alternative B provides for a tool that has a maximum life of 2.0 hours when machining 3-in.-diameter stock with a 0.23-in. depth of cut at 2250 rpm with a feed rate of 0.0045 in. per revolution. 2,500,000 of these inserts are expected to be sold per year with sales starting in the beginning of year 3 and lasting until the end of year 10. Selling prices are expected to be: year 3, $1.25 per insert; years 4 to 6, $1.30; years 7 to 10, $1.50. Design and development costs incurred in year 1 are expected to be $235,000. Cost to implement alternative B (e.g., salaries, training, facilities, etc.) incurred during year 2 are expected to be $545,000. Marketing costs incurred during year 3 are expected to be $200,000, and then $40,000 per year through year 10. Actual manufacturing costs (starting in year 3 and continue through year 10) are expected to be: maintenance and operating costs, $23,500 per year; power, $10,000 per year; and direct labor, $97,000 per year. Product phase-out will occur in year 10, and will result in no cost.

(a) Compare the two alternatives using a decision evaluation display.

(b) Determine which alternative should be adopted.

(c) Explain why the alternative chosen is best.

Life-Cycle Costing
Methodology

Experience has shown that a major portion of the projected life-cycle cost for a given product and system stems from the consequences of decisions made during early planning as part of system conceptual design. These decisions deal with system operational requirements, performance and effectiveness factors, the maintenance concept, the system design configuration, number of items to be produced, utilization factors, logistic support, and so on. Such decisions guide subsequent design and production activities, product distribution functions, and the various aspects of sustaining system support. Thus, if the ultimate life-cycle cost is to be controlled, it is essential that a high degree of cost emphasis be applied in the early stages of system/product development in a structured manner.[1]

6.1 THE LIFE-CYCLE COSTING SITUATION

The recent combination of economic trends, rising inflation, cost growth experienced for many systems and products, the continuing reduction in buying power, budget limitations, increased competition, and so on, has created an awareness and interest in total system and product cost. Not only are the ac-

---

[1] A structured approach for the process of life-cycle cost analysis is outlined in Appendix A and should be studied in conjunction with this Chapter.

quisition costs associated with new systems rising, but the costs of operating and maintaining systems already in use are increasing at alarming rates. This is due primarily to a combination of inflation and cost growth from causes such as:

1. Cost growth due to the poor quality of products and systems in use.
2. Cost growth due to engineering changes occurring throughout the design and development of a product or system (for the purposes of improving performance, adding capability, etc.).
3. Cost growth due to changing suppliers in the procurement of system components.
4. Cost growth due to system production and/or construction changes.
5. Cost growth due to changes in the logistic support capability.
6. Cost growth due to initial estimating inaccuracies and changes in estimating procedures.
7. Cost growth due to unforeseen problems.

Experience indicates that cost growth due to these various causes has ranged from 5 to 10 times the rate of inflation over the past several decades.[2] At the same time, budget allocations for many programs are decreasing from year to year. The result is that less money is available for acquiring and operating new systems or products and for maintaining and supporting systems already existing. Available funds for projects (i.e., buying power), when inflation and cost growth are considered, are decreasing at a rapid rate.

The current economic situation is further complicated by some additional problems related to the actual determination of system and/or product cost. Some of these are:

1. Total system cost is often not visible, particularly those costs associated with system operation and support. The cost visibility problem can be related to the iceberg effect illustrated in Figure 6.1. One must address not only system acquisition cost, but other costs as well.
2. In estimating cost, individual factors are often improperly applied. For instance, costs are identified and often included in the wrong category; variable costs are treated as fixed costs (and vice versa); indirect costs are treated as direct costs; and so on.
3. Existing accounting procedures do not always permit a realistic and timely assessment of total cost. In addition, it is often difficult (if not impossible) to determine costs on a functional basis.
4. Budgeting practices are often inflexible regarding the shift in funds from

[2] Cost growth compares the initial cost estimate for a system to subsequent cost estimates of the same system at a later point in the life cycle.

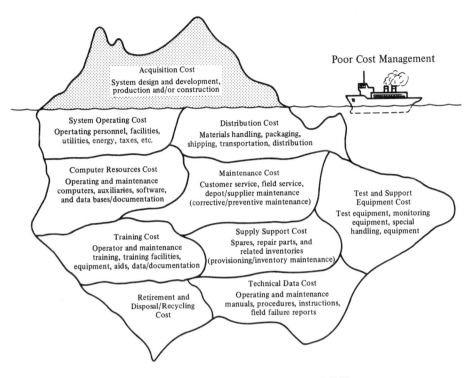

Figure 6.1 The problem of total cost visibility.

one category to another, or from year to year, to facilitate improvements in system acquisition and utilization.

The current trends of inflation and cost growth, combined with these additional problems, have caused inefficiencies in the utilization of valuable resources. Systems and products have been developed that are not cost-effective. Further, it is anticipated that conditions will become worse unless an increased degree of cost consciousness is assumed in day-to-day activities. Economic feasibility studies must address all aspects of life-cycle cost, not just segments thereof.

Life-cycle cost is determined by identifying the applicable functions in each phase of the life cycle, costing these functions, applying the appropriate costs by function on a year-to-year schedule, and ultimately accumulating the costs for the entire span of the life cycle. Life-cycle cost includes all producer and consumer costs as defined in Chapter 2.[3]

[3] It should be noted that *all* life-cycle costs may be difficult (if not impossible) to predict and measure. For instance, some indirect costs caused by the interaction effects of one system on another, social costs, and so on, may be impossible to quantify. Thus the emphasis should relate primarily to those costs that can be directly attributed to a given system or product.

The application of life-cycle costing methods in system and product design and development is realized through the accomplishment of life-cycle cost analyses. A life-cycle cost analysis may be defined as a systematic analytical process of evaluating various alternative courses of action with the objective of choosing the best way to employ scarce resources.

6.2 COST GENERATED OVER THE LIFE CYCLE

Life-cycle cost refers to all costs associated with the product or system as applied to the defined life cycle. The life cycle and the major functions associated with each phase were illustrated in Figure 1.3. The life cycle, tailored to the specific system being addressed, forms the basis for life-cycle costing.

Life-cycle costing is employed in the evaluation of alternative system design configurations, alternative production schemes, alternative logistic support policies, and so on. The analysis constitutes a step-by-step approach employing life-cycle cost figures of merit as criteria to arrive at a cost-effective solution. The analysis process is iterative in nature and can be applied to any phase of the system or product life cycle.

Actions Affecting Life-Cycle Cost

Throughout the system/product life cycle, there are many actions required, both technical and nontechnical. The majority of the actions, particularly those at the earlier stages, have life-cycle implications and definitely affect life-cycle cost. It may appear initially that a specific action will not directly affect life-cycle cost; however, the indirect effects on cost may turn out to be very significant. In general, life-cycle cost falls into categories based on organizational activity over the life cycle. These are:

1. *Research and development cost:* initial planning; market analysis; feasibility studies; product research; requirements analysis; engineering design; design data and documentation; software; test and evaluation of engineering models; and associated management functions.

2. *Production and construction cost:* industrial engineering and operations analysis; manufacturing (fabrication, assembly, and test); facility construction; process development; production operations; quality control; and initial logistic support requirements (e.g., initial consumer support, the manufacture of spare parts, the production of test and support equipment, etc.).

3. *Operation and support cost:* consumer or user operations of the system or product in the field; product distribution (marketing and sales, transportation, and traffic management); and sustaining maintenance and lo-

gistic support throughout the system or product life cycle (e.g., customer service, maintenance activities, supply support, test and support equipment, transportation and handling, technical data, facilities, system modifications, etc.).

4. *Retirement and disposal cost:* disposal of nonrepairable items throughout the life cycle; system/product retirement; material recycling; and applicable logistic support requirements.

The initial step in life-cycle costing is to establish cost targets or firm goals [i.e, one or more quantitative figures of merit to which the system or product should be designed, produced (or constructed), and supported for a designated period of time]. Second, these cost targets are then allocated to specific subsystems or elements as design constraints or criteria. With the progression of design, various alternative configurations are evaluated in terms of compliance with the allocated targets, and a preferred approach is selected. As the system or product continues to evolve through various stages of development, life-cycle cost estimates are made and the results are compared against the initially specified targets. Areas of noncompliance are noted and corrective action is initiated where appropriate. Cost emphasis throughout the system/product life cycle is illustrated in Figure 6.2 and discussed below.

Conceptual System Design (Figure 6.2, Block 1)

In the early stages of planning and conceptual design, as system requirements are being defined, quantitative cost figures of merit should be established to which the system or product is to be designed, tested, produced (or constructed), and supported. A *design-to-cost* (DTC) concept may be adopted to establish cost as a system or product *design constraint,* along with performance, effectiveness, capacity, accuracy, size, weight, reliability, maintainability, supportability, and so on. Cost must be an *active* rather than a *resultant* factor throughout the design process.

Design-to-cost figures of merit are usually specified at the system level. However, DTC parameters sometimes are established at a lower level to facilitate improved cost visibility and closer control throughout the life cycle. For example,

1. *Design to unit acquisition cost:* a factor that includes only research and development cost and production or construction cost.

2. *Design to unit operation and support cost:* a factor that includes only operation and maintenance support cost.

When suboptimizing by considering only a single segment of life-cycle cost, one must be sure that decisions are not based on that one segment alone,

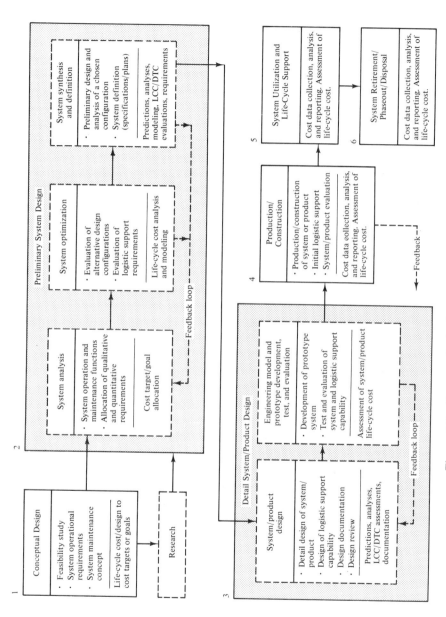

Figure 6.2 Cost emphasis throughout the system life cycle.

Conceptual Design

1

· Feasibility study
· System operational requirements
· System maintenance concept

Life-cycle cost/design to cost targets or goals

Research

Preliminary System Design

2

System analysis

· System operation and maintenance functions
· Allocation of qualitative and quantitative requirements

Cost target/goal allocation

System optimization

· Evaluation of alternative design configurations
· Evaluation of logistic support requirements

Life-cycle cost analysis and modeling

System synthesis and definition

· Preliminary design and analysis of a chosen configuration
· System definition (specifications/plans)

Predictions, analyses, modeling, LCC/DTC evaluations, requirements

Feedback loop

Detail System/Product Design

3

System/product design

· Detail design of system/product
· Design of logistic support capability
· Design documentation
· Design review

Predictions, analyses, LCC/DTC assessments, documentation

Engineering model and prototype development, test, and evaluation

· Development of prototype system
· Test and evaluation of system and logistic support capability

Assessment of system/product life-cycle cost

Feedback loop

Production/Construction

4

· Production/construction of system or product
· Initial logistic support
· System/product evaluation

Cost data collection, analysis, and reporting. Assessment of life-cycle cost.

System Utilization and Life-Cycle Support

5

Cost data collection, analysis, and reporting. Assessment of life-cycle cost.

System Retirement/ Phaseout/Disposal

6

Cost data collection, analysis, and reporting. Assessment of life-cycle cost.

Feedback

without considering the overall effects on total life-cycle cost. For example, one can propose a given design configuration on the basis of a low unit acquisition cost, but the projected operation and support cost, and life-cycle cost, for that configuration may be considerably higher than necessary. Ideally, acquisition cost should not be addressed without consideration for operation and support cost (and vice versa), and both segments of cost must be viewed in terms of life-cycle cost. As conceptual design evolves and various system design approaches are being considered, life-cycle cost considerations are included in the criteria.

Preliminary System Design (Figure 6.2, Block 2)

With the quantitative cost requirements established, the next step includes an iterative process of synthesis, trade-off and optimization, and system/product definition. The criteria defined in block 1 are initially allocated, or apportioned, to various segments of the system to establish guidelines for the design and/or the procurement of the applicable element(s). As illustrated in Figure 6.3, allocation is accomplished from the system level down to the level necessary to provide an input to design and to ensure

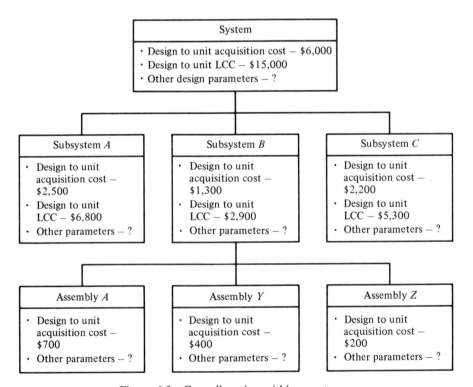

Figure 6.3 Cost allocation within a system.

adequate control. The factors projected reflect the target cost per individual unit (i.e., a single system or product in a total population) and are based on system operational requirements, the system maintenance concept, and so on.

As the development evolves, various alternative approaches are considered in leading to a preferred system configuration. Life-cycle cost analyses are accomplished in evaluating each possible candidate with the objective of (1) ensuring that the candidate selected is compatible with the established cost targets, and (2) determining which of the various candidates being considered is preferred from an overall cost-effectiveness standpoint. Numerous trade-off studies are accomplished, using life-cycle cost analysis as an evaluation tool, until a preferred design configuration is chosen. Areas of compliance are justified, and noncompliant approaches are discarded. This is an iterative process with the necessary feedback and corrective action loop as illustrated by block 2 of Figure 6.2.

Detail Design and Development
(Figure 6.2, Block 3)

As system or product design is further refined and design data become available, the life-cycle cost analysis effort involves the evaluation of specific design characteristics (as reflected by design documentation and engineering or prototype models), the prediction of cost-generating variables, the estimation of costs, and the projection of life-cycle cost as a cost profile. The results are compared with the initial requirement and corrective action is taken as necessary. Again, this is an iterative process, but at a lower level than what is accomplished during preliminary system design.

Production, Utilization, and Support
(Figure 6.2, Blocks 4 and 5)

Cost concerns in these latter stages of the system or product life cycle are addressed through data collection, analysis, and assessment function. High-cost contributors are identified, cause-and-effect relationships are defined, and valuable information can be gained and utilized for the purposes of product improvement.

In summary, life-cycle costing is applicable in all phases of system design, development, production, construction, operation use, and logistic support. Cost emphasis is created early in the life cycle by establishing quantitative cost factors as "design to" *requirements*. As the life cycle progresses, cost is employed as a major parameter in the evaluation of alternative design configurations and in the selection of a preferred approach. Subsequently, cost data are generated based on established design and production characteristics and used in the development of life-cycle cost projections. These projections, in turn, are compared with the initial requirements to determine degree of compliance and the ultimate necessity for corrective action. In essence, life-cycle cost evolves from a series of rough estimates to a relatively refined methodology, and is employed as a management tool for decision-making purposes.

6.3 LIFE-CYCLE COST ANALYSIS

Where there are possible alternative solutions to a specific problem, and a decision is required in the selection of a preferred approach, there is an overall analysis process that should be followed. Specifically, one should (1) define the need for analysis, (2) establish the analysis approach, (3) select a model to facilitate the evaluation process, (4) generate the appropriate information for each alternative being considered, (5) evaluate the alternatives, and (6) recommend a proposed solution in response to the problem at hand.

Cost Analysis Goals See p. 371

The possible applications of life-cycle cost analysis are numerous. Specifically, life-cycle cost analysis may be employed in evaluation of the following:

1. Alternative system/product operational scenarios and utilization approaches.
2. Alternative system maintenance concepts and logistic support policies.
3. Alternative system/product design configurations involving technology applications, equipment packaging schemes, diagnostic routines, built-in test versus external test, manual functions versus automation, hardware versus software approaches, component selection and standardization, reliability versus maintainability, levels of repair versus discard decisions, and so on.
4. Alternative supplier sources for a given item.
5. Alternative production approaches, such as continuous versus discontinuous production, quantity of production lines, number of inventory points and levels of inventory, levels of product quality, inspection and test alternatives, and so on.
6. Alternative product distribution channels, transportation and handling methods, warehouse locations, and so on.
7. Alternative logistic support plans, such as customer service levels, sustaining supply support levels, maintenance functions and tasks, and so on.
8. Alternative product disposal and recycling methods.
9. Alternative management policies and their impact on the system.

There are many different facets of a system that one can study, and it is relatively easy to become overwhelmed by undertaking too large an effort, or by proceeding in the wrong direction. Thus an important initial step constitutes the clarification of analysis objectives, defining the issues of concern, and bounding the problem such that it can be studied in an efficient and timely manner. In many cases, the nature of the problem appears to be obvious, whereas the precise definition of the problem may be the most difficult part of the entire process. The problem at hand must be defined clearly, precisely, and presented in such a manner as to be easily understood by all concerned. Otherwise, it is highly doubtful whether an analysis of any type will be meaningful.

From the problem statement, the cost analyst needs to identify specific goals. For instance, is it the objective to evaluate many different alternatives on the basis of life-cycle cost? Is there a requirement to determine the life-cycle cost of system XYZ for budgetary purposes? Does the evaluation need to show system performance in terms of design to unit acquisition cost? Is it necessary to evaluate supply support costs as a function of the equipment design packaging configuration?

Actually, there are many such questions that the decision maker might wish to address. There may be a single overall analysis goal (e.g., design to minimum life-cycle cost) and any number of subgoals. The primary question is: What is the purpose of the analysis, and what is to be learned through the analysis effort?

Identifying the goals of the analysis may seem elementary, but is extremely important. It is not uncommon to find instances where the analysis effort becomes the driving force and the original goals are lost in the process; or the goals have unintentionally shifted as a result of the analyst becoming too involved in the details and losing sight of the overall picture. The analyst must be careful to ensure that realistic goals are established at the start of the analysis process, and that these goals remain in sight throughout the process.

Analysis Guidelines and Constraints

Subsequent to definition of the problem and the goals, the cost analyst must define the guidelines and constraints (or bounds) within which the analysis is to be accomplished. Guidelines are composed of information concerning such factors as the resources available for conducting the analysis (e.g., necessary labor skills, availability of appropriate computer software, etc.), the time schedule allowed for completion of the analysis, and/or related management policy or direction that in any way will effect the analysis.

In many instances, a manager may not completely understand the problem or the analysis process and direct that certain tasks be accomplished in a prescribed manner and at a designated time which, in turn, may not be compatible with the analysis objectives. On other occasions, a manager may have a preconceived idea as to a given decision outcome and direct that the analysis support the decision, whether realistic or not. Thus at times there are external inhibiting factors that may affect the validity of the analysis effort. In such cases, the cost analyst should make every effort to alleviate the problem through education. Should any unresolved problems exist, the analyst should document them as part of the analysis report and relate their effects to the analysis results.

Relative to the technical characteristics of a system or product, the analysis output may be constrained by bounds (or limits) that are established through the definition of system performance features, operational requirements, the maintenance concept, and/or through advanced program planning. For instance, there may be a maximum weight requirement for a given product, a minimum reliability requirement, a maximum allowable unit life-cycle cost goal (e.g., the allocated value in Figure 6.3), a minimum capacity output for a plant, and so on. These various bounds, or constraints, must be defined in terms of the trade-off areas allowable in the evaluation of alternatives. All alternative candidates that fall within the trade-off area are eligible for consideration, while those that fall outside this area are not even though one of these alternatives may turn out to be more cost-effective in the long run.

Identification of Alternatives

Chapter 4 described the formal process for developing and evaluating alternatives. Within the established bounds and constraints, there may be any number of approaches leading to a possible solution. All possible alternatives should be considered, with the most likely candidates selected for further evaluation in accordance with the process depicted in Figure 6.4. All possible alternatives are not necessarily attainable. Alternatives are frequently proposed for analysis even though there seems to be little likelihood that they will prove feasible. This is done with the thought that it is better to consider many alternatives than to overlook one that may be very good. Alternatives not considered cannot be adopted, no matter how desirable they may actually be.

Developing the Cost Breakdown Structure

Developing the cost breakdown structure is one of the most significant steps in life-cycle costing. The CBS constitutes the framework for defining life-cycle costs and provides the communications link for cost reporting, analysis, and ultimate cost control. Section 2.4 provided a detailed description of CBS and Figure 2.4 illustrated the major categories. The CBS is the basic reference point for much of the material presented in subsequent sections of this chapter.

In developing the CBS, one needs to expand to the depth required to (1) provide the necessary information for a true and valid assessment of the sys-

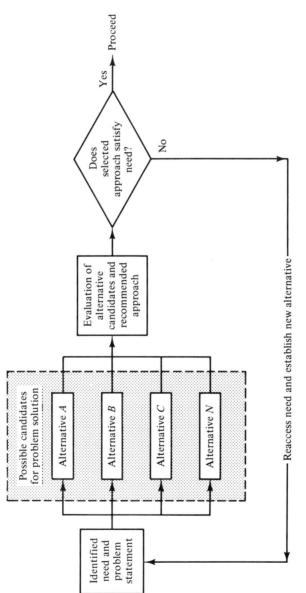

Figure 6.4 Process for evaluating a group of alternatives.

tem or product life-cycle cost, (2) identify high-cost contributors and enable determination of the cause-and-effect relationships, and (3) illustrate the various cost parameters and their application in the analysis. Traceability from the system-level LCC figure of merit to the specific input factor is required.

Selecting a Cost Model

After defining the cost breakdown structure, it is necessary to develop a model (or a series of models) to facilitate the life-cycle economic evaluation process. The model may be a simple series of parameter relationships or a complex set of computer subroutines, depending on the phases of the system life cycle in which the model is used and the nature of the problem at hand. Life-cycle cost analyses during the conceptual or preliminary design phases may require the use of basic accounting techniques and the model may be rather simple in construction. On the other hand, life-cycle cost analyses accomplished during detail design and development may be more extensive and require a series of models as illustrated in Figure 6.5. In either case, the model should:

1. Be comprehensive and include all relevant factors, and be reliable in terms of repeatability of results.
2. Represent the "dynamics" of the system or product being evaluated, and be sensitive relative to the relationships of key input parameters.
3. Be flexible to the extent that the analyst can evaluate overall system requirements, as well as the individual relationships of various system components. In the analysis process, one may wish to view the system as a whole, identify high-cost contributors, evaluate one or more specific components of the system as necessary independent of other elements, initiate changes at the component level, and present the results in the context of the overall system.
4. Be designed in such a way as to be simple enough to allow for timely implementation. Unless the model can be utilized in a timely and efficient manner by the analyst, it is of little value.
5. Be designed such that it can be easily modified to incorporate additional capabilities. It may be necessary to expand certain facets of the cost breakdown structure in order to gain additional visibility.

The illustration presented in Figure 6.5 reflects a conceptual approach for life-cycle cost analyses as they are accomplished for relatively large-scale systems. The "life-cycle cost model" (block 6) represents the subroutine where the individual cost categories in the CBS can be compiled into an overall figure of merit for the system. The other subroutines cover key activities considered important and requiring visibility in the analysis process. For

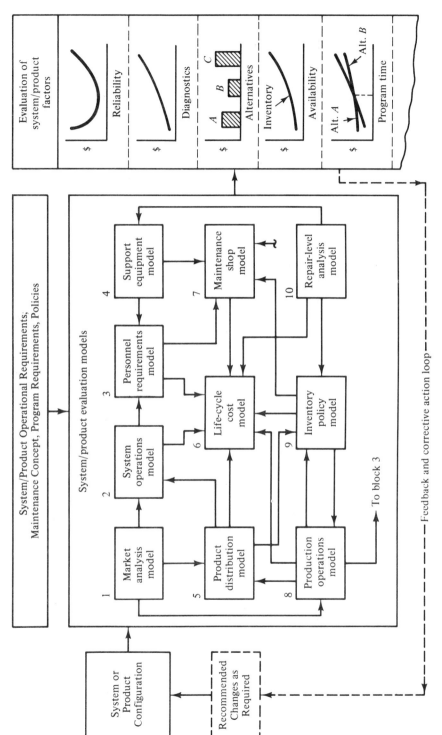

Figure 6.5 Models in the life-cycle costing process.

135

instance, if the supply support cost represents a high-cost contributor in the LCC summary presented from block 6, the analyst may wish to evaluate the spare/repair part assumptions through use of the "inventory policy model" (block 9). Additionally, various repair-level decisions may be evaluated on the basis of system operational requirements by using the models represented by blocks 2 and 10.

Decisions at this level (and below) may be tested through the use of a well-designed tool that will reflect the sensitivities among key system characteristics, as well as providing the necessary visibility with regard to major components of the system and its critical program activities. While there are many LCC models currently in existence, extreme care must be taken to ensure that the model to be used is tailored to the problem at hand. If an appropriate model is not readily available, a new model must be developed.

6.4 COST TREATMENT OVER THE LIFE CYCLE

With the system/product cost breakdown structure defined and cost estimating approaches established, it is appropriate to apply the resultant data to the system life cycle. To accomplish this, one needs to understand the steps required in developing cost profiles, aspects of inflation, the effects of learning curves, the time value of money, and so on. These are discussed in this section.

Developing the Cost Profile

In developing a cost profile, there are different procedures that may be followed. The following steps are suggested:

1. Identify all activities throughout the life cycle that will generate costs of one type or another. This includes functions associated with planning, research and development, test and evaluation, production, construction, product distribution, system/product operational use, maintenance and logistic support, and so on, as illustrated in Figure 6.2.
2. Relate each activity identified in item 1 to a specific cost category in the cost breakdown structure. All program activities should fall into one or more of the CBS categories.
3. Establish the appropriate cost factors in constant dollars for each activity in the CBS, where constant dollars reflect the general purchasing power of the dollar at the time of decision (i.e., today). Relating costs in terms of constant dollars will allow for a direct comparison of activity levels from year to year prior to the introduction of inflationary cost factors, changes in price levels, economic effects of contractual agreements with suppliers, and so on, which often cause some confusion in the evaluation of alternatives.

4. Within each cost category in the CBS, the individual cost elements are projected into the future on a year-to-year basis over the life cycle as applicable. The result should be a cost stream in constant dollars for the activities that are included.

5. For each cost category in the CBS, and for each applicable year in the life cycle, introduce the appropriate inflationary factors, economic effects of learning curves, changes in price levels, and so on. The modified values constitute a new cost stream and reflect realistic costs as they are anticipated for each year of the life cycle (i.e., expected 1991 costs in 1991, 1992 costs in 1992, etc.). These costs may be used directly in the preparation of future budget requests, since they reflect the actual dollar needs anticipated for each year in the life cycle.

6. Summarize the individual cost streams by major categories in the CBS and develop a top-level cost profile.

The results from the foregoing sequence of steps are presented in Figure 6.6. First, it is possible and often beneficial to evaluate the cost stream for individual activities of the life cycle such as research and development, production, operation and support, and so on. Second, these individual cost streams may be shown in the context of the total cost spectrum. Finally, the total cost profile may be viewed from the standpoint of the logical flow of activities and the proper level and timely expenditure of dollars. The profile in Figure 6.6 represents a budgetary estimate covering future resource needs, with the estimates accomplished in accordance with methods to be discussed in Chapter 7.

When dealing with two or more alternative system configurations, each will include different levels of activity, different design approaches, different logistic support requirements, and so on. No two alternatives will be identical. Thus individual profiles will be developed for each alternative and ultimately compared on an equivalent basis utilizing the economic analysis techniques of Chapter 3. Figure 6.7 illustrates several alternative profiles.

Incorporating Inflationary Factors

The reality of inflation should be considered for each future year in the life cycle when developing time-phased cost profiles. During the past several decades, inflation has been a significant factor in the rising costs of products and services and in the reduction of the purchasing power of the dollar. Inflation is a broad term covering the general increase(s) in the unit cost of an item or activity and is related primarily to labor and material costs, as follows:

1. Inflation factors applied to labor costs are due to salary and wage increases, cost-of-living increases, and increases in overhead rates due to the rising costs of personnel fringe benefits, retirement benefits, insur-

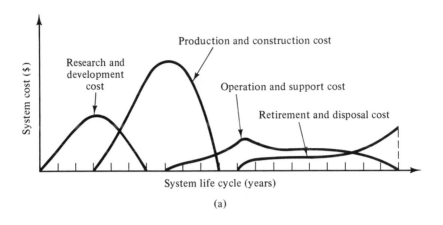

(a)

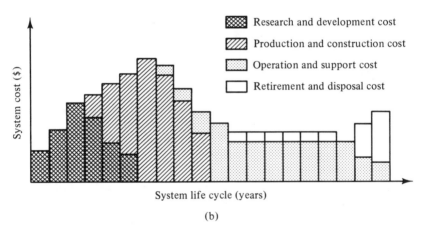

(b)

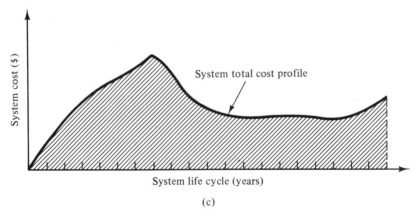

(c)

Figure 6.6   Development of life-cycle cost profiles.

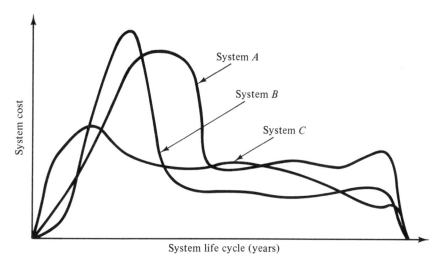

Figure 6.7   Life-cycle cost profiles of alternatives.

ance, and so on. Inflation factors should be determined for different categories of labor (i.e., engineering labor, technician labor, manufacturing labor, construction labor, customer service personnel labor, management labor, etc.) and should be estimated for each year in the life cycle.

2. Inflation factors applied to material costs are due to material availability (or unavailability), supply and demand characteristics, the increased costs of material processing, and increases in material handling and transportation costs. Inflation factors will often vary with each type of material and should be estimated for each year in the life cycle.

Increasing costs of an inflationary nature often occur as a result of new contract provisions with suppliers, new labor agreements and union contracts, revisions in procurement policies, shifts in sources of supply, the introduction of engineering changes, program schedule shifts, changes in productivity levels, changes in item quantities, and for other comparable reasons. Also, inflation factors are influenced to some extent by geographical location and competition. When reviewing the various causes of inflation, one must be extremely careful to avoid overestimating and double counting for the effects of inflation. For instance, a supplier's proposal may include provisions for inflation, and unless this fact is noted, there is a chance that an additional factor for inflation will be included for the same reason.

Inflation factors should be estimated on a year-to-year basis if at all possible. Since inflation estimates may change considerably with general economic conditions at the national level, cost estimates far out in the future (i.e., five years and more) should be reviewed at least annually and adjusted as required. Inflation factors may be established by using price indices or by the application of a uniform escalation rate as was illustrated in Chapter 3. Additional applications will be discussed in Chapter 7.

Considering Learning Effects

When performing a repetitive activity or process, learning takes place and the experience gained often results in reduced cost. Although learning and the associated cost variations occur at different activity points throughout the life cycle, the greatest impact of learning on cost is realized in the production of large quantities of a given item. In such instances, the cost of the first unit produced is generally higher than the cost of the second unit, which may be higher than the cost of the fourth unit, and so on. This is due primarily to job familiarization by workers in a production facility, development of more efficient methods for item fabrication and assembly, the use of more efficient tools, and improvement in overall management. The effects of learning generally result in the largest portion of any cost savings taking place relatively early in a program, with a leveling off taking place later.

Learning effects are commonly modeled on the basis of an assumed constant percentage cost savings for each doubling of the quantity of production units. For example, an 80% unit learning curve implies that the second unit costs 80% of the first, the fourth unit costs 80% of the second, the eighth units costs 80% of the fourth, and so on. This learning curve is then applied to find the production cost profile.

Unit learning curves may vary considerably, depending on the expected magnitude of the cost savings estimated for the second unit, the tenth unit, the twentieth unit, and so on. Because of product complexity, an 80% unit cost reduction may not be realized until the production of the tenth unit. In this case, an 80% learning curve will be based on the tenth, twentieth, fortieth, and eightieth units as being the major milestones for cost measurement. Thus one still may utilize an 80% learning curve, but the cost factors will be different. The analyst should evaluate the complexity of tasks in the production process and attempt to determine the type of unit learning curve that is most appropriate for the situation at hand.

Learning curves can also be applied to material cost, although the percentage(s) may be different. While labor costs relate to both the required personnel skill levels and labor-hours to accomplish a given function, material costs may vary as a function of factory tooling, material scapage rates (or percent of raw material utilized after the fabrication process), procurement methods, inventory policies, and worker skill. Again, there are many factors involved, and different learning curves may be applied, depending on the specific situation.

In the application of learning curves the cost analyst must ensure that the process is indeed continuous and relatively void of design changes, manufacturing changes in producing the product, and/or organization changes that will ultimately cancel out the effects of a learning curve altogether, if not create a negative learning curve where producing the tenth unit is more costly than the first. The proper application of learning curves is considered significant in life-cycle costing. Accordingly, models for learning are presented in Chapter 7.

Determining Cost Equivalence

The development of a given system or product requires many decisions to be made. Such decisions evolve from the evaluation of alternative proposals of one type or another. Each proposal considered in the evaluation process represents a potential investment and should be viewed from the standpoint of anticipated revenues (i.e., benefits) and costs that will occur over the designated life cycle. Alternatives such as the investment in configuration A, configuration B, or the investment of money in a bank, are evaluated in a like manner.

Since revenues and costs are related to different activities at a different point in time over the life cycle, a common point of reference must be assumed so that all alternatives can be compared on an equivalent basis. The flow of revenues and costs, having time value, for each alternative being considered must be equated to a common reference point. This point is generally the present time or now, when decisions that have a significant impact on the future are made; thus all future revenues and costs for each year in the life cycle may be discounted to their present equivalent amounts.

The time value of money and the calculation of equivalence was presented in detail in Chapter 3. In performing life-cycle cost analyses for decision-making purposes, the principles discussed in that chapter must be incorporated. In the evaluation of alternatives, such as those illustrated by the cost profiles in Figure 6.6, all costs must be converted to a common point in time to view these alternatives on an equivalent basis. On occasion, optimization using the models in Chapter 5 must also be applied before alternatives can be compared equivalently.

6.5 DESIGN TO COST[4]

It is the policy of the U.S. Department of Defense that all relevant life-cycle cost elements be considered in the selection and design of weapon systems. These costs include development costs, production costs, operation and support costs, and where applicable, disposal costs.

---

[4] This section was adapted from DOD-STD-337, "Design to Cost." Nondirective guidance implementing DTC may be found in the DOD *Design to Cost Handbook,* DOD-HDBK-787. The top DOD reference is DOD Directive 4245.3, "Design to Cost."

Overall *design to cost* (DTC) optimizes the use of the critical life-cycle acquisition functions and data base management procedures, reports progress against cost targets, and takes appropriate action to achieve a realistic balance between cost targets and system performance requirements. This approach helps to assure that cost effective military systems are developed within the cost, performance, and time frameworks.

The crucial importance of cost as a system parameter prompts a more aggressive approach to contracting for cost-effective products which are affordable to buy, operate, support, and in some cases, for their disposition. During the early phases of a weapon system development, achieving a proper balance of cost, performance, readiness, supportability, and schedule in a changing world requires continual communication between the government and the contractor. In some cases these program parameters will be in conflict and will require compromise. The government program office is the proper and most knowledgeable authority for guiding these decisions since it is ultimately responsible for the final product. Consequently, during the course of a contract, particularly where cost is critical and the cost risk is high, provisions must be made to obtain guidance from the government. This should be accomplished through appropriate contracting channels to update priorities and to clarify what is an acceptable mix of product characteristics.

Cost is a major consideration during the selection of subsystems and major components for the production end item. The DTC process uses relevant life-cycle cost elements to the extent they discriminate between design choices. Later in the acquisition cycle, DTC is used as the means to compare current estimates against targets and to encourage cost reduction initiatives when a target breach appears imminent.

An issue that needs to be addressed is the conflict between cost-effective choices and affordable choices for design alternatives. The desire for cost-effectiveness may, at some point, be sacrificed to the practical considerations of the funding available to the government program office. However, a prematurely imposed and unrealistic affordability requirement can needlessly preclude design choices that could have saved money. The application of cost targets is, therefore, an important issue, requiring the contractor's technical expertise and the government program office's knowledge of the total program issues to determine the proper timing and magnitude of cost targets.

Careful consideration and disposition of these cost issues is critical to an effective engineering cost control effort. Also, high-quality cost analysis, concise and timely cost information, and rapid communication among the designers and decision makers are the essential ingredients for successful design to cost. Given proper guidance, information, and resources, the designers of military systems can better achieve cost-effective and affordable designs that can be produced and employed economically.

DTC is more than just another requirement related to cost analysis; it is a concept of managing life-cycle cost elements. Properly implemented, this becomes a basic way of conducting defense business by making financial and system design decisions in terms of meeting requirements at the least total system cost. In most cases, a design to cost program will not require new organizational entities to meet the requirements. Critical functional areas (such as systems engineering, producibility, reliability, maintainability, logistics, materials, quality, and manufacturing engineering) are likely to be active in the design of military systems and will require only nominal additional effort to support cost trade-off studies.

Design to cost is mainly a matter of management direction of existing functions toward cost-conscious design decisions, organizing existing data bases to support cost understanding by design decision makers, reporting cost progress against cost targets, and taking appropriate action to achieve the latter. The level of effort for a design-to-cost program should be commensurate with the risk involved in meeting the cost goals and the benefits derived.

QUESTIONS AND PROBLEMS

1. Describe life-cycle cost and discuss what is included (excluded).
2. Describe cost-effectiveness, life-cycle cost analysis, and economic feasibility.
3. How would you create cost emphasis in the planning and development of a new system or product?
4. What is the purpose of cost allocation as illustrated in Figure 6.3?
5. Why consider life-cycle cost? Name some of the benefits associated with life-cycle costing. *Causes focus on downstream effect*
6. What purpose does the cost breakdown structure serve in life-cycle costing methodology?
7. Discuss how inflation should be treated in determining life-cycle cost.
8. How do learning curves affect LCC? What factors influence learning curves?
9. Itemize the cost elements to be considered in performing a life-cycle cost of a personal automobile.
10. Describe design to cost as a cost control methodology.
11. How can suboptimization be avoided in the application of design to cost?
12. Describe design to cost as an approach for assuring market penetration for a commercial product.

7

Estimating Cost and Economic Elements

Estimating in the physical environment approximates certainty in many situations. Examples are the pressure that a confined gas will develop under a given temperature, the current flowing in a conductor as a function of the voltage and resistance, and the velocity of a falling body at a given point in time. Much less is known with certainty about the economic environment within which life-cycle costing must be done. Economic laws depend on the behavior of people, whereas physical laws depend on well-ordered cause-and-effect relationships. Cost estimating is an inexact endeavor that will result in only an approximation of what will occur. In this chapter, attention is directed to methods and techniques for estimating cost and other economic elements.

7.1 COST ESTIMATING METHODS[1]

A *cost estimate* is an opinion based on analysis and judgment of the cost of a product, system, or structure. This opinion may be arrived at in either a formal or an informal manner by several methods, all of which assume that

---

[1]The subject of cost estimation is a significant area for study. For additional material, see P. F. Ostwald, *Cost Estimating*, 2nd ed. (Englewood Cliffs, NJ: Prentice-Hall, Inc., 1984) and R. D. Stewart, *Cost Estimating*, (New York: John Wiley & Sons, Inc., 1982).

experience is a good basis for predicting the future. In many cases the relationship between past experience and future outcome is fairly direct and obvious; in other cases it is unclear, because the proposed product or system differs in some significant way from its predecessors. The challenge is to project from the known to the unknown by using experience with existing entities. The techniques used for cost estimating range from intuition at one extreme to detailed mathematical analysis at the other.

Estimating by Engineering Procedures

Estimating by engineering procedures involves an examination of separate segments at a low level of detail. The engineering estimator begins with a complete design and specifies each production or construction task, equipment and tool need, and material requirement. Costs are assigned to each element at the lowest level of detail. These are then combined into a total for the product and system.

Time standards for production operations exist for many common tasks. These are usually developed by industrial engineers and constitute the minimum time required to complete a given task with normal worker skills and tools. Standards are best applied in engineering estimating procedures when a long, stable production run of identical items is contemplated. They are normally not useful in estimating for complex systems in which one of a kind is to be fabricated. For example, production runs of advanced military and space systems are normally short, with both the design configuration and production requirements continuing to evolve rapidly over time.

Engineering estimating procedures may require more hours of effort and data than are likely to be available in the development of some systems or products. Also, combining thousands of detailed estimates into an overall estimate can lead to an erroneous result, for the whole often turns out to be greater than the sum of its parts. The engineering estimator works from sketches, engineering drawings, or descriptions for some items that have not been completely designed. He or she can assign costs only to activities that he/she knows about. The effect of low estimates may be compounded because detail estimating is attempted on only a portion of the labor hours. A number of construction or production labor elements, such as planning, rework, coordination, and testing, are usually factored in as a percentage of the detail estimates. Other cost elements, such as maintenance, inspection, and production control, are factored in as a percentage of the production labor required. Thus small errors in detailed estimates can result in large errors in the total cost estimate.

Another source of error in estimates made by the engineering method is the significant variability that occurs in the fabrication of successive units. Production runs of like models may be of limited length and often are subject to design changes. In the case of defense systems, production rates vary frequently and unexpectedly. The proportion of new components may be significant from model year to model year as the manufacturer seeks to adapt a product to market needs. Sometimes the effect of these forces can be represented by mathematical or statistical functions that describe technological progress.

Estimating by Analogy

When a firm is entering into a new activity, estimating by analogy can be very effective. For example, aircraft companies bidding on missile programs in the 1950s drew analogies between aircraft and missiles as a basis for estimating. Appropriate adjustments were made for differences in size, number of engines, and performance. This is an example of estimating by analogy at the macrolevel.

Estimating by analogy may also occur at the microlevel. The direct labor hours required to make a component part may be estimated by referring to the hours required on similar jobs. The basis for the estimate is the similarity that exists between the known item and the proposed part. Some estimators with backgrounds as mechanics, toolmakers, or technicians are able to estimate the required times very closely. Accordingly, they are often consulted when an estimate is needed quickly.

The cost of direct labor is sometimes estimated in relation to the cost of direct material. These relationships are known with reasonable accuracy for different kinds of activities. For example, the cost of labor to lay 1,000 bricks is approximately equal to the cost of the bricks and the necessary mortar.

At all levels of aggregation, much estimating is performed by analogy. For example, project A required 10,000 direct labor hours and 4,000 equipment hours. Given the similarities and differences between project A and proposed project B, the direct labor hours and equipment hours might be estimated to be 8,000 and 3,200, respectively. By applying current labor- and equipment-hour rates, and an applicable overhead rate, a total project cost can be estimated. Or the estimator may find elements in project A that are analogous to elements in project B. From this the cost of project B may be estimated. In this example, analogy becomes part of the engineering method of estimating.

A major disadvantage of estimating by analogy is the high degree of judgment required. Considerable experience and expertise are required to identify and deal with appropriate analogies and to make adjustments for perceived differences. However, because the cost of estimating by analogy is low, it can be used as a check on other methods. Often it is the only method that can be used because the product, system, or service is only in a preliminary stage of development.

Parametric Estimating Methods

The parametric method of cost estimating may utilize statistical techniques ranging from simple graphical curve fitting to multiple correlation analysis. In either case, the objective is to find a functional relationship between changes in cost and the factor or factors upon which the cost depends, such as output rate, weight, lot size, and so forth.

Although parametric cost estimating techniques are preferred in most situations, there are cases in which engineering methods or estimating by analogy are required because the data for a systematic historical base do not exist. The product may utilize some new unfamiliar manufacturing method, thus invalidating data from previous items as a statistical base.

There will always be situations in which analogy or engineering methods are required, but the statistical approach is judged to be sufficient in long-range planning. Total cost may be estimated directly as a function of power output, weight, square feet, volume, and the like. Industrywide data or maintenance experience and energy consumed can be treated statistically and added to statistically estimated costs associated with the item itself.

Parametric estimating techniques will vary according to the purpose of the study and the information available. In conceptual design, it is desirable to have a procedure that gives the total expected cost of the product or system. Allowances for contingencies are to compensate for unforeseen changes that will have to be made. Later, as the product or system moves closer to detail design, it is desirable to have a procedure that will yield estimates of its component parts. Additional engineering effort can then be applied to reduce the cost of those components which are found to be high contributors to overall cost.

Application of Estimating Methods

In planning, industrywide labor and overhead rates can be obtained from statistical publications and used to give a rough cost estimate for a given item. As the item nears the time for bidding in its design cycle, data that are specific for a particular contractor and particular location can be used. As more is known, more specific statistical data can be used, as is the case for a product currently in production. In this stage of the product, accounting records can be used to produce a relatively precise cost figure.

In the development of cost data, the requirements may vary considerably, depending on the program phase, the extent of system/product definition, and the type and depth of the analysis being accomplished. During the early planning and conceptual design stages of system development, available data are limited, and the cost analyst must depend primarily on the use of various parametric cost estimating techniques in the development of cost data, as indicated in Figure 7.1. As the system design progresses, more complete design information becomes available and the analyst is able to develop cost estimates by comparing the characteristics of the new system with similar systems where historical cost data are available. The generation of cost data is based on analogous estimating methods. Finally, as the system design configuration becomes firm, design data (to include drawings, specifications, parts lists, predictions, etc.) are produced which allow for the development of detail engineering, manufacturing, and logistic support estimates.

7.2 DEVELOPING COST DATA

In developing cost data for a life-cycle cost analysis, the cost analyst should initially investigate all possible data sources to determine what is available for direct application in support of analysis objectives. If the required data are not available, the use of parametric cost estimating techniques may be appropriate. However, the analyst should first determine what can be derived from existing data banks, initial system planning data, supplier documentation, reliability and maintainability predictions, logistic support analyses, test data, field data, and so on. Some of the these data sources are discussed in this section.

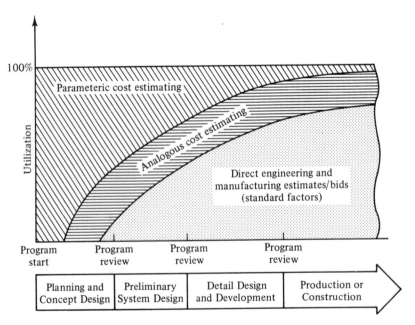

Figure 7.1 Estimating methods versus program phase.

Cost Data Requirements

The acquisition of the right type of data in a timely manner, and presented in a manageable format, is one of the most important steps in the overall process of life-cycle cost analysis. The requirements for data must be carefully defined since the application of too few data, too many data, the wrong type of data, and so on, can invalidate the overall analysis, resulting in poor decisions that may be quite costly in the long term. Further, every effort should be made to avoid the unnecessary expenditure of valuable resources in generating data that may turn out not to be required at all. Often, there is a tendency to undertake elaborate analytical exercises to develop precise quantitative factors at times when only top system-level estimates are required to satisfy the need.

Definition of the analysis goals and guidelines, combined with the identification of specific evaluation criteria, will normally dictate the data output requirements for the life-cycle cost analysis (i.e., the type of data desired from the analysis and the preferred format in which the data are to be presented). With the analysis output requirements defined, the cost analyst develops the methodologies and relationships necessary to produce the desired results. This is accomplished through the development of the cost breakdown structure and the selection of the cost model, where system parameters, estimating relationships, and cost factors are identified. The completion of these steps leads to the identification of the input data necessary to accomplish the cost analysis.

Sources of Cost Data

The sources of cost data are many and varied, as illustrated in Figure 7.2. In this section, five main sources of data for life-cycle costing purposes are presented in a summary manner to provide an overview as to what the cost analyst should look for. In pursuing the data requirements further, the analyst will find that a great deal of experience has been gained in determining research and development and production/construction costs. However, very few historical cost data are currently available in the operations and support area.

Existing data banks.   Historical information on existing systems similar in configuration and function to the item(s) being developed may be used when applicable. Often it is feasible to employ such data and apply adjustment factors as necessary to compensate for any differences in technology, configuration, projected operational environment, and time frame. Included in this category of existing data are standard cost factors which have been derived from historical experience that can be applied to specific functions or activities. Standard cost factors may cover such areas as:

Figure 7.2   Some sources of data for life-cycle costing.

1. *Cost of engineering labor:* dollars per labor hour for principal engineer, senior engineer, technician, and so on
2. *Cost of manufacturing labor by classification:* dollars per labor hour per classification
3. *Overhead rate:* dollars per direct labor cost (or percent)
4. *Training cost:* dollars per trainee week
5. *Shipping cost:* dollars per pound per mile
6. *Cost of fuel:* dollars per gallon
7. *Cost of maintaining inventory:* percent of the inventory value per year
8. *Cost of facilities:* dollars per cubic foot occupied
9. *Cost of material x:* dollars per pound or per foot

These and comparable factors, where actual quantitative values can be applied directly, are usually established from known rates and costs in the market place, and are a direct input to the analysis. However, care must be exercised to ensure that the necessary inflationary and deflationary adjustments are incorporated on a year-to-year basis.

Advanced product planning data.   Advanced planning data for the system or product being evaluated usually includes market analysis data, definition of system operational requirements and the maintenance concept, the results of technical feasibility studies, and program management data. The cost analyst needs information pertaining to the proposed physical configuration and major performance features of the system, the anticipated mission to be performed and associated utilization factors, system effectiveness parameters, the geographical location and environmental aspects of the system, the maintenance concept and logistic support philosophy, and so on. This information serves as the baseline from which all subsequent program activities evolve. If the basic information is not available, the analyst must make some assumptions and proceed accordingly. These assumptions must then be thoroughly documented.

Individual cost estimates and predictions.   Throughout the early phases of a program, cost estimates are usually generated on a somewhat continuing basis. These estimates may cover research and development activities, production or construction activities, and/or system operating and support activities. Research and development activities, which are basically nonrecurring in nature, are usually covered by initial engineering cost estimates or by cost-to-complete projections. Such projections primarily reflect labor costs and include inflationary factors, cost growth due to design changes, and so on.

Production cost estimates are often presented in terms of both nonrecurring costs and recurring costs. Nonrecurring costs are handled in a manner similar to research and development costs. On the other hand, recurring costs are frequently based on individual manufacturing cost standards, value engineering data, industrial engineering standards, and so on. Quite often, the individual standard cost factors that are used in estimating recurring manufacturing costs are documented separately, and are revised periodically to reflect labor and material inflationary effects, supplier price changes, learning effects, and so on.

System operating and support costs are based on the projected activities throughout the operational use and logistic support phase of the life cycle and are usually the most difficult to estimate. Operating costs are a function of system or product mission requirements and utilization factors. Support costs are basically a function of the inherent reliability and maintainability characteristics in the system design and the logistical requirements necessary to support all scheduled and unscheduled maintenance actions throughout the programmed life cycle. Logistic support requirements include maintenance personnel and training, supply support (spares, repair parts, and inventories), test and support equipment, transportation and handling, facilities, computer resources, and certain facets of technical data. Thus individual system support cost estimates are based on the predicted frequency of maintenance or the mean time between maintenance (MTBM) factor, and on the logistic support resources required when maintenance actions occur. These costs are derived from reliability and maintainability prediction data, logistic support analysis (LSA) data, and other supporting information, all of which is supported by system/product engineering design data.[2]

Supplier documentation and data.   Proposals, catalogs, design data, and reports covering special studies conducted by suppliers (or potential suppliers) may be used as a data source when appropriate. Quite often, major elements of a system are either procured off the shelf or developed through a subcontracting arrangement of some type. Potential suppliers will submit proposals for consideration, and these proposals may include not only acquisition cost but life-cycle cost projections (in some instances). If supplier cost data are used, the cost analyst must become completely knowledgeable as to what is and is not included. Omissions and/or the double counting of costs must not occur.

Engineering test and field data.   During the latter phases of system development and production and when the system or product is being tested or is in operational use, the experience gained represents the best source of data for actual analysis and assessment purposes. Such data are collected and used as an input to the life-cycle cost analysis. Also, field data are utilized to the extent possible in assessing the life-cycle cost impact that may result from any proposed modifications on prime equipment, software, and/or the elements of logistic support.

7.3 ADJUSTMENT OF COST DATA

Data must be consistent and comparable if they are to be useful in an estimating procedure. Inconsistency is often inherent in cost data because there are differences in definitions and in production quantity, missing cost elements, inflation, and so on. In this section some approaches found useful in coping with this inherent inconsistency are presented.

Cost Data Categories

Different accounting practices make it necessary to adjust basic cost data. Organizations record their costs in different ways; often they are required to report costs to governmental agencies in categories that differ from those used internally. These categories also change from time to time. Because of these definitional differences, the first step in cost estimating should be to adjust all data to the definition being used.

---

[2]Refer to Appendix C for the relevant terms and definitions.

Consistency is also needed in defining physical and performance characteristics. The weight of an item depends on what is included. Gross weight, empty weight, and airframe weight apply to aircraft, with each term differing in exact meaning. Speed can be defined in many ways: maximum speed, cruising speed, and so on. Differences such as these can lead to erroneous cost estimates in which the estimate is statistically derived as a function of a physical characteristic. When cost data are collected from several sources, an understanding of the definitions of physical and performance characteristics is as important as an understanding of the cost elements.

Another area requiring clear definition is that of nonrecurring and recurring costs. Recurring costs are a function of the number of units produced, whereas nonrecurring costs are not. If research and development effort on new products is charged off as an expense against current production, it does not appear against the new product. In this case, the cost of initiating a new product would be understated and the cost of existing products overstated. Separation of nonrecurring and recurring costs should be made by means of a downward adjustment of the production costs for existing products and the establishment of an account to collect research and development costs for the new product.

In addition to the first cost needed to construct or produce a new structure or system, there are recurring costs of a considerable magnitude associated with operations, maintenance, and disposal. Power, fuel, lubricants, spare parts, operating supplies, operator training, maintenance labor, and logistic support are some of these recurring costs. The life of many complex systems, when multiplied by recurring costs such as these, leads to an aggregate expenditure that may be large when compared with the first cost. Limited cost estimating effort is often applied to the category of costs associated with operations and maintenance. This is unfortunate, for the life-cycle cost of the structure of system is the only correct basis for judging its worth.

Price-Level Changes

The price of goods and services and of the labor, material, and energy required in their production changes over time. Inflationary pressures have acted to increase the price of most items. These increases have been very significant in recent years. Prices have decreased for only very brief periods.

Table 7.1 shows the change in average hourly earnings of workers in various industries over the last 25 years. The hourly wage rate in manufacturing has increased by a factor of about 3.0 from 1970 to 1990. Thus, if the labor cost component of an automobile was $1,500 in 1970, it would be almost $4,500 in 1990. Fortunately, increased productivity has kept the labor cost of the automobile at about the same percentage over this 20-year period.

Adjustments in cost data are often made by means of an index constructed from data in which one year is selected as the base. The value of that

TABLE 7.1 Average Hourly Earnings for U.S. Workers

Year	Construction	Manufacturing	Services	Transportation and Public Utilities	Total Private
1965	$ 3.70	$ 2.61	$2.05	$ 3.03	$2.46
1966	3.70	2.71	2.17	3.11	2.56
1967	4.11	2.82	2.29	3.23	2.68
1968	4.41	3.01	2.42	3.42	2.85
1969	4.79	3.19	2.61	3.63	3.04
1970	5.24	3.35	2.81	3.85	3.23
1971	5.69	3.57	3.04	4.21	3.45
1972	6.06	3.82	3.27	4.65	3.70
1973	6.41	4.09	3.47	5.02	3.94
1974	6.81	4.42	3.75	5.41	4.24
1975	7.31	4.83	4.02	5.88	4.53
1976	7.71	5.22	4.31	6.45	4.86
1977	8.10	5.68	4.65	6.99	5.25
1978	8.66	6.17	4.99	7.57	5.69
1979	9.27	6.70	5.36	8.16	6.16
1980	9.94	7.27	5.85	8.87	6.66
1981	10.82	7.99	6.41	9.70	7.25
1982	11.63	8.49	6.92	10.32	7.68
1983	11.94	8.83	7.31	10.79	8.02
1984	12.13	9.19	7.59	11.12	8.32
1985	12.32	9.54	7.90	11.40	8.57
1986	12.48	9.73	8.18	11.70	8.76
1987	12.71	9.91	8.49	12.03	8.98
1988	13.01	10.18	8.91	12.32	9.29
1989	13.37	10.47	9.39	12.57	9.66
1990[a]	14.04	10.99	9.86	13.20	10.14

[a]Estimated.
SOURCE: Bureau of Labor Statistics, Employment and Earnings.

year is expressed as 100, and the other years in the series are then expressed as a percentage of this base. Hourly earnings from 1965 through 1990 for U.S. workers could be converted to an index by using any of the years as a base. Table 7.2 uses 1967 as a base.

Price level changes are dependent on the country in question, and there are some differences within a given country. Table 7.3 gives a comparison of average hourly costs for a selected group of industrialized countries (by industry category) and with the U.S. = 1.00.

Table 7.4 gives an index for plant erection costs by country for the past several years, with the U.S. = 1.00. This index is an example of how the costs for labor, materials, and other items can be combined into one composite index.

The adjustment of costs for early price increases based on indexes is not

TABLE 7.2 Index of Average Hourly Earnings for U.S. Workers

Year	Construction	Manufacturing	Services	Transportation and Public Utilities	Total Private
1965	90	93	90	94	92
1966	95	96	95	96	96
1967	100	100	100	100	100
1968	107	107	106	106	106
1969	117	113	114	112	113
1970	128	119	123	119	121
1971	138	127	133	130	129
1972	147	136	143	144	138
1973	156	145	152	155	147
1974	166	157	164	168	158
1975	178	171	176	182	169
1976	188	185	188	200	181
1977	197	201	203	216	196
1978	211	219	218	234	212
1979	226	238	234	253	230
1980	242	258	256	275	249
1981	263	283	280	300	271
1982	283	301	302	320	287
1983	291	313	319	334	299
1984	295	326	331	344	311
1985	300	338	345	353	320
1986	304	345	357	362	327
1987	309	351	371	373	335
1988	317	361	389	381	347
1989	325	371	410	389	360
1990[a]	342	390	431	409	378

[a]Estimated.
SOURCE: Bureau of Labor Statistics, Employment and Earnings.

always easy. While the average labor rate may increase by 6% in a given year, the labor rate of a particular firm may be either more or less. Also, indexes may not be available for specific material items or for certain purchased parts. A third problem arises when expenditures are made over a number of years for a project of long duration. In the latter case, the costs in early years will require less adjustment that those in later years.

Whenever price-level changes are contemplated, one should consider the fact that increasing productivity tends to offset increased labor costs. The increase in productivity is not uniform from firm to firm or even within a specific company. However, it is a well-known economic fact that the upper limit on wage increases is set by the attainable productivity increase. Wage increases that exceed increases in productivity tend to depress profits and/or increase prices, which, in turn, adds to inflation.

TABLE 7.3 Comparison of Average Hourly Labor Costs, with U.S. = 1.0[a, b]

Country	Industry[c]	1981	1982	1983	1984	1985	1986	1987	1988
U.S.	1	1.00	1.00	1.00	1.00	1.00	1.00	1.00	1.00
	2	1.00	1.00	1.00	1.00	1.00	1.00	1.00	1.00
	3	1.00	1.00	1.00	1.00	1.00	1.00	1.00	1.00
Canada	1	0.72	0.72	0.72	0.67	0.63	0.64	0.68	0.74
	2	0.88	0.91	0.88	0.83	0.76	0.76	0.81	0.88
	3	0.99	0.99	0.85	0.79	0.73	0.71	0.80	0.85
U.K.	1	0.58	0.53	0.48	0.40	0.47	0.51	0.59	0.72
	2	0.58	0.57	0.50	0.42	0.51	0.55	0.63	0.79
	3	0.45	0.41	0.37	0.33	0.38	0.41	0.48	0.59
Japan	1	0.72	0.59	0.66	0.62	0.70	0.99	1.00	1.22
	2	0.72	0.60	0.66	0.62	0.70	0.96	0.98	1.20
	3	0.53	0.42	0.48	0.48	0.53	0.74	0.77	0.94
W. Germany	1	0.81	0.74	0.67	0.56	0.63	0.86	0.94	1.05
	2	0.90	0.84	0.77	0.65	0.75	1.02	1.13	1.28
	3	0.70	0.63	0.59	0.51	0.57	0.74	0.85	0.93
Sweden	1	NA	NA	NA	NA	NA	NA	NA	NA
	2	0.88	0.84	0.64	0.64	0.72	0.85	0.95	1.14
	3	0.89	0.78	0.59	0.59	0.67	0.84	0.96	1.13

SOURCE: *Engineering Costs and Production Economics*, July 1989.

[a] Note that all years except 1987 and 1988 are values for October. 1987 and 1988 occur in the month of December.

[b] NA, not available.

[c] 1, Manufacture of industrial chemicals; 2, manufacture of machinery excluding electrical; 3, construction.

TABLE 7.4 Comparison of Plant Erection Costs by Country, with U.S. = 1.0[a]

Country	1980	1981	1982	1983	1984	1985	1986	1987	1988
U.S.	1.00	1.00	1.00	1.00	1.00	1.00	1.00	1.00	1.00
Canada	0.90	0.90	0.92	0.92	0.86	0.81	0.76	0.80	0.84
U.K.	0.94	1.08	0.86	0.79	0.68	0.59	0.70	0.81	0.92
Japan	0.79	0.77	0.73	0.60	0.62	0.58	0.65	0.94	0.99
W. Germany	1.20	1.13	0.88	0.85	0.76	0.64	0.73	1.01	1.09
Sweden	1.26	1.29	0.99	0.90	0.76	0.70	0.79	1.03	1.16

These are currency adjusted?

SOURCE: *Engineering Costs and Production Economics*, July 1989.

[a] Note that all index measurements occur at January 1.

Improvements Due to Learning

     Learning takes place within an individual or within an organization as a function of the number of units produced. It is commonly accepted that the amount of time required to complete a given task or produce a unit of output will be less each time the task is undertaken. The unit time will decrease at a decreasing rate, and this time reduction will follow a predictable pattern.

The empirical evidence supporting the concept of a *learning curve* was first noted in the aircraft industry. The reduction in direct labor hours required to build an aircraft was observed and found to be predictable. Since then, the learning curve has found applications in other industries as a means for adjusting costs for items produced beyond the first one.

Most learning curves are based on the assumption that the direct labor hours needed to complete a unit of product will decrease by a constant percentage each time the production quantity is doubled. A typical rate of improvement in the aircraft industry is 20% between doubled quantities. This establishes an 80% learning function and means that the direct labor hours needed to build the second aircraft will be 80% of the hours required to build the first aircraft. The fourth aircraft will require 80% of the hours that the second required, the eighth aircraft will require 80% of the fourth, and so on. This relationship is given in Table 7.5.

An analytical expression for the learning curve may be developed for the assumption of constant percentage reduction for doubled quantities. Let

x = unit number

Y_x = number of direct labor hours required to produce the xth unit

K = number of direct labor hours required to produce the first unit

ϕ = the slope parameter of the learning curve

From the assumption of a constant percentage reduction in direct labor hours for doubled production units,

$$Y_x = K\phi^0 \quad \text{where } x = 2^0 = 1$$
$$Y_x = K\phi^1 \quad \text{where } x = 2^1 = 2$$
$$Y_x = K\phi^2 \quad \text{where } x = 2^2 = 4$$
$$Y_x = K\phi^3 \quad \text{where } x = 2^3 = 8$$

TABLE 7.5   Unit, Cumulative, and Cumulative Average Direct Labor Hours for an 80% Function

Unit Number x	Unit Direct Labor Hours	Cumulative Direct Labor Hours	Cumulative Average Direct Labor Hours
1	100.00	100.00	100.00
2	80.00	180.00	90.00
4	64.00	314.21	78.55
8	51.20	534.59	66.82
16	40.96	892.01	55.75
32	32.77	1,467.86	45.87
64	26.21	2,392.45	37.38

Therefore,

$$Y_x = K\phi^d \qquad \text{where } x = 2^d$$

Taking the common logarithm gives

$$\log Y_x = \log K + d \log \phi$$

where

$$\log x = d \log 2$$

Solving for d gives

$$d = \frac{\log Y_x - \log K}{\log \phi}$$

and

$$d = \frac{\log x}{\log 2}$$

from which

$$\frac{\log Y_x - \log K}{\log \phi} = \frac{\log x}{\log 2}$$

$$\log Y_x - \log K = \frac{\log x (\log \phi)}{\log 2}$$

Let

$$n = \frac{\log \phi}{\log 2}$$

Therefore,

$$\log Y_x - \log K = n \log x$$

Taking the antilog of both sides gives

$$\frac{Y_x}{K} = x^n$$

$$Y_x = Kx^n \qquad\qquad (7.1)$$

Application of Equation 7.1 can be illustrated by reference to the example of an 80% progress function with unit 1 at 100 direct labor hours. Solving for Y_8, we see that the number of direct labor hours required to build the eighth unit gives

$$Y_8 = 100(8)^{\log 0.8 / \log 2}$$

$$= 100(8)^{-0.322}$$

$$= \frac{100}{1.9535} = 51.2$$

The information from the learning curve can be extended to cost estimates for labor by multiplying by the labor rate that applies. In doing this, the analyst must take into consideration that the subsequent units may be completed months or years after the initial units. Adjustments for labor-rate increases might have to be made along with the adjustment for learning that is inherent in the application of the learning curve.

7.4 COST ESTIMATING RELATIONSHIPS

Estimates of a result will usually be more accurate if they are based on estimates of the factors having a bearing on the result than if the result is estimated directly. For example, in estimating the volume of a room it will usually prove more accurate to estimate the several dimensions of the room and calculate the volume than to estimate the volume directly. Similar reasoning applies to estimates of cost and other economic elements.

Cost estimating methods often lead to mathematically fitted functions called *cost estimating relationships* (CERs). A cost estimating relationship is a functional model that mathematically describes the cost of a structure, system, or service as a function of one or more independent variables. Of course, there must be a logical or theoretical relationship of the variables to cost, a statistical significance of the contribution of the variables, and independence among the variables.

Parametric Estimating Functions

Parametric cost estimating relationships are basically "rules of thumb" that relate various categories of cost-to-cost-generating or explanatory variables of one form or another. These explanatory variables usually represent characteristics of system performance, physical features, effectiveness factors, or even other cost elements. Estimating relationships may take different forms (i.e., continuous or discontinuous, mathematical or nonmathematical, linear or nonlinear, etc.). Some of these are presented in the following paragraphs:

Simple linear functions.   A simple linear estimating function is expressed as

$$y = a + bx$$

where y and x are the dependent and independent variables, and a and b are parameters. Linear functions are useful because many cost relationships are of this form. Sometimes linear relationships are developed employing curve-fitting techniques (i.e., least squares) or normal regression analysis. Such linear functions are utilized for forecasting purposes and may relate one cost parameter to another, a cost parameter to a noncost parameter, and/or a non-

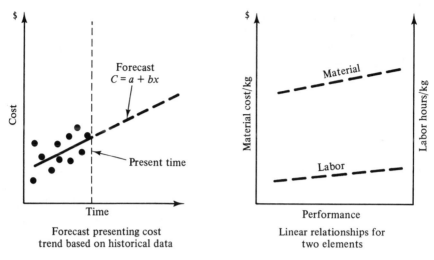

Figure 7.3   Simple linear cost estimating relationships.

cost parameter to another noncost parameter. Two illustrations are given in Figure 7.3.

Simple nonlinear functions.   Not all cost functions are linear. Some cost relationships may be exponential in nature, hyperbolic, or may fit some other curve. Examples of nonlinear forms involving a single explanatory variable are

$$y = ab^x \qquad \text{(exponential)}$$

$$y = a + bx - cx^2 \qquad \text{(parabolic)}$$

$$y = \frac{1}{a + bx} \qquad \text{(hyperbolic)}$$

Figure 7.4 illustrates two nonlinear applications.

Discontinuous step functions.   The estimating relationships introduced imply a continuous function involving cost and other variables. However, in many instances cost can be constant over a specific range of the explanatory variable, then suddenly increase to a higher level at some point, remain constant again, then increase to another level, and so on. This type of relationship, known as a *step function*, is illustrated in Figure 7.5. These kinds of functions are useful in illustrating the cost behavior of quantity procurement in production, support activities that are represented in small non-continuous increments, price–quantity relationships, and so on.

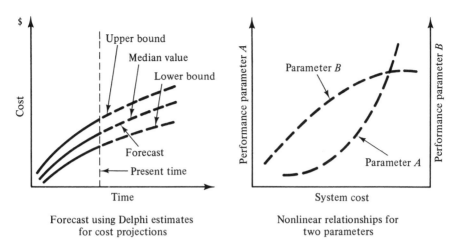

Forecast using Delphi estimates
for cost projections

Nonlinear relationships for
two parameters

Figure 7.4   Simple nonlinear cost estimating relationships.

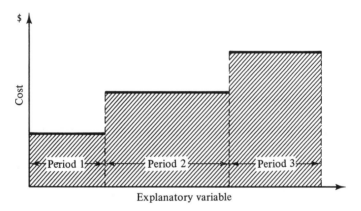

Figure 7.5   Discontinuous step function for cost.

Statistical distribution functions.   When analyzing historical cost data, one will find that the actual cost of a given activity, when completed on a number of occasions, will vary. This variance may assume any form of distribution, such as illustrated in Figure 7.6. In the prediction of future costs for comparable activities on a new program, the cost analyst may wish to assume a distribution and determine the median or mean value, variance, standard deviation, and so on, in order to assess risk in terms of probabilities of possible cost variations. The distributions associated with historical costs will facilitate this task.

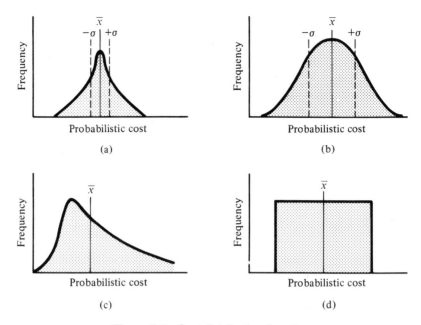

Figure 7.6 Cost distribution functions.

Other estimating forms.   Of a more general nature, the analyst may use analogies as a form of estimating. Historical data from events in the past may be employed in terms of future estimates on the basis of similarity. Such estimates may be used directly or may be factored to some extent to compensate for slight differences.

Another approach may involve *rank-order cost estimation*. A series of comparable activities are evaluated in terms of cost and then ranked on the basis of the magnitude of the cost (i.e., the highest-cost activity on down to the lowest-cost activity). After the ranking is accomplished, the various activities are viewed in relation to each other, and the initial cost values may be adjusted if the specific relationships appear to be unrealistic. This may require an iterative process.

Some Examples of CERs

Numerous examples of specific cost estimating relationships could be presented that follow one or more of the categories discussed above. In this section two generally applicable relationships are developed and illustrated numerically. The first uses the learning curve to estimate item cost and the second uses the power law and sizing model to estimate equipment cost.

Determining item cost involving learning.   As one example of the development of a cost estimating relationship consider the production of a lot of N units. The cumulative number of direct labor hours required to produce N units may be expressed as

$$T_N = Y_1 + Y_2 + \cdots + Y_N = \sum_{x=1}^{N} Y_x \tag{7.2}$$

where Y_x is the number of direct labor hours required to produce the xth unit. This was derived as Equation 7.1 as

$$Y_x = Kx^n$$

An approximation for the cumulative direct labor hours is given by

$$T_N \cong \int_0^N Y_x \, dx$$

$$\cong \int_0^N Kx^n \, dx$$

$$\cong K \left(\frac{N^{n+1}}{n+1} \right) \tag{7.3}$$

Dividing by N gives an approximation for the cumulative average number of direct labor hours expressed as

$$V_N \cong \frac{1}{n+1} (KN^n) \tag{7.4}$$

Item cost per unit may be expressed in terms of the direct labor cost, the direct material cost, and the overhead cost. Let

LR = direct labor hourly rate
DM = direct material cost per unit
OH = overhead rate expressed as a decimal fraction of the direct labor hourly rate

Item cost per unit, C_i, can be expressed as

$$C_i = V_N (\text{LR}) + \text{DM} + V_N (\text{LR})(\text{OH})$$

or, by substituting for V_n,

$$C_i = \frac{KN^n}{n+1} (\text{LR})(1 + \text{OH}) + \text{DM} \tag{7.5}$$

As an example of the application of this cost estimating relationship, consider a situation in which 8 units are to be produced. The direct labor rate is \$9 per hour, the direct material cost per unit is \$600, and the overhead rate is 0.90. It is estimated that the first unit will require 100 direct labor hours and that an 80% learning curve is applicable. The item cost per unit is then estimated from Equation 7.5 to be

$$C_i = \left[\frac{100(8)^{-0.322}}{-0.322 + 1} \right] (\$9)(1.90) + \$600$$

$$= \left[\frac{\$51.19}{0.678} \right] (\$9)(1.90) + \$600$$

$$= \$1,291 + \$600 = \$1,891$$

This cost estimating relationship gives the cost per unit as a function of the direct labor cost, the direct material cost, and the overhead cost. It also adjusts the direct labor hours for learning in accordance with an estimated rate.

Power law and sizing model.   Equipment cost estimating can often be accomplished by using the power law and sizing model. Equipment to which this cost estimating relationship applies must be similar in type and vary only in size. The economies of scale in terms of size are expressed in the relationship

$$C = C_r \left(\frac{Q_c}{Q_r} \right)^m \tag{7.6}$$

where

C = cost for design size Q_c
C_r = known cost for reference size Q_r
Q_c = design size
Q_r = reference design size
m = correlating exponent, $0 < m < 1$

If $m = 1$, a linear relationship exists and the economies of scale do not apply. For most equipment m will be approximately 0.5, and for chemical processing equipment it is approximately 0.6.

As an example of the application of Equation 7.6, assume that a 200-gallon reactor with glass lining and jacket cost \$9,500 in 1980. An estimate is required for a 300-gallon reactor to be purchased and installed in 1990. The price index in 1980 was 180 and is anticipated to be 235 in 1990. An estimate of the correlating exponent for this type of equipment is 0.50. Therefore, the estimated cost in 1980 dollars is

$$C_{1980} = \$9,500 \left(\frac{300}{200} \right)^{0.5} = \$11,635$$

and the cost in 1990 dollars is

$$C_{1990} = \$11,635\left(\frac{235}{180}\right) = \$15,190$$

This cost estimating relationship relates a known cost to a future cost by means of an exponential relationship. Determination of the exponent is essential to the estimation process.

Other estimating relationships.   The widespread use of estimating relationships speaks of their value in a wide range of situations. These relationships are available in the form of equations, sets of curves, nomograms, and tables.

In the aircraft and defense industry it is common to express the cost of airframe, power plant, avionics, and so on, as a function of weight, impulse, speed, and other factors. It is normally the next generation of aircraft or missile that is of interest. The estimated cost is determined by an extrapolation from known values for a sample group to an unknown proposed vehicle. This information is then used in cost-effectiveness studies and in budget requests.

Pollution control equipment such as sewage plants can be estimated from functions that relate the investment cost to the capacity in gallons per day. A municipality considering a plant with primary and secondary treatment capability may refer to estimating relationships based on plants already built. The estimator then would make two adjustments, one for the difference in construction cost due to the passage of time since the relationship was derived, the other for cost differences based on location.

Cost estimating relationships are probably most plentiful for estimating the cost of buildings. These relationships are normally based on square feet and/or volume. They take into consideration costs due to labor differentials for location. A person beginning discussions about the construction of a new home will almost always begin thinking in terms of the cost per square foot.

Engineering costs for complex projects are available as a function of the installed cost of the structure or system being designed. These costs are expressed as a percentage of the installed cost of such projects as office buildings and laboratories, power plants, water systems, and chemical plants. In each case the engineering cost is a decreasing percentage as the installed project cost increases.

7.5 ESTIMATING MANUFACTURING COST

To estimate item cost for manufacturing, it is essential that direct material and direct labor costs be accurately collected and appropriately allocated (along with factory burden costs) to the product being produced. The methods commonly used to allocate burden costs are the direct-material-cost method and the direct-labor-cost method. These, and the direct-resource-cost method, as well as the determination of factory burden cost and manufacturing cost, are illustrated in the following example.[3]

PLASCO Company, a small plastic manufacturing company, has plant facilities as shown in Figure 7.7. The cost of land for the plant is $18,000 and the cost of the plant is $90,000. Two-thirds of each of these costs, namely, $12,000 and $60,000, is attributed to the production department. The initial cost of machine X and machine Y was $36,000 and $60,000, respectively. In addition, other assets of the firm are factory furniture, with a first cost of $8,000; small tools and dies, which cost $8,800; and stores and stock inventory, with a value of $12,000.

The labor costs during the current year (50 weeks per year at 40 hours per week) are estimated as follows:

Foreman F supervises factory operations	$24,000
Handyman H moves material and takes care of stores	11,000
Total indirect labor	$35,000
Worker W_1 operates machine X, $9/hr × 2000 hr/yr	$18,000
Worker W_2 operates machine Y, $7/hr × 2000 hr/yr	14,000
Total direct labor	$32,000

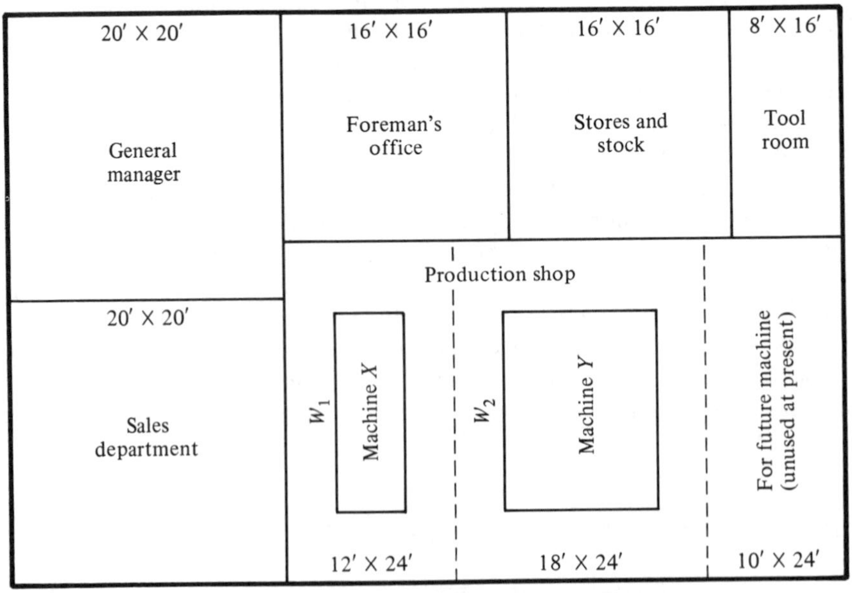

Figure 7.7   PLASCO facilities for manufacturing.

[3] The general outline for this example was adopted from G. J. Thuesen and W. J. Fabrycky, *Engineering Economy*, 7th ed. (Englewood Cliffs, NJ: Prentice-Hall, Inc., 1989).

PLASCO Company makes three products, A, B, and C. Estimated output, material cost, direct labor hours, and machine hours are given in Table 7.6. The estimation of PLASCO Company factory burden costs during the current year may be summarized as follows:

1. Indirect expenses for building and land:

Depreciation, insurance, and maintenance of property	$ 8,800
Taxes and interest on present value of property	10,400
Utilities for factory	3,700
Total	$22,900

2. Miscellaneous indirect expenses:
   Depreciation, insurance, maintenance, taxes, and interest on present value of

Factory furniture	$2,060
Small tools	710
Stores and stock inventory	1,750
Office and general supplies	1,600
Total	$6,120

3. Indirect labor and related expenses:

Salaries of employees F and H	$35,000
Payroll taxes	7,800
Total	$42,800

4. Indirect expenses due to machine X:

Depreciation, insurance, maintenance, and taxes	$6,100
Interest on present value of machine	2,800
Supplies and power	$1,240
Total	$10,140

5. Indirect expenses due to machine Y:

Depreciation, insurance, maintenance, and taxes	$ 9,400
Interest on present value of machine	4,300
Supplies and power	1,800
Total	$15,500

Grand total (all factory burden items)	$97,460

On the basis of the information given, factory burden allocation rates may be computed as follows:

$$\text{direct-material-cost rate} = \frac{\text{total factory burden}}{\text{total direct material cost}}$$

$$= \frac{\$97,460}{\$30,800} = 3.16$$

TABLE 7.6 Estimated Production Activity and Cost

Product	Estimated Output	Material Cost Each	Material Cost Total	Worker W_1 Each	Worker W_1 Total	Worker W_2 Each	Worker W_2 Total	Machine X Each	Machine X Total	Machine Y Each	Machine Y Total
A	100,000	$0.10	$10,000	0.01	1,000	—	—	0.01	1,000	—	—
B	140,000	0.08	11,200	—	—	0.01	1,400	—	—	0.01	1,400
C	80,000	0.12	9,600	0.0125	1,000	0.0075	600	0.0125	1,000	0.0075	600
			$30,800		2,000		2,000		2,000		2,000

(Direct Labor Hours: Worker W_1, Worker W_2; Machine Hours: Machine X, Machine Y)

TABLE 7.7 Item Cost per Unit for Manufacturing Using Different Methods of Allocating Factory Burden

Product	Direct-Material-Cost Method	Direct-Labor-Cost Method	Direct-Resource-Cost Method
A	Direct material $0.100	Direct material $0.100	Direct material $0.100
	Direct labor, 0.01 × $9 0.090	Direct labor, 0.01 × $9 0.090	Direct labor, 0.01 × $9 0.090
	Factory burden, $0.10 × 3.16 0.316	Factory burden, $0.09 × 3.05 0.275	Factory burden, $0.19 × 1.55 0.294
	$0.506	$0.465	$0.484
B	Direct material $0.080	Direct material $0.080	Direct material $0.080
	Direct labor, 0.01 × $7 0.070	Direct labor, 0.01 × $7 0.070	Direct labor, 0.01 × $7 0.070
	Factory burden, $0.08 × 3.16 0.253	Factory burden, $0.07 × 3.05 0.214	Factory burden, $0.15 × 1.55 0.232
	$0.403	$0.364	$0.382
C	Direct material $0.120	Direct material $0.120	Direct material $0.120
	Direct labor, 0.0125 × $9 + 0.0075 × $7 0.165	Direct labor, 0.0125 × $9 + 0.0075 × $7 0.165	Direct labor, 0.0125 × $9 + 0.0075 × $7 0.165
	Factory burden, $0.12 × 3.16 0.379	Factory burden, $0.165 × 3.05 0.503	Factory burden, $0.285 × 1.55 0.442
	$0.664	$0.788	$0.727

$$\text{direct-labor-cost rate} = \frac{\text{total factory burden}}{\text{total direct labor cost}}$$

$$= \frac{\$97,460}{\$32,000} = 3.05$$

$$\text{direct-resource-cost rate} = \frac{\text{total factory burden}}{\text{total direct resource cost}}$$

$$= \frac{\$97,460}{\$62,800} = 1.55$$

The item cost of products A, B, and C may now be determined by each of the three methods of allocating factory burden cost. The calculations are given in Table 7.7.

Item cost of manufacturing is obtained by summing the estimates of direct cost and factory burden cost. An accurate determination of these costs is essential for an accurate estimate of item cost. Direct material cost may be inaccurate because of variations in pricing, charging a product with more material than is actually used, and due to the use of estimates in place of actual values. Similar reasons may apply to direct-labor-cost estimates. Good control and accounting procedures are therefore necessary to obtain reliable cost estimates.

Additional difficulties are experienced in connection with the allocation of factory burden and general overhead costs. An examination of Table 7.7 reveals that there can be a significant difference in the estimates of item cost of manufacturing obtained by the three methods of allocating factory burden costs. In reality, factory burden consists of a great number and variety of costs. It is therefore not surprising that the use of a single, simple method will not allocate factory burden costs to specific products with precision. The use of a single method may, however, be quite satisfactory in most situations, even though wide variations may result in some specific instances.

7.6 ACCOUNTING DATA IN ESTIMATING

Since accounting data are the basis for many life-cycle cost studies, caution should be exercised in their use. An understanding of the relevance of accounting data is essential for its proper utilization. Two examples of the pertinence of cost accounting data are presented in this section.

Effect of Activity-Level Changes

In the determination of rates for the allocation of overhead, the activity of the PLASCO Company for the year was estimated in terms of products A,

B, and C. This estimate served as a basis for determining annual material cost, annual direct labor cost, and annual direct resource cost. These items then became the denominator of the several allocation rates.

The numerator of the allocation rates was the estimated factory overhead, totaling $97,460. This numerator quantity will remain relatively constant for changes in activity, as an examination of the items of which it is composed will reveal. For this reason the several rates for allocating factory overhead will vary in some generally inverse proportion with activity. Thus if the actual activity is less than the estimated activity, the overhead rate charged will be less than the amount necessary to absorb the estimated total overhead. The reverse is also true.

In cost estimating the effect of activity on overhead charges and overhead rates is an important consideration. The total overhead charges of the PLASCO Company would remain relatively constant over a range of activity represented, for example, by 1,200 to 2,000 hours of activity for each of the two machines. Thus, after the total overhead has been allocated, the incremental cost of producing additional units of product will consist only of direct material and direct labor costs.

Inadequacy of Average Costs

An important function of cost accounting is to provide data for decisions relative to the reduction of production costs and the increase of profit from sales. Cost data that are believed to be accurate may lead to costly errors in decisions. Cost data that give true average values and are adequate for overall analysis may be inadequate for specific detailed analyses. Thus cost data must be carefully scrutinized and their accuracy established before they can be used with confidence in economy studies.

In Table 7.8 actual and estimated cost data relative to the cost of three products have been tabulated. The actual production costs of products X, Y, and Z are $9, $10, and $11, respectively, but because of inaccuracies in overhead costs are believed to be $10 for each. Even though the average of a number of costs may be correct, there is no assurance that this average is a

TABLE 7.8   Actual and Estimated Cost Data

Product	Direct Labor and Material Costs	Overhead Costs, Actual	Overhead Costs, Believed to Be	Production Cost, Actual	Production Cost, Believed to Be
X	$6.50	$2.50	$3.50	$ 9.00	$10.00
Y	7.00	3.00	3.00	10.00	10.00
Z	7.50	3.50	2.50	11.00	10.00
Average	7.00	3.00	3.00	10.00	10.00

good indication of the cost of individual products. For this reason the accuracy of each cost should be ascertained before it is used in a cost analysis.

For example, if the selling price of the products is based on their believed production cost, product X will be overpriced and product Z will be underpriced. Buyers may be expected to shun product X and to buy large quantities of product Z. This may lead to a serious unexplained loss of profit. Average values of cost data are of little value in making decisions relative to specific products.

7.7 JUDGMENT IN ESTIMATING

Mature judgment is an essential ingredient in the estimating process as often discussed. Although the need for judgment is self-evident, one problem in the past has been too much reliance on judgment and too little on analytical approaches.

Because people are involved in applying judgment, the problem of personal bias arises. A person's assigned role or position seems to influence his or her forecasts. Thus a tendency toward low estimates appears among those whose interests they serve, principally proponents of a new product, structure, or system. Similarly, estimates by people whose interests are served by caution are likely to be higher than they would otherwise.

The primary use of judgment should be to decide whether or not an estimating relationship can be used. Second, judgment must determine what adjustments will be necessary to take into account the effect of a technology that is not present in the sample. Judgment is also required to decide whether or not the results obtained from an estimating relationship are reasonable in comparison with the past cost of similar items.

When a proposed project contains considerable uncertainty, it is often wise to hold capital equipment investment to a minimum until outcomes become clearer, even though such a decision may result in higher maintenance and operation costs for the present system. Such action amounts to a decision to incur higher costs temporarily in order to reserve the privilege of making a second decision when the situation becomes clearer.

The accuracy of estimates with respect to events in the future is, to some extent, inversely proportional to the span of time between the estimate and the event. It is often appropriate to incur expense for the privilege of deferring the decision until better estimates can be made.

QUESTIONS AND PROBLEMS

1. Contrast estimating in the physical environment with estimating in the economic environment.

2. Why must life-cycle costing rely heavily on estimates?
3. Briefly describe the advantages and disadvantages of the three cost estimating methods.
4. What are some of the important requirements in the development of cost data?
5. List some of the sources of cost data.
6. Explain why an estimate of a result will probably be more accurate if it is based upon estimates of the factors that have a bearing on the result than if the result is estimated directly.
7. If the total cost for construction labor on a project was $520,000 in 1978, estimate the cost in 1990 from the information in Table 7.1.
8. If the manufacturing labor cost per unit of product produced in the United States was $6.10 in 1985, what was the labor cost in that year in the United Kingdom? In Japan? In West Germany?
9. Describe three sources which contribute to manufacturing improvement through learning.
10. Sketch the progress curve with $K = 12$ hours and $\phi = 0.80$ on arithmetic graph paper through 20 units. How long should units 8 and 16 take to complete?
11. Suppose that 5,000 hours are required to build a certain system for which the rate of learning for subsequent systems will be 15% on doubled quantities.
    (a) Calculate the labor hours to build the second, fourth, eighth, and sixteenth systems, and plot the results.
    (b) Estimate the labor hours required for the tenth and twentieth units and compare this estimate to the result obtained from the formula.
12. Use the information in Problem 11 to compute the cumulative labor hours for the group of 16 systems by both the exact and the approximate methods.
13. Estimate the cumulative average number of direct labor hours for a product requiring 8 hours for the first unit if 16 units are to be produced with an improvement of 20% between doubled production quantities.
14. Estimate the item cost per unit for a production lot of 1,000 units if the first unit requires 4 labor hours, the 70% learning curve applies, the labor rate is $9.10 per hour, the direct material cost is $20 per unit, and the overhead rate is 1.80.
15. A heat exchanger cost $7,500 in 1983 and must be replaced soon with a larger unit. The present unit has an effective area of 250 sq feet and its replacement should have an area of 350 sq feet. Replacement is anticipated in 1990 when the price index is estimated to be 170 with 1983 as the base year. Estimate the cost of the unit in 1990 if the correlating coefficient for this type of equipment is 0.6.
16. The following data were collected on alternate production units:

Unit Number	Direct Labor Hours
2	100
4	90
6	80
8	75
10	60
12	50

What is the best estimate of the cumulative average time to complete a total of 100 such units? Solve graphically.

17. The following data are provided for Problem 16:

Direct material cost	$3.50 per piece
Direct labor rate	$7.50 per hour
Factory burden rate	1.10

What is the average unit cost of the 100 units? If the units can be purchased for $37.50 per unit, how many units should be produced so that the cost of manufacturing and purchasing will be equal?

18. A product can be manufactured under a direct labor hourly rate of $9.00 per hour, a direct material cost of $21 per unit, and a factory burden rate of 1.20. The first production unit will require 4 hours to complete. Improvements of 25 percent between doubled quantities can be expected. The product can also be purchased for $70. At what total quantity are the two alternatives equal in cost?

19. A small factory is divided into four departments for accounting purposes. The direct labor and direct material expenditures for a given year are as follows:

Department	Direct Labor-Hours	Direct Labor Cost	Direct Material Cost
A	900	$14,500	$19,000
B	945	14,900	6,800
C	1,050	15,050	11,200
D	1,335	13,900	15,000

Distribute an annual overhead charge of $42,000 to departments A, B, C, and D on the basis of direct labor cost and direct resource cost.

20. What precautions should be exercised in utilizing accounting data in life-cycle costing and economic analysis?

21. Describe a situation in which a person's role or position has influenced his or her estimate of an undertaking.

8

Evaluating Errors
in Estimating

There are many factors to be considered in life-cycle economic analysis. Assumptions must be made, data must be collected and evaluated, functional relationships must be established, and so on. The process allows for the introduction of error. In making a final recommendation as to a proposed course of action, the economic analyst should review the overall analysis process in terms of problem definition, validity of stated assumptions, functional relationships, inclusions or exclusions, adequacy of data input, and stated conclusions. In this chapter several methods for dealing with errors in estimates are presented.

8.1 A DECISION BASED ON ESTIMATES

The future outcome of an activity can be predicted accurately if sufficient knowledge is available. Considerable emphasis is usually placed on obtaining appropriate data and using them carefully to arrive at estimates that are representative of anticipated outcomes. When all facts about alternatives are known in accurate quantitative terms, the relative merit of each may be expressed in terms of a single decision number. Decision making in this case is simple.[1]

---

[1] The decision evaluation theory of Chapter 5 assumed that the facts about each alternative were known.

Decisions must often be made even though quantitative considerations are based on estimates that are subject to error. As an example, suppose that special equipment for processing a microchip circuit is considered likely to result in a saving. It is known with absolute certainty that the equipment will cost $260,000. All other economic factors pertinent to the decision are un-known and must be estimated.

Cost Saving Estimate

From a study of past data and the result of judgment, it has been esti-mated that a total of 6,000 units of the circuit will be made during the next five years. The number to be made each year is not known. However, it is be-lieved that production will be fairly well distributed over the period, making the annual production to be 1,200 units. A detailed consideration of materials used, time studies of the methods employed, technician rates and the like, gives an estimated saving of $150 per unit, exclusive of the costs incident to the operation of the equipment. Combining the estimated production and the estimated unit saving results in an estimated saving (income) of $1,200 \times$ $150 = $180,000 per year.

Capital Recovery with Return Estimate

The equipment is single-purpose and no use is seen for it except in processing the microchip circuit under consideration. Its service life has been taken to be five years to coincide with the estimated production period of five years. It is believed that the salvage value of the equipment will be $60,000. Interest is considered to be an expense based on the cost of money, and the rate has been estimated at 12%. The next step is to combine the estimates of first cost, service life, and salvage value to determine the estimated annual cost of capital recovery with a return. For the first cost of $260,000, a service life of five years, a salvage value of $60,000, and an interest rate of 12%, the annual cost of capital recovery and return is estimated to be

$$\overset{A/P,12,5}{(\$260,000 - \$60,000)\,(\,0.2774\,) + \$60,000\,(0.12)} = \$62,680$$

Operation and Maintenance Cost Estimate

Operation and maintenance costs are normally made up of several items such as power, supplies, spare parts, and labor. For simplicity, consider the operation and maintenance expenses of the equipment in this example to consist of four items. Each is estimated on the basis of the number of units of product to be processed per year as shown in Table 8.1.

TABLE 8.1   Operation and Maintenance Costs

O&M Item	Annual Cost
Power	$ 40,000
Maintenance labor	10,500
Operating and maintenance supplies	6,000
Operating labor with indirect	48,000
Total	$104,500

The estimated net annual saving for the project may be summarized as shown in Table 8.2. This final statement means that the project will result in an equivalent annual saving of $12,820 per year for a period of five years if the several estimates prove to be accurate.

TABLE 8.2   Computation of Net Annual Saving

Saving or Cost Item	Cost	Saving
Estimated total annual saving		$180,000
Estimated annual capital recovery with return cost	$ 62,680	
Estimated annual operation and maintenance cost	104,500	
Estimated total annual cost	$167,180	
Estimated net annual saving		$ 12,820

The equivalent annual saving is itself an estimate, and experience indicates that the most certain characteristic of estimates is that they nearly always prove to be inaccurate, sometimes in small degree and often in large degree. However, once the best possible estimates have been made, whether they eventually prove to be good or bad, they remain the most objective basis on which to base decisions.

8.2 ALLOWING FOR ERRORS IN ESTIMATES

The better the estimate, the less allowance needs to be made for error. However, allowances for errors do not make up for a deficiency of knowledge in the sense that they correct error. The allowances presented in this section are *rule-of-thumb* approaches for eliminating some of the consequences of error.

Allowing for Error by High Interest Rates

A common policy in many firms is to require that proposed undertakings be justified on the basis of a high minimum acceptable rate of return, say 25%. One basis for this practice is that there are many opportunities that will result in a return of 25% or more. Those yielding less can be ignored. Since this is a much greater return than most firms make on the average, the high rate of return provides an allowance for error. It is anticipated that if the undertaking of ventures is limited to those that promise a high rate of return, few will be undertaken that will result in a loss.

Returning to the example of microchip circuit production given in Section 8.1, suppose that the estimated saving and the estimated cost of carrying on the venture when the interest rate is taken at 25% are as shown in Table 8.3. If the calculated loss based on the high interest rate is the deciding factor, the venture will not be undertaken. Although the estimates as given above, except for the interest rate of 25%, might have been correct, the venture would have been rejected. The arbitrary high interest rate taken is the cause for rejection even though the resulting rate of return would be almost 25%.

TABLE 8.3 Computation of Net Annual Saving at i = 25%

Saving or Cost Item	Cost	Saving
Estimated total annual saving		$180,000
Estimated annual capital recovery with return cost		
$(\$260,000 - \$60,000) \overset{A/P,25,5}{(\ 0.3719\ )} + \$60,000\,(0.25)$	$ 89,380	
Estimated annual operating and maintenance cost	104,500	
Estimated total annual cost	$193,880	
Estimated net annual profit		$-13,880

Suppose that the total operating costs had been estimated as above, but that the annual saving had been estimated at $195,000. On the basis of a policy to accept ventures promising a return of 25% on investment, the venture would be accepted. But if it turned out that the annual saving was only $170,000, the venture would result in loss regardless of the calculated income with the high interest rate. Accordingly, an allowance for error embodied in a high rate of return does not prevent a loss that stems from incorrect estimates if a venture is undertaken that will, in fact, result in loss.

Allowing for Error by Rapid Payout

The effect of allowing for error in estimates by rapid payout is essentially the same as that of using high interest rates. For example, assume that a policy exists that equipment purchases must be based on a three-year payout period when the interest rate is taken at 12%.

Returning to the prior example, suppose that the estimated saving and the estimated cost of carrying on the venture when a three-year payout period are adopted as shown in Table 8.4. Under these conditions the project would not have been undertaken. The effect of choosing conservative values for

TABLE 8.4 Computation of Net Annual Saving for $n = 3$

Saving or Cost Item	Cost	Saving
Estimated annual saving (estimated for five years but taken as three years to conform to policy)		$180,000
Estimated annual capital recovery with return cost		
$(\$260,000 - \$60,000) (\overset{A/P,\ 12,3}{0.4164}) + \$60,000\ (0.12)$	$ 90,480	
Estimated annual operating and maintenance cost	104,500	
Estimated total annual cost	$194,980	
Estimated net annual saving		$-14,980

the components making up an estimate is to improve the certainty of a favorable result if the outcome results in values that are more favorable than those chosen.

8.3 CONSIDERING A RANGE OF ESTIMATES

A popular method for the treatment of estimates is to make a least favorable estimate, a *fair estimate*, and a most favorable estimate of each situation. The fair estimate is the estimate that appears most reasonable after a diligent search for and a careful analysis of data. This estimate is also termed the most likely estimate.

The *least favorable estimate* is the estimate that results when each item is given the least favorable interpretation that the estimator feels may reasonably be realized. The least favorable estimate is not the very worst that could happen. This is a difficult estimate to make. Each element of each item should be considered independently insofar as possible. The least favorable estimate should not be determined from the fair estimate by multiplying the latter by a factor.

The *most favorable estimate* is the estimate that results when each item is given the most favorable interpretation that the estimator feels may reasonably be realized. Comments similar to those made in reference to the least favorable estimate, but of reverse effect, apply to the most favorable estimate. The use of the three estimates will be illustrated by application to the example of previous sections. Table 8.5 gives the example estimates.

An important feature of the least favorable, fair, and most favorable basis for comparison is that it brings additional information to bear on the situation under study. Additional information results from the estimator's analysis and judgment in answering two questions relative to each item: "What is the least favorable value that this item may reasonably be expected to have?" and the reverse, "What is the most favorable value that this item may reasonably be expected to have?"

TABLE 8.5 Example Estimated Values

Item Estimated	Least Favorable Estimate	Fair Estimate	Most Favorable Estimate
Annual number of units	1,000	1,200	1,500
Savings per unit	$ 140	$ 150	$ 160
Annual savings	$ 140,000	$180,000	$240,000
Period of annual savings, n	4	5	6
Capital recovery with return			
$(\$260,000 - \$60,000)(\overset{A/P,12,n}{\quad}) + \$60,000\,(0.12)$	$ 73,040	$ 62,680	$ 55,840
Operating and maintenance cost			
Item a: power	$ 50,000	$ 40,000	$ 30,000
Item b: maintenance	13,897	10,500	7,103
Item c: O&M supplies	9,000	6,000	3,137
Item d: labor	55,178	48,000	40,822
Estimated total of capital recovery, return, and operating items	$ 201,115	$167,180	$136,902
Estimated net annual saving in prospect for n years	$-61,115	$ 12,820	$103,098

Judgment should be made item by item. A summation of judgments is expected to be more accurate than a single judgment of the whole. A second advantage of the three-estimate approach is that it reveals the consequences of deviations from the fair or most likely estimate. Even though the calculated consequences are themselves estimated, they show what is in prospect for different sets of conditions. It may be found that the small deviations in the direction of unfavorableness will have disastrous consequences in some situations. In other situations, even a considerable deviation may not result in serious consequences.

8.4 SENSITIVITY ANALYSIS

The crude techniques of the previous sections are limited in their rigor, even though they are widely used. Decision makers are typically interested in the full range of possible outcomes that would result from variances in estimates. Sensitivity analysis permits a determination of how sensitive final results are to changes in the values of estimates.

Sensitivity Involving a Single Alternative

As a simple example illustrating the concept of sensitivity analysis, assume that a present investment of $10,000 is anticipated to return $20,000 five years hence. The expected rate of return on this investment may be computed from Equation 3.5, which relates F and P as

$$F = P(1 + i)^n$$

from which

$$i = \sqrt[n]{\frac{F}{P}} - 1$$

For the stated example, the expected rate of return is

$$i = \sqrt[5]{\frac{\$20,000}{\$10,000}} - 1$$

$$= 0.1487 \quad \text{or} \quad 14.87\%$$

The anticipated return of $20,000 may be more or less, which will make the expected rate of return more or less than 14.87%. Table 8.6 gives a range of possible values for F and rates of return that result. Also shown is the percentage change in i related to the percentage change in F. From this it can be concluded that the rate of return is quite sensitive to errors in the estimates of F, with the sensitivity being greater for underestimates of F than for overestimates. Figure 8.1 illustrates this situation for arbitrarily chosen maximum and minimum values of F.

TABLE 8.6   Sensitivity of i to F, Given P and n

F	$i\,(\%)$	Percent Change in F	Percent Change in i
$16,000	9.86	-20	-33.7
18,000	12.45	-10	-16.3
20,000	14.87	0	0
22,000	17.08	$+10$	$+14.9$
24,000	19.14	$+20$	$+28.7$

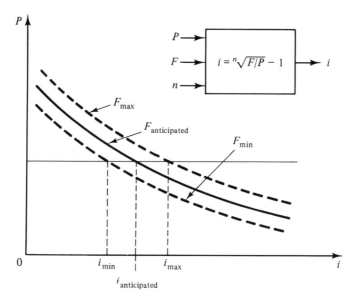

Figure 8.1   Sensitivity of i to the estimate of F.

In the previous example, only one estimated input was varied as a basis for examining its impact on the anticipated rate of return. As an example of sensitivity analysis for a single alternative with two inputs varying jointly, consider an extension of the previous example to allow both F and n to vary. Suppose that F is to be studied over the same range as before ($16,000 to $24,000) and that n is to be taken as 4, 5, or 6. The resulting values for rate of return are given in Table 8.7. Information such as this can be very useful in deciding whether or not to pursue the alternative.

Another view of multiple input sensitivity analysis can be obtained by varying only one input at a time but exhibiting all simultaneously. Consider the single alternative depicted by the money flow in Figure 8.2. At an interest rate of 10%, the present equivalent amount of the money flow is

$$\text{PE}(10) = \$-20{,}000 + \$4{,}000(\overset{P/A,\,10,\,10}{}) = \$4{,}578$$

TABLE 8.7 i^* for Different Values of F and n

			F		
n	\$16,000	\$18,000	\$20,000	\$22,000	\$24,000
4	12.47	15.83	18.92	21.79	24.47
5	9.86	12.45	14.87	17.08	19.14
6	8.15	10.29	12.75	14.04	15.71

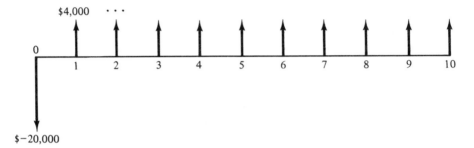

Figure 8.2 Money flow for a single alternative.

This result is valid only if all parameter estimates are estimated correctly. It is likely that errors will be made in estimating one or more of these parameters. To illustrate their individual impacts on the present equivalent amount, assume that A, i, and n can vary between $+50\%$ and -50% of their anticipated or estimated values.

If the estimate of the interest rate is incorrect and the estimates of A and n are assumed to be correct, the present equivalent of this investment can be expressed as a function of i as

$$PE(i) = \$-20{,}000 + \$4{,}000(\overset{P/A,\,i,\,10}{})$$

A $\pm50\%$ variation in i has an effect on PE as shown in Table 8.8. If, however, the estimate of A is incorrect and the estimates of i and n are assumed to be correct, the present equivalent of this investment can be expressed as a function of A as

$$PE(A) = \$-20{,}000 + A(\overset{P/A,\,10,\,10}{})$$

A $\pm50\%$ variation in A has an effect on PE as shown in Table 8.9. Finally, if the estimate of n is incorrect and the estimate of i and A are assumed to be correct, the present equivalent of this investment can be expressed as a function of n as

$$PE(n) = \$-20,000 + \$4,000(\overset{P/A,\,10,\,n}{})$$

A $\pm 50\%$ variation in n has an effect on PE as shown in Table 8.10.

TABLE 8.8 Sensitivity of PE to i, Given A and n

i (%)	PE
5	$10,887
6	9,440
7	8,094
8	6,840
9	5,671
10	4,578
11	3,557
12	2,601
13	1,705
14	864
15	75

TABLE 8.9 Sensitivity of PE to A, Given i and n

A	PE
$2,000	$-7,711
2,400	-5,253
2,800	-2,795
3,200	-337
3,600	2,121
4,000	4,578
4,400	7,036
4,800	9,494
5,200	11,952
5,600	14,410
6,000	16,868

TABLE 8.10 Sensitivity of PE to n, Given i and A

n	PE
5	$-4,837
6	-2,579
7	-526
8	1,340
9	3,036
10	4,578
11	5,980
12	7,255
13	8,414
14	9,467
15	10,424

Sensitivity of the present equivalent amount to changes in A, n, and i may be illustrated graphically as shown in Figure 8.3. Present equivalent is plotted versus the percentage error in the estimate of A, n, and i, from the information in Tables 8.8, 8.9, and 8.10. Figure 8.3 can now be used to reach conclusions about the desirability of pursuing the alternative under study. First, the PE is positive for all interest rates less than 15% (50% above the estimated value of 10%). PE is positive for project durations exceeding approximately 7.5 years (25% below the estimated value of 10 years). Finally, PE is positive for annual returns exceeding about $325 (18.75% below the estimated value of $400).

Sensitivity analysis simultaneously considering multiple estimated inputs can give insight into planned actions by the decision maker. The same analysis can also be performed to determine the sensitivity of annual equivalent or other criteria that the decision maker may prefer.

Sensitivity Involving Multiple Alternatives

As an illustration of sensitivity analysis for multiple alternatives, consider the three mutually exclusive alternatives summarized in Table 8.11. The first cost of each alternative is known with a high degree of certainty. Simi-

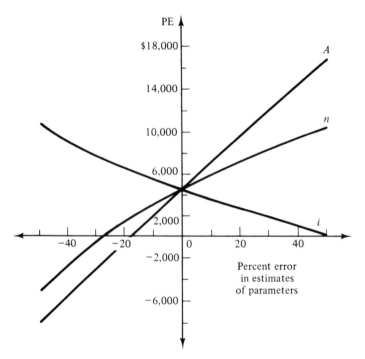

Figure 8.3　Sensitivity of PE to estimates of A, n, and i.

larly, assume that the anticipated service lives of 10 years are fixed and the cost of money is certain to be 10%. Annual maintenance and operating costs are uncertain but are expected to be the amounts given in Table 8.11.

TABLE 8.11 Three Mutually Exclusive Alternatives

Economic Element	A	B	C
First cost	$30,000	$44,000	$50,000
M&O cost	18,000	14,500	13,500

A general expression for the annual equivalent cost for this decision situation is derived as follows:

$$AE = P(\overset{A/P,i,n}{\qquad}) + M\&O$$

To reflect changes in AE as a function of deviations in the M&O cost from its expected value, the expression above can be altered to the following form:

$$AE(\pm \Delta M\&O\%) = P(\overset{A/P,10,10}{\qquad}) + (M\&O)(\pm \Delta M\&O\%)$$

For the specific situation of Table 8.11, the annual equivalent cost as a function of deviations in the M&O cost is shown in Figure 8.4. The decision is between alternative A and alternative C for all % changes in M&O cost.

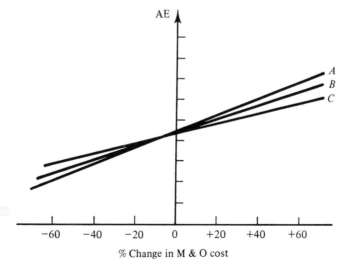

Figure 8.4 Annual equivalent cost sensitivity to changes in M&O cost.

Alternative B is dominated. The break-even (or decision reversal point) between alternatives A and C can be found exactly as follows:

$$\overset{A/P,10,10}{\$30,000(\ 0.1628\ )} + \$18,000(1+\Delta) = \overset{A/P,10,10}{\$50,000(\ 0.1628\ )} + \$13,500(1+\Delta)$$

$$\$20,000(0.1628) = \$4,500(1+\Delta)$$

$$\$3,256 = \$4,500(1+\Delta)$$

$$\Delta = \frac{\$3,256}{\$4,500} - 1$$

$$\Delta = -0.28 \quad \text{or} \quad -28\%$$

Thus if the M&O cost were to turn out to be 28% less than the anticipated amount, the preference would pass from alternative C to alternative A.

8.5 MONTE CARLO ANALYSIS

Monte Carlo is the name given to a class of simulation approaches to decision making in which probability distributions are used to describe certain economic elements. In many of these cases, an analytical solution is not possible because of the way in which the probabilities must be manipulated. In other cases, the Monte Carlo approach is preferred because of the level of detail it provides.

Decision situations to which Monte Carlo analysis may be applied are characterized by empirical or theoretical distributions. The Monte Carlo approach utilizes these distributions to generate random outcomes. These outcomes are then combined in accordance with the economic analysis technique being applied to find the distribution of the present equivalent, the annual equivalent, rate of return, and so on.

Suppose that a defense contractor wishes to bid on a project that will require special computer-controlled instrumentation.[2] Two alternatives are being considered by the contractor. The first has a high cost and low O&M costs. Although the first cost of each instrumentation alternative is known with certainty, the annual O&M cost is uncertain, as is the contract duration.

The possible contract durations and O&M costs are shown in Table 8.12 along with their associated probabilities. Also shown in Table 8.12 are the simulation techniques chosen to generate random outcomes. It is noted that the tossing of two coins will be used to generate contract durations. For O&M

[2] This example is taken from G. J. Thuesen and W. J. Fabrycky, *Engineering Economy*, 7th ed. (Englewood Cliffs, NJ: Prentice-Hall, Inc., 1989).

TABLE 8.12   Generation of Simulated Values

Simulated Value	Possible Outcome	Probability of Outcome	Simulation Technique	Assignment of Outcome
Contract	1	$\frac{1}{4}$	Tossing two coins	HH
duration, n	2	$\frac{1}{2}$		HT or TH
	3	$\frac{1}{4}$		TT
O&M	$ 2,000	$\frac{1}{6}$	Tossing one die	1
costs for	3,000	$\frac{1}{2}$		2, 3, or 4
alternative A	5,000	$\frac{1}{3}$		5 or 6
O&M	$12,000	$\frac{1}{6}$	Tossing one die	1
costs for	25,000	$\frac{1}{3}$		2 or 3
alternative B	30,000	$\frac{1}{3}$		4 or 5
	40,000	$\frac{1}{6}$		6

costs, the tossing of one die will be used. These methods of generating a sequence of economic outcomes are mechanical in nature.[3]

The process for generating simulated contract durations and O&M costs for the alternatives presented in Table 8.12 can now be applied with the techniques of life-cycle cost analysis over several trials. This is shown in Table 8.13 for 100 trials with a summary at 10 trials. After 10 trials the annual equivalent cost for alternative A is $48,630. For alternative B the annual equivalent cost is $41,623 after 10 trials. The annual equivalent cost difference is $7,007, as shown in the last column of Table 8.14.

Although alternative B appears to be best, it must be recognized that only 10 trials lead to this conclusion. It is entirely possible for a larger sample to yield different results. Consider the behavior of the mean annual equivalent cost for alternative A as the number of trials increases to 100, as shown in Figure 8.5. Note how the average annual equivalent cost fluctuates early in the simulation and then stabilizes as the number of trials increases. It may be concluded that at least 100 trials are required to obtain sufficiently stabilized results on which to base a comparison.

The simulated data from Table 8.12 can be used to develop additional information about the cost of alternative A and alternative B. Tables 8.13 and 8.14 give the possible annual equivalent cost values for each alternative together with the frequency of occurrence for each. The mean and variation for the annual equivalent cost under each alternative can be estimated from the frequencies given in Tables 8.14 and 8.15. For alternative A the mean is

$$0.04(\$30,147) + 0.13(\$31,147) + \cdots + 0.08(\$82,000) = \$50,229$$

[3] It is necessary to generate values at random from the distributions representing problem parameters in performing a Monte Carlo analysis. There are many ways of doing this, including mechanical, mathematical, digital computer, and others.

TABLE 8.13 Monte Carlo Comparison of Two Alternatives

Trial Number	Outcome of Coin Tossing	Contract Duration, n	(a) Capital Recovery Cost, Alternative A; $70,000 $A/P,10,n$ ( )	(b) Capital Recovery Cost, Alternative B; $20,000 $A/P,10,n$ ( )	Outcome of Die Toss, Alternative A	(c) Annual O&M Costs, Alternative A	(d) = (a) + (c) Annual Equivalent Cost, Alternative A	Outcome of Die Toss, Alternative B	(e) Annual O&M Costs, Alternative B	(f) = (b) + (e) Annual Equivalent Cost, Alternative B	(d) − (f) Difference in Annual Equivalent Cost, Alternative A − Alternative B
1	HH	1	$77,000	$22,000	2	$3,000	$80,000	3	$25,000	$47,000	$33,000
2	HT	2	40,334	11,524	4	3,000	43,334	3	25,000	36,524	6,810
3	TH	2	40,334	11,524	1	2,000	42,334	6	40,000	51,524	−9,190
4	TH	2	40,334	11,524	5	5,000	45,334	2	25,000	36,524	8,810
5	TT	3	28,147	8,042	2	3,000	31,147	1	12,000	20,042	11,105
6	HH	1	77,000	22,000	3	3,000	80,000	5	30,000	52,000	28,000
7	TH	2	40,334	11,524	6	5,000	45,334	4	30,000	41,524	3,810
8	HT	2	40,334	11,524	1	2,000	42,334	5	30,000	41,524	810
9	TT	3	28,147	8,042	3	3,000	31,147	6	40,000	48,042	−16,895
10	TH	2	40,334	11,524	6	5,000	45,334	4	30,000	41,524	3,810
							$486,300			$416,228	$70,070
							Mean AEC = 48,630			Mean AEC = $41,623	Mean Diff. = $7,007
·	·	·	·	·	·	·	·	·	·	·	·
100	HT	2	40,334	11,524	2	3,000	43,334	4	30,000	41,524	1,810

TABLE 8.14 Frequency Distribution of the
Annual Equivalent Cost for Alternative *A*

Annual Equivalent Cost	Frequency in 100 Trials	Probability
$30,147	4	0.04
31,147	13	0.13
33,147	9	0.09
42,334	8	0.08
45,334	22	0.22
45,334	18	0.18
79,000	5	0.05
80,000	13	0.13
82,000	8	0.08
	100	1.00

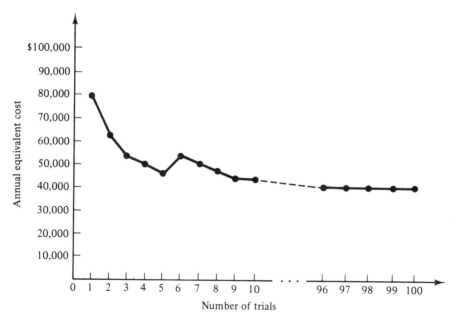

Figure 8.5 Convergence of the annual equivalent cost with increasing
trials for Alternative *A*.

TABLE 8.15 Frequency Distribution of the
Annual Equivalent Cost for Alternative *B*

Annual Equivalent Cost	Frequency in 100 Trials	Probability
$20,042	4	0.04
23,524	9	0.09
33,042	9	0.09
34,000	4	0.04
36,524	17	0.17
38,042	8	0.08
41,524	17	0.17
47,000	7	0.07
48,042	4	0.04
51,524	8	0.08
52,000	8	0.08
62,000	5	0.05
	100	1.00

and the variance is

$$0.04(\$30,147)^2 + 0.13(\$31,147)^2 + \cdots + 0.08(\$82,000)^2 - (\$50,229)^2$$

$$= \$346,802,000$$

For alternative *B* the mean is

$$0.04(\$20,042) + 0.09(\$23,524) + \cdots + 0.05(\$62,000) = \$40,158$$

and the variance is

$$0.04(\$20,042)^2 + 0.13(\$23,524)^2 + \cdots + 0.05(\$62,000)^2 - (\$40,158)^2$$

$$= \$101,232,300$$

The annual equivalent cost difference between alternative *A* and alternative *B* can now be estimated more precisely. It is $50,229 − $40,158 = $10,071. This compares with a difference of $7,007 after 10 trials. Thus alternative *B* is favored on the basis of the expected-value approach.

It should be noted that alternative *B* also leads to a smaller variance in the annual equivalent cost than does alternative *A*. Thus, from an expectation-variance viewpoint, alternative *B* is clearly superior to alternative *A*. It is unlikely that this conclusion would be altered by pursuing the Monte Carlo analysis beyond 100 trials.

QUESTIONS AND PROBLEMS

1. Additional equipment must be purchased for use at a shipping facility to meet an increased shipping load. It is estimated that the equipment would handle an additional 135,000 tons of goods annually, for which the estimated income would

be $8 per ton. The equipment will cost $1,500,000, its service life is estimated to be 10 years, and the estimated annual maintenance and operation costs are $750,000. If the interest rate is 12%, compute the estimated net annual profit.

2. Would the equipment in Problem 1 be purchased if the additional shipping load were estimated to be 120,000 tons per week?

3. Would the equipment in Problem 1 be purchased if the minimum acceptable rate of return (MARR) were 20%?

4. Compute the least favorable, fair, and most favorable estimates of the cost per mile for an automobile you would personally use from estimates of the least favorable, fair, and most favorable first costs, service life, salvage value, interest rate, maintenance and operating costs, and miles driven per year. Your estimates should be those which you might personally experience.

5. Suppose that the following most favorable estimates apply to the equipment in Problem 1:

Additional tonnage handled	5,500
Income per ton	$11
Service life in years	12
Annual maintenance and operation costs	$600,000

What is the annual net profit for this most favorable estimate?

6. A project is estimated in the face of an interest rate of 10% as follows:

	Optimistic	Most Likely	Pessimistic
Investment	$45,000	$50,000	$55,000
Service life	6 years	5 years	4 years
Salvage value	$15,000	$12,000	$10,000
Net annual return	$16,000	$13,000	$10,000

(a) Find the annual equivalent amount for each possible outcome.
(b) Tabulate the annual equivalent amount for all combinations of the estimates for service life and net annual return. Assume that the salvage value decreases at a linear rate for all three cases.

7. An epoxy mixer purchased for $7,000 has an estimated salvage value of $700 and an expected life of three years. An average of 25 pounds of epoxy per month will be produced by the mixer. Calculate the annual equivalent cost of capital recovery plus return per pound of epoxy with an interest rate varying from 8 to 16%.

8. An asset was purchased for $5,200 with the anticipation that it would serve for 12 years and be worth $600 as scrap. After five years of operation the asset was sold for $1,800. The interest rate is 14%.
(a) What was the anticipated annual equivalent cost of capital recovery plus return?
(b) What was the actual annual equivalent cost of capital recovery plus return?

9. A special machine was purchased for $75,000. It was estimated that the machine would result in a saving on production cost of $14,000 per year for 20 years. With a zero salvage value at the end of 20 years, what is the anticipated rate of return? It now appears that the machine will soon become inadequate. If it is sold after six years of use for $20,000, what is the change in the anticipated rate of return resulting from the incorrect service life estimate?

10. A firm invests $10,000 into a piece of equipment that will be used for 10 years. Salvage value of the equipment is uncertain and can range up to 20% of the original equipment cost. If the interest rate is 10% compounded annually, derive an expression that expresses the capital-recovery cost of the equipment as a function of its salvage value.

11. A design department must determine the annual equivalent cost that might be experienced by a machine currently being designed. It is estimated that it will cost $75,000 to design and build the machine. A service life of seven years with a salvage value of $7,000 is anticipated, but these estimates are subject to error. A service life of six years with a salvage value of $8,000 and a service life of eight years with a salvage value of $6,000 are also possible. If the interest rate is 10%, analyze the sensitivity of the annual equivalent cost to changes from the anticipated values.

12. A company is considering investing $10,000 in a heat recapture device. The device will last 10 years, at which time it will be worth $2,000. Maintenance costs for the device are estimated to increase by $200 per year over its life with maintenance cost for the first year estimated to be $1,000. As an alternative, the company may lease the equipment for $X per year, including maintenance. For what range of $X should the company lease the heat exchanger? The cost of money is 10%.

13. A small CAD system for an engineering office can be purchased for $25,000. The system is expected to be used for 10 years, have an annual maintenance cost of $3,000, and have a salvage value of $5,000. Alternatively, the system can be leased for $50 per day, including maintenance costs. It will cost $50 per day to operate the system under either acquisition alternative. It is not necessary to treat daily expenditures within the year with interest.
  (a) If the MARR is 15% compounded annually, how many days per year must the CAD system be used for the purchase alternative to break even with the lease alternative?
  (b) Sketch a graph of the break-even number of days per year as a function of MARR, for MARR = 10%, 15%, and 20% compounded annually, to illustrate break-even sensitivity to the MARR.

14. A testing function can be performed by an automated diagnostic computer that will cost $100,000. Net annual savings in technician time are estimated to be $36,000. This equipment will serve for six years, but must be reprogrammed at the end of three years of operation at a cost estimated to be $40,000. Find the internal rate of return anticipated and then calculate the sensitivity of the IRR to the reprogramming cost.

15. The best estimates for a certain investment opportunity are as follows:

Initial investment	$100,000
Estimated life	8 years

Salvage value	$20,000
Net annual return	$30,000

If the MARR is 12%, calculate and graph over a range of $\pm 40\%$ the sensitivity of the annual equivalent amount to:
(a) The interest rate.
(b) The net annual return.
(c) The salvage value.

16. A $10,000 investment into a renovation project now will avoid an expense five years hence with the exact amount saved described as a probability distribution as follows:

Amount Saved	Probability
$18,000	0.25
20,000	0.50
22,000	0.25

Utilize Monte Carlo analysis to develop the probability distribution of the rate of return in prospect. What are the exact probabilities of the rate of return taking on specific values?

17. In Problem 16, assume that the time before the expense is avoided is either five or six years with equal probability. Also assume that the amount saved is in accordance with the probability distribution as Problem 13. Find the theoretical probabilities of the rate of return taking on all possible values. Also, perform a few Monte Carlo trials for this situation.

9

Life-Cycle Economic
Evaluations

Previous chapters dealt primarily with essential concepts and methodology for the application of life-cycle costing. Although this background is important, a good understanding of the subject can only be acquired by examining some of the details for establishing a cost breakdown structure, defining cost estimating relationships, and determining specific segments of cost. Accordingly, several example economic evaluations are introduced in this chapter. In presenting each example, only enough detail is included to provide an understanding of the requirements involved in the evaluation process. A more complete step-by-step procedure covering each element of the process is presented in Appendix A.

9.1 COST EVALUATION OF TWO ALTERNATIVES

When two mutually exclusive alternatives provide essentially the same service, it is desirable to compare them directly to each other on the basis of life-cycle cost. Where benefits of unequal value are provided by multiple alternatives, each alternative must be evaluated as a single alternative and accepted or rejected as discussed in Section 5.7. However, when available alternatives do provide outputs that are identical or equal in value the objective is to select the alternative that provides the desired service at least cost.

Evaluating Equipment Purchase Alternatives[1]

Assume that a defense contractor is considering the purchase of new test equipment. Semiautomatic test equipment will cost $110,000 and can be expected to last six years, with a salvage value of $10,000. Operating costs will be $28,000 per year. Fully automatic equipment will cost $170,000, should last six years, and have a salvage value of $14,000. The operating costs will be $12,000 per year. Figure 9.1 illustrates the money flow diagram for estimated costs and salvage values. The service provided by each equipment alternative is identical. With an assumed interest rate of 14%, the alternative that meets the criterion of least cost should be selected.

Present equivalent evaluation.   Under this evaluation method, the alternatives may be compared using equivalent costs at a time taken to be the present. The present equivalent cost of the semiautomatic test equipment is

$$\$110,000 + \$28,000 \; \overset{P/A,\,14,6}{(\;3.8887\;)} - \$10,000 \; \overset{P/F,\,14,6}{(\;0.4556\;)} = \$214,327$$

The present equivalent cost of the fully automatic equipment is

$$\$170,000 + \$12,000 \; \overset{P/A,\,14,6}{(\;3.8887\;)} - \$14,000 \; \overset{P/F,\,14,6}{(\;0.4556\;)} = \$210,286$$

This comparison shows the present equivalent cost of the fully automatic test equipment to be less than the present equivalent cost of the semiautomatic test equipment by $214,327 less $210,286, or $4,041.

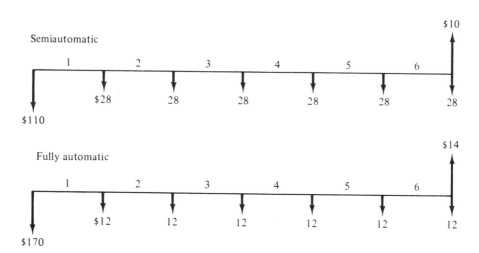

Figure 9.1   Equipment purchase alternatives (thousands of dollars).

[1] Refer to Figure 5.1 for the general money flow pattern for procurement by purchase.

Annual equivalent evaluation. The annual equivalent costs are taken as an equal-cost series over the life of the assets. The annual equivalent cost of the semiautomatic test equipment is

$$\overset{A/P,\,14,\,6}{\$110{,}000\ (\ 0.2572\ )} + \$28{,}000 - \$10{,}000\ \overset{A/F,\,14,\,6}{(\ 0.1175\ )} = \$55{,}118$$

and the annual equivalent cost of the fully automatic test equipment is

$$\overset{A/P,\,14,\,6}{\$170{,}000\ (\ 0.2572\ )} + \$12{,}000 - \$14{,}000\ \overset{A/F,\,14,\,6}{(\ 0.1175\ )} = \$54{,}079$$

The annual equivalent difference of $55,118 less $54,079 or $1,039 is the equivalent cost superiority of the fully automatic test equipment. As a verification, the present equivalent amount of the annual equivalent difference is

$$\overset{P/A,\,14,\,6}{\$1{,}039\ (\ 3.8887\ )} = \$4{,}041$$

Future equivalent evaluation. Under this evaluation method, the alternatives may be compared in equivalent cost at the time when their service lives end. The future equivalent cost of the semiautomatic test equipment is

$$\overset{F/P,\,14,\,6}{\$110{,}000\ (\ 2.195\ )} + \$28{,}000\ \overset{F/A,\,14,\,6}{(\ 8.536\ )} - \$10{,}000 = \$470{,}458$$

The future equivalent cost of the fully automatic equipment is

$$\overset{F/P,\,14,\,6}{\$170{,}000\ (\ 2.195\ )} + \$12{,}000\ \overset{F/A,\,14,\,6}{(\ 8.536\ )} - \$14{,}000 = \$461{,}582$$

This evaluation shows the future equivalent cost of the fully automatic test equipment to be less than the future equivalent cost of the semiautomatic test equipment by $470,458 less $461,582 or $8,876. The present equivalent of $8,876 is

$$\overset{P/F,\,14,\,6}{\$8{,}876\ (\ 0.4556\ )} = \$4{,}043$$

Rate-of-return evaluation. The previous cost comparisons indicated that the fully automatic test equipment was more desirable at an interest rate of 14%. At some higher interest rate, the two alternatives will be identical in cost, and beyond that interest rate, the semiautomatic test equipment will be less expensive because of its lower initial cost.

The interest rate at which the costs of the two alternatives are identical can be determined by setting the present equivalent amounts for the alternatives equal to each other and solving for the interest rate, i. Thus

$$\$110{,}000 + \$28{,}000\ \overset{P/A,\,i,\,6}{(\qquad)} - \$10{,}000\ \overset{P/F,\,i,\,6}{(\qquad)}$$

$$= \$170{,}000 + \$12{,}000\ \overset{P/A,\,i,\,6}{(\qquad)} - \$14{,}000\ \overset{P/F,\,i,\,6}{(\qquad)}$$

$$\$16,000 \left(\overset{P/A,i,6}{} \right) + \$4,000 \left(\overset{P/F,i,6}{} \right) = \$60,000$$

For $i = 15\%$,

$$\$16,000 \left(\overset{P/A,15,6}{3.7845} \right) + \$4,000 \left(\overset{P/F,15,6}{0.4323} \right) = \$62,281$$

For $i = 20\%$,

$$\$16,000 \left(\overset{P/A,20,6}{3.3255} \right) + \$4,000 \left(\overset{P/F,20,6}{0.3349} \right) = \$54,548$$

Then, by interpolation,

$$i = 15 + 5 \left[\frac{\$62,281 - \$60,000}{\$62,281 - \$54,548} \right] = 16.47\%$$

When funds are considered to earn between 0 and 16.47%, the fully automatic test equipment will be most desirable. When funds are worth more than 16.47%, the semiautomatic equipment would be preferred. This may be illustrated by the equivalence function diagram in Figure 9.2.

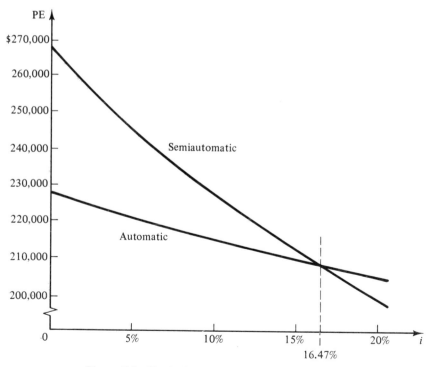

Figure 9.2 Equivalence function diagram for i.

Payout evaluation. The service life of six years for each of the two test equipment alternatives is the result of estimates. It may be in error. If the services are needed for shorter or longer periods of time, and if the assets are capable of providing the service for a longer period of time, the advantage may pass from one alternative to the other.

Just as there is an interest rate at which two alternatives may be equal, there may be a service life at which the equivalent cost may be identical. This service life may be obtained by calculating the present equivalent cost of the alternatives, seeking the duration for which the costs are equal. For an interest rate of 14%:[2]

For $n = 3$ years,

$$PE(\text{automatic}) = \$170,000 + \$12,000 \ (\overset{P/A,14,3}{2.3216}) - \$92,000 \ (\overset{P/F,14,3}{0.6750})$$

$$= \$135,759$$

$$PE(\text{semiautomatic}) = \$110,000 + \$28,000 \ (\overset{P/A,14,3}{2.3216}) - \$60,000 \ (\overset{P/F,14,3}{0.6750})$$

$$= \$134,505$$

For $n = 4$ years,

$$PE(\text{automatic}) = \$170,000 + \$12,000 \ (\overset{P/A,14,4}{2.9137}) - \$66,000 \ (\overset{P/F,14,4}{0.5921})$$

$$= \$165,886$$

$$PE(\text{semiautomatic}) = \$110,000 + \$28,000 \ (\overset{P/A,14,4}{2.9137}) - \$43,333 \ (\overset{P/F,14,4}{0.5921})$$

$$= \$165,926$$

Then, by interpolation,

$$n = 3 + 1\left[\frac{\$1,254}{\$1,254 - (\$-40)}\right] = 3.97 \text{ years}$$

If the test equipment were to be used less than 3.97 years, the semiautomatic choice would be the best. For a utilization period greater than 3.97 years, the automatic equipment should be purchased. An equivalence function diagram for this payout situation is shown in Figure 9.3.

Evaluating Equipment Design Alternatives[3]

Suppose that there is a need for new complex equipment to perform a certain function five years from now. Two potential designs are proposed pro-

---

[2] In the calculations that follow, the salvage value is adjusted linearly to reflect the value of the asset at the payout year under consideration.

[3] Refer to Figure 5.1 for the general money flow pattern for procurement by development.

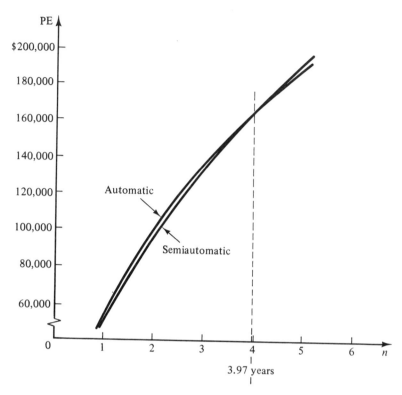

Figure 9.3   Equivalence function diagram for n.

viding anticipated costs and activities (i.e., research and development, production, and system operation and maintenance). The alternative cost flows,
represented by design A and design B, are shown in Figure 9.4. These cost
flows are illustrated for each year in millions of dollars. The objective is to
select either design A or design B on the basis of the given life-cycle cost information, assuming an annual interest rate of 10%. The life-cycle cost flows can
be compared on an equivalent bases at any point in time. In Table 9.1, the
present equivalent comparison is made. The preference is for design A.

Consideration should be given next to when the preferred alternative
actually assumes a favorable position. In some instances, a given alternative
may be preferable on the basis of the life-cycle cost figure of merit; but the
time preference of the cost profile may not be favorable when compared to
other opportunities, particularly if the perceived advantage is not realized
until a point far out in the life cycle. Therefore, a break-even analysis should
be done prior to arriving at a final decision.

Figure 9.5 illustrates the application of the break-even concept to the
design alternatives shown in Figure 9.4. The cumulative life-cycle cost of each

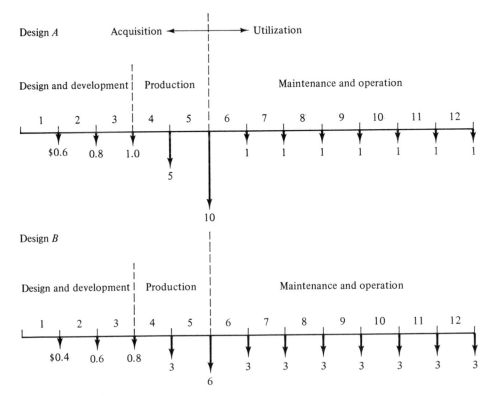

Figure 9.4 Two design alternatives for complex equipment (hundreds of thousands of dollars).

TABLE 9.1 Present Equivalent Cost Comparison

Year,	Estimated Cost (dollars × 100,000)		$P/F, 10, n$	Present Equivalent Cost (dollars × 100,000)	
n	Design A	Design B	( )	Design A	Design B
1	0.6	0.4	0.9091	0.5455	0.3636
2	0.8	0.6	0.8265	0.6612	0.4959
3	1.0	0.8	0.7513	0.7512	0.6010
4	5.0	3.0	0.6830	3.4150	2.0490
5	10.0	6.0	0.6209	6.2090	3.7254
6	1.0	3.0	0.5645	0.5645	1.6935
7	1.0	3.0	0.5132	0.5132	1.5369
8	1.0	3.0	0.4665	0.4665	1.3995
9	1.0	3.0	0.4241	0.4241	1.2723
10	1.0	3.0	0.3856	0.3856	1.1568
11	1.0	3.0	0.3505	0.3505	1.0515
12	1.0	3.0	0.3186	0.3186	0.9558
Total				14.6050	16.3012

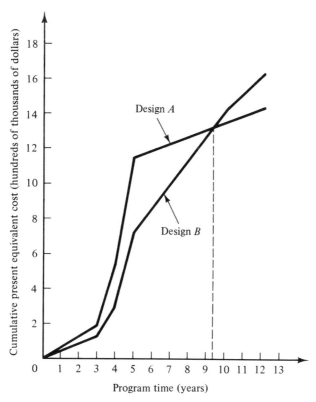

Figure 9.5   Cumulative present equivalent cost and break even.

alternative is calculated. The least costly approach assumes a favorable position in approximately nine years and seven months.

The following question may be asked: Is the break-even point (or crossover point) reasonable in terms of possible system obsolescence, competition,
and business risk and uncertainty? If the break-even point is far out in time,
it may be more feasible to select design *B* in lieu of design *A*. Also, if the magnitude of the benefits derived are small by accepting *A* (i.e., potential cost
savings), then *B* may be preferable when considering other factors. When
evaluating all factors in this example, design *B* may actually be the preferred
alternative.

9.2 COST EVALUATION OF MULTIPLE ALTERNATIVES

As an example of the cost evaluation of multiple alternatives consider the
problem of selecting a used automobile for personal use from one of five possible choices. Each of the five automobiles is currently available, and the cri-

teria for selection are based on acquisition cost plus operation and support cost over the life cycle.

The Analysis Approach

The needed automobile is expected to last for a period of at least five years, and the average usage will be 10,000 miles per year (i.e., 50,000 miles for the defined life cycle). Suppose that the choice is narrowed to the five possible candidates listed in Table 9.2.

In evaluating the various candidates, the purchaser is interested in acquiring a four-door sedan but is also willing to consider a small two-door vehicle (i.e., automobile *D*). The objective is to make a selection based on life-cycle cost, where the life-cycle cost includes acquisition cost plus all operation and support costs over the five-year period of use. As a start, one should identify the cost breakdown structure of cost categories applicable to the acquisition, operation, and support of each automobile. The significant categories of cost are discussed below and summarized in Table 9.3.

Acquisition cost.   Acquisition cost constitutes the consumer purchase price, which includes dealer preparation, delivery cost, and the costs associated with product warranty (if any).

Operation cost.   Operation cost includes the cost of the fuel and other consumables (e.g., lubricants) required in operating the automobile throughout its planned life cycle. To this must be added the cost of insurance and taxes.

Maintenance cost.[4]   Maintenance cost is divided between scheduled and unscheduled maintenance. Scheduled maintenance involves the periodic

TABLE 9.2   Five Used Automobile Purchase Alternatives

Alternative	Characteristics	Acquisition Cost
Automobile *A*	Large size, low performance, four-door, 10 miles per gallon	$5,000
Automobile *B*	Large size, medium performance, four-door, 18 miles per gallon	6,000
Automobile *C*	Medium size, medium performance, four-door, 15 miles per gallon	4,200
Automobile *D*	Small size, high performance, two-door, 30 miles per gallon	3,600
Automobile *E*	Medium size, high performance, four-door, 26 miles per gallon	5,500

[4] Unscheduled and scheduled maintenance costs include maintenance personnel labor cost, supply support cost, cost of test and support equipment utilization, cost of facility utilization, and related costs applicable to the consumer.

TABLE 9.3 Operation and Maintenance Costs

Cost Category	Automobile	Cost of Ownership (dollars)					Total Cost	Description and Justification
		Year 1	Year 2	Year 3	Year 4	Year 5		
1. Cost of operating the vehicle (gasoline)	A	990	1,035	1,080	1,125	1,245	$5,475	Assume an average usage of 10,000 miles per year. Gasoline cost is $0.99 in year 1, $1.035 in year 2, $1.08 in year 3, $1.125 in year 4, and $1.245 in year 5.
	B	550	575	600	625	691	3,041	
	C	660	690	720	750	830	3,650	
	D	330	345	360	375	415	1,825	
	E	381	398	415	433	479	2,106	
2. Unscheduled maintenance cost (labor and material)	A	90	240	280	420	500	$1,530	Maintenance actions include unscheduled performance checks, repairs, new tires, etc., accomplished at gas station and/or garage.
	B	80	210	290	360	430	1,370	
	C	120	270	320	570	760	2,040	
	D	85	195	200	220	250	950	
	E	100	250	300	400	430	1,480	
3. Scheduled maintenance cost (labor and material)	A	80	75	75	75	75	$ 380	Maintenance actions include oil changes, filter changes, lubrication, periodic checks, etc., accomplished at gas station and/or garage.
	B	70	60	60	60	60	310	
	C	65	50	50	50	50	265	
	D	45	30	30	30	30	165	
	E	50	45	45	45	45	230	

inspections accomplished at 3,000 miles, 6,000 miles, and so on, and includes engine oil changes, filter changes, lubrication, and the normal preventive maintenance requirements for a typical automobile. Unscheduled maintenance includes visits to the gas station or garage as a result of suspected problems, repairs due to failures, new tires, overhauls, and the like. Maintenance labor cost, the cost of material spares and consumables, allocated test and support equipment utilization cost, facilities utilization cost, and related direct and indirect costs.

An analysis of each of the five candidate automobiles in terms of operation and support costs is presented in Table 9.4. Operation cost is based on an average utilization rate throughout the five-year life cycle. Support cost relates to the number of scheduled and unscheduled maintenance actions, and the anticipated logistics support resources required per maintenance action. Each cost entry in Table 9.4 is calculated from the sum of operation and maintenance costs for each year given in Tables 9.3 times the $(P/F,8,n)$ factor; the opportunity cost of money taken to be 8%.

TABLE 9.4 Present Equivalent Analysis of Automobile Alternatives

Automobile	Acquisition Cost	Present Equivalent Operation and Support Cost (dollars)					Total Present Cost
		Year 1	Year 2	Year 3	Year 4	Year 5	
A	$5,000	1,074	1,157	1,139	1,191	1,239	$10,800
B	6,000	648	724	754	768	804	9,698
C	4,200	782	866	865	1,006	1,115	8,834
D	3,600	426	489	468	453	473	5,909
E	5,500	492	594	603	645	694	8,528

Analysis of Results

The results of the life-cycle cost evaluation indicate that automobile D is clearly favored. Figure 9.6 includes the acquisition plus operation and support cost, and illustrates the consumer life-cycle cost profiles for each alternative. Since the various alternatives are compared on a present equivalent basis, the costs are moved to the present using the specified interest rate. Note that the discounted cost profiles tend to show increasing costs as the various automobiles reach the 40,000-mile point and beyond, which is fairly characteristic.

If the consumer decides to accept the small high-performance two-door automobile, the decision is strongly in favor of automobile D. However, if customer preference is overwhelmingly in favor of a larger four-door sedan for one reason or another, automobile D ceases to be a feasible alternative, and the other four candidates must be considered. Although the acquisition cost of automobile E is $5,500 (the second highest), the present equivalent life-

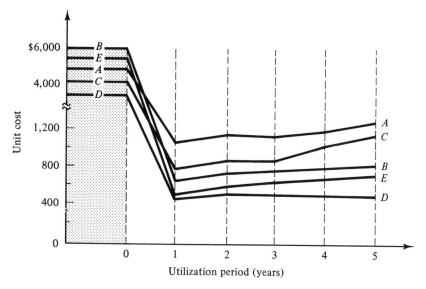

Figure 9.6   Acquisition plus operation and support costs.

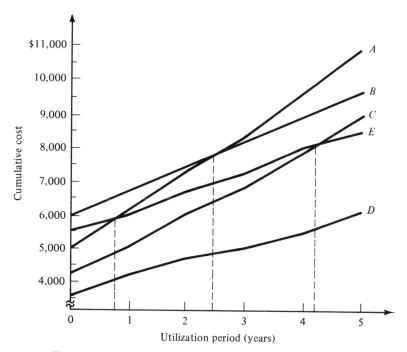

Figure 9.7   Cumulative present equivalent life-cycle cost.

cycle cost is $8,528, which is the next lowest overall. In such a situation, automobile E assumes the preferred position.

Prior to a final selection of automobile E, one may wish to determine the point in time when this automobile assumes the lead position. The break-even cost projections in Figure 9.7 indicate that automobile E becomes less costly after approximately four years and three months of ownership (i.e., the crossover point between automobiles C and E). Accordingly, if use of this automobile is planned for a time period greater than the crossover point, it is probably worthwhile remaining with E; otherwise, the preference may shift to C.

As a final step, one may wish to address the sensitivities of the input data. For example, the cost of fuel over the next five years may increase at a much faster rate than indicated in Table 9.3. If this occurs, the break-even point in Figure 9.7 may shift. Another major input factor is the frequency of unscheduled maintenance. By varying the number of maintenance actions over a realistic range of values, one can readily reevaluate the decision in terms of the projections in Figure 9.7 (refer to Section 8.4).

9.3 PROFITABILITY EVALUATION OF ALTERNATIVES

FABCorp is considering the possibility of introducing product X into the market. A market analysis indicates that the corporation could sell over 500 units of this product per year (if available) at a price of $75 each for at least 10 years into the future. The product is not repairable. It is to be discarded at failure. To manufacture the product, the corporation needs to procure capital equipment. Based on a survey of potential sources, there are three alternatives considered feasible.

1. *Machine A* is automatic, will produce up to 350 units per year, and can be purchased at a price of $11,050. The expected reliability (MTBF) of this machine is 210 hours and the anticipated cost per corrective maintenance action is $75. Preventive maintenance is required every six months, and the cost per maintenance action is $50. The average machine operation cost is $0.50 per hour, and the estimated salvage value after 10 years of operation is $300.

2. *Machine B* is also automatic, will produce 440 units per year, and can be purchased at a price of $9,725. The expected reliability (MTBF) of this machine is 385 hours, and the anticipated cost per corrective maintenance action is $100. Preventive maintenance is required every six months, and cost per maintenance action is $60. The average machine operation cost is $0.65 per hour, and the estimated salvage value after 10 years of operation is $550.

3. *Machine C* is semiautomatic (requiring a part-time machine operator), will produce 300 units per year, and can be purchased at a price of

$5,075. The expected reliability (MTBF) of this machine is 150 hours, and the anticipated cost per corrective maintenance action is $50. Preventive maintenance is required every six months, and the cost per maintenance action is $80. The average machine operation cost is $1.20 per hour, and the estimated salvage value after 10 years of operation is $100.

The expected utilization will be 8 hours per day for 270 days per year. Machine output is expected to be 50% during the first year of operation, at full capacity during year 2, through the end of year 10. The manufacturing cost (materials and labor associated with material procurement, material handling, quality control, inspection and test, and packaging) for product X is $20 using machine A, $30 using machine B, and $40 using machine C. The expected allocated distribution cost (transportation, warehousing, etc.) is $3 per unit. These machines should be evaluated on the basis of life-cycle cost and selection made based on the lowest LCC. An 8% interest rate is assumed for evaluation purposes.

The Analysis Approach

The first step is to identify the major categories of revenue and cost that are applicable to the problem at hand. Of primary concern are the revenues and costs associated with the new product itself, and the costs of acquisition, operation, and support of the machine. These factors are discussed in the following paragraphs:

Product X revenues.   It is expected that machine A will manufacture 175 units during year 1 and 350 units per year thereafter. Machine B will manufacture 220 units during year 1 and 440 units per year from there on. Machine C will manufacture 150 units during year 1 and 300 units every year thereafter. All units are sold during the year of manufacture. From these data, product revenues are calculated using the $75 selling price as a basis.

Product X manufacturing cost.   Manufacturing costs cover materials and the labor associated with material procurement, material handling, product quality control, inspection and test, and packaging. The effects of learning and inflation are considered and averaged over the life cycle. Manufacturing costs per unit will be $20 on machine A, $30 on machine B, and $40 on machine C.

Product X distribution cost.   This category includes the transportation, warehousing, and distribution costs associated with the product. The expected allocated product distribution cost is $3 per item.

Operation cost.   The costs included in this category primarily cover the energy consumption associated with the operation of each machine. The allocated cost is $0.50 per hour for machine A, $0.65 per hour for machine B, and $1.20 per hour for machine C.

Maintenance cost. Both scheduled and unscheduled maintenance costs are included herein. For machine A, scheduled (or preventive) maintenance constitutes two maintenance actions per year at an average cost of $50 per maintenance action. Machine B requires two maintenance actions per year at an average cost of $60 per maintenance action. Machine C also requires two preventative maintenance actions each year at an average cost of $80 per maintenance action.

Unscheduled maintenance cost is based on the estimated number of corrective maintenance actions, which is a function of the machine reliability. The expected reliability (MTBF) of machine A is 210 hours, of machine B is 385 hours, and machine C is 150 hours. The cost per corrective maintenance action for machine A is $75, for machine B it is $100, and for machine C it is $50. The effects of inflation are included in the maintenance cost and averaged over the defined life cycle.

A summary of investment, product manufacturing, distribution, operation, and maintenance costs is presented in Figure 9.8 for each of the three machines being considered. The recurring costs are presented in Table 9.5. It is now necessary to convert these projected revenues and costs to present equivalent values.

Analysis of Results

Table 9.6 shows the present equivalent value of the money flows illustrated in Table 9.5. Based on the results of this analysis, the selection of machine B is preferred over that of machines A and C, since the net present equivalent value for B is $92,647 versus a net of only $90,406 for A, and $33,135 for C, calculated as follows:

net present equivalent value of machine A = $163,985 − $73,579
                                                                 = $90,406
net present equivalent value of machine B = $206,154 − $113,507
                                                                 = $92,647
net present equivalent value of machine C = $140,561 − $107,426
                                                                 = $33,135

Prior to making a final choice, one should perform a break-even analysis and establish the payback points for each alternative. Although other factors may affect the ultimate decision, the project exhibiting an early payback is usually desirable when considering risk and uncertainty. Figure 9.9 illustrates money flows and payback points. Machine B retains its preferred status. Greater detail on payback is exhibited in Figure 9.10.

Machine *A*

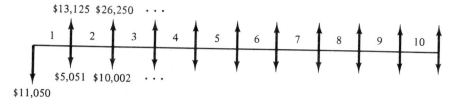

Machine *B*

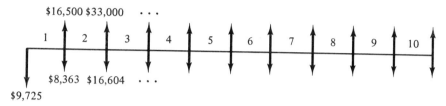

Machine *C*

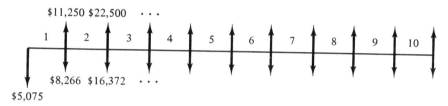

Figure 9.8   Revenue/cost projections for the three machines.

Another approach to selecting the preferred machine configuration is to use the present equivalent on incremental investment method presented in Section 4.5. This analysis begins by comparing the differences in the initial investment and subsequent net money flows for the least expensive and next more expensive machine. Machine *C* is selected as the initial current best and compared with machine *B* as follows:

$$\overset{P/F,8,1}{\text{PE}(8)_{\text{B-C}} = -\$4{,}650 + \$5{,}153(0.9259)} + \overset{P/A,8,9}{\$10{,}268\ (6.2469)}\ \overset{P/F,8,1}{(0.9259)} = \$59{,}511$$

Since this value is positive, machine *B* becomes the new current best. It is now compared with machine *A* as follows:

$$\overset{P/F,8,1}{\text{PE}(8)_{\text{A-B}} = -\$1{,}325 - \$63(0.9259)} - \overset{P/A,8,9}{\$148\ (6.2469)}\ \overset{P/F,8,1}{(0.9259)} = -\$2{,}239$$

A negative result for this increment leaves machine *B* as the current best. This

TABLE 9.5 Production and Machine Costs

Evaluation Category	Costs per Program Year (dollars)										Total Actual Cost
	1	2	3	4	5	6	7	8	9	10	
Machine A											
1. Product X Manufacturing	3,500	7,000	7,000	7,000	7,000	7,000	7,000	7,000	7,000	7,000	
2. Product X Distribution	525	1,050	1,050	1,050	1,050	1,050	1,050	1,050	1,050	1,050	
3. Machine Operation	540	1,080	1,080	1,080	1,080	1,080	1,080	1,080	1,080	1,080	
4. Scheduled Maintenance	100	100	100	100	100	100	100	100	100	100	
5. Unscheduled Maintenance	386	772	772	772	772	772	772	772	772	772	
Total Cost	5,051	10,002	10,002	10,002	10,002	10,002	10,002	10,002	10,002	10,002	$95,069
Machine B											
1. Product X Manufacturing	6,600	13,200	13,200	13,200	13,200	13,200	13,200	13,200	13,200	13,200	
2. Product X Distribution	660	1,320	1,320	1,320	1,320	1,320	1,320	1,320	1,320	1,320	
3. Machine Operation	702	1,404	1,404	1,404	1,404	1,404	1,404	1,404	1,404	1,404	
4. Scheduled Maintenance	120	120	120	120	120	120	120	120	120	120	
5. Unscheduled Maintenance	281	560	560	560	560	560	560	560	560	560	
Total Cost	8,363	16,604	16,604	16,604	16,604	16,604	16,604	16,604	16,604	16,604	$157,799
Machine C											
1. Product X manufacturing	6,000	12,000	12,000	12,000	12,000	12,000	12,000	12,000	12,000	12,000	
2. Product X distribution	450	900	900	900	900	900	900	900	900	900	
3. Machine operation	1,296	2,592	2,592	2,592	2,592	2,592	2,592	2,592	2,592	2,592	
4. Scheduled maintenance	160	160	160	160	160	160	160	160	160	160	
5. Unscheduled maintenance	360	720	720	720	720	720	720	720	720	720	
Total Cost	8,266	16,372	16,372	16,372	16,372	16,372	16,372	16,372	16,372	16,372	$155,614

TABLE 9.6 Analysis of Production Alternatives

Program Year, n	$P/F, 8, n$	Machine A Present Equivalent Revenues	Costs	Machine B Present Equivalent Revenues	Costs	Machine C Present Equivalent Revenues	Costs
0	—	—	$11,050	—	$ 9,725	—	$ 5,075
1	0.9259	$ 12,152	4,677	$ 15,277	7,743	$ 10,416	7,653
2	0.8573	22,504	8,575	28,291	14,235	19,289	14,036
3	0.7938	20,837	7,940	26,195	13,180	17,861	12,996
4	0.7350	19,294	7,351	24,255	12,204	16,538	12,033
5	0.6806	17,866	6,807	22,460	11,301	15,314	11,143
6	0.6302	16,543	6,303	20,797	10,464	14,180	10,318
7	0.5835	15,317	5,836	19,256	9,688	13,129	9,553
8	0.5403	14,183	5,404	17,830	8,971	12,157	8,846
9	0.5002	13,130	5,003	16,507	8,305	11,255	8,189
10	0.4632	12,159	4,633	15,286	7,691	10,422	7,584
Total		$163,985	$73,579	$206,154	$113,507	$140,561	$107,426

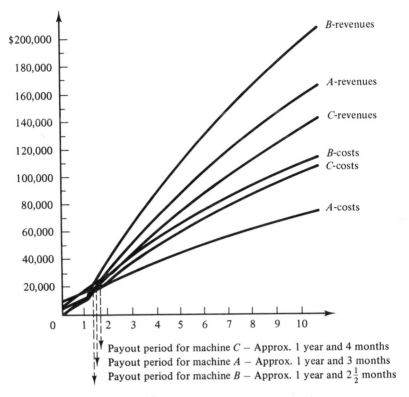

Figure 9.9 Profitability evaluation of three machines.

approach verifies the present equivalent finding used initially and could be applied in a break-even mode.

9.4 EVALUATING SYSTEM DESIGN ALTERNATIVES

A ground vehicle currently under development requires the incorporation of radio communication equipment. A decision is needed to establish the type of equipment deemed most feasible from the standpoint of performance, reliability, and life-cycle cost. Budget limitations require that the equipment unit cost (based on life-cycle cost) not exceed $20,000. Review of all possible supplier sources indicates that there are two design configurations that appear (based on preliminary design data) to meet the specified requirements. Each is to be evaluated on an equivalent basis in terms of reliability and total life-cycle cost.

The communication equipment is to be installed in a light vehicle. The equipment shall enable communication with other vehicles within a range of

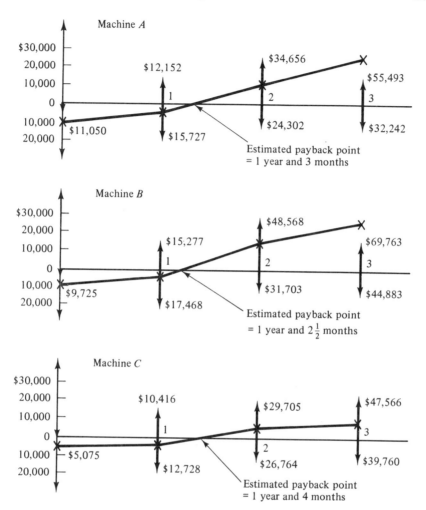

Figure 9.10   Payback detail for profitability evaluation.

200 miles, overhead aircraft at an altitude of 10,000 feet or less, and a central-ized area communication facility. The system must have an MTBF of 450 hours, a $\overline{\text{M}}$ct of 30 minutes, and a MLH/OH requirement of 0.2. The opera-tional and maintenance concepts and program time frame are illustrated in Figure 9.11.

The decision maker should evaluate each of the two proposed design configurations on the basis of total cost. Research and development costs and investment (or production) costs are determined from engineering and manu-facturing cost estimates prepared by the respective suppliers. Operation and maintenance cost is also provided based on reliability prediction reports,

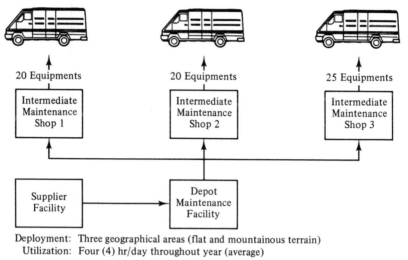

Deployment: Three geographical areas (flat and mountainous terrain)
Utilization: Four (4) hr/day throughout year (average)

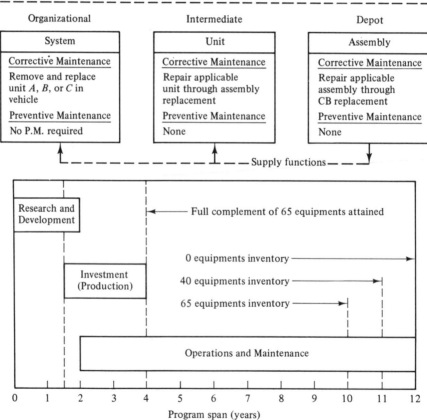

Organizational	Intermediate	Depot
System	**Unit**	**Assembly**
<u>Corrective Maintenance</u>	<u>Corrective Maintenance</u>	<u>Corrective Maintenance</u>
Remove and replace unit A, B, or C in vehicle	Repair applicable unit through assembly replacement	Repair applicable assembly through CB replacement
<u>Preventive Maintenance</u>	<u>Preventive Maintenance</u>	<u>Preventive Maintenance</u>
No P.M. required	None	None

— Supply functions —

Figure 9.11 System attributes for communication equipment installation.

214

maintainability prediction reports, and the results of the logistic support analysis. These costs are related to the cost breakdown structure, and the analysis is accomplished following the steps described earlier.

A breakdown of life-cycle cost is presented in Table 9.7. The CBS used here is different than that illustrated in Figure 2.5 in that it is tailored to the evaluation being made. Note that the acquisition cost (research and development, and investment) is higher for configuration *A* ($478,033 versus $384,131). This is partially due to a better design using more reliable components. Although the initial cost is higher, the overall life-cycle cost is lower, owing to a reduction in anticipated maintenance actions which result in lower operation and maintenance costs. Thus configuration *A* is preferred.

Figure 9.12 shows the relationship of the two configurations in terms of the specified reliability requirement and the design to unit life-cycle cost goal.

TABLE 9.7 Life-Cycle Cost Breakdown

Cost Category	Configuration *A* PE Cost	Configuration *A* Percent of Total	Configuration *B* PE Cost	Configuration *B* Percent of Total
1. Research and development	$ 70,219	7.8	$ 53,246	4.2
(a) Program management	9,374	1.1	9,252	0.8
(b) Advanced R&D	4,152	0.5	4,150	0.4
(c) Engineering design	41,400	4.5	24,581	1.9
(d) Engineering development and test	12,176	1.4	12,153	0.9
(e) Engineering data	3,117	0.3	3,110	0.2
2. Production	407,814	45.3	330,885	26.1
(a) Manufacturing	333,994	37.1	262,504	20.8
(b) Construction	45,553	5.1	43,227	3.4
(c) Initial logistic support	28,267	3.1	25,154	1.9
3. Operations and maintenance	422,217	46.9	883,629	69.7
(a) Operations	37,811	4.2	39,301	3.1
(b) Maintenance	384,406	42.7	844,328	66.6
• Maintenance personnel and support	210,659	23.4	407,219	32.2
• Spare/repair parts	103,520	11.5	228,926	18.1
• Test and support equipment maintenance	47,713	5.3	131,747	10.4
• Transportation and handling	14,404	1.6	51,838	4.1
• Maintenance training	1,808	0.2	2,125	Neg.
• Maintenance facilities	900	0.1	1,021	Neg.
• Technical data	5,402	0.6	21,452	1.7
(c) Equipment modifications	—	—	—	—
(d) Phaseout and disposal	—	—	—.	—
Total	$900,250	100	$1,267,760	100

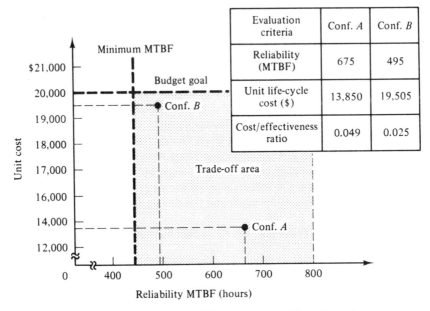

Evaluation criteria	Conf. *A*	Conf. *B*
Reliability (MTBF)	675	495
Unit life-cycle cost ($)	13,850	19,505
Cost/effectiveness ratio	0.049	0.025

Figure 9.12   Reliability versus unit life-cycle cost.

Both configurations meet the specified requirements. However, configuration *A* is clearly preferred, owing to a higher reliability and a lower unit life-cycle cost. As stated, configuration *A* is preferred on the basis of total life-cycle cost. Prior to a final decision the analyst should perform a break-even analysis to determine the point in time that configuration *A* becomes more desirable than configuration *B*. Figure 9.13 illustrates a payback point of six years and five months. This is early enough in the life cycle to support the decision.

By referring to Table 9.7, the analyst can readily pick out the high-cost contributors (those that contribute more than 10% of the total cost). These are the areas where a more refined analysis is required and greater emphasis is needed in providing valid input data. For instance, maintenance personnel and support cost and spare/repair parts cost contribute 23.4% and 11.5%, respectively, to the total cost for configuration *A*. This leads the analyst to reevaluate the design in terms of impact on personnel support and spares; the prediction methods used in determining maintenance frequencies and inventory requirements; the analytical model to ensure that the proper parameter relationships are established; and cost factors such as personnel labor cost, spares material costs, inventory holding cost; and so on. If the analyst wishes to determine the sensitivity of these areas to input variations, he or she may perform a sensitivity analysis. In this instance, it is appropriate to vary MTBF as a function of maintenance personnel and support cost and spare/repair parts cost. Figure 9.14 presents the results of this sensitivity analysis.

The analyst (or decision maker) should review the break-even analysis in Figure 9.13 and determine how far out in time he or she is willing to go and

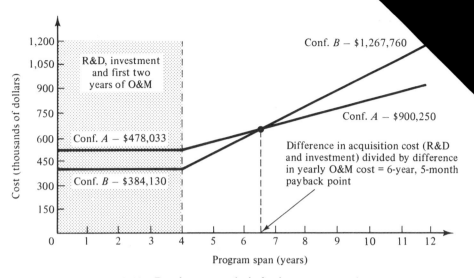

Figure 9.13 Break-even analysis for investment payback.

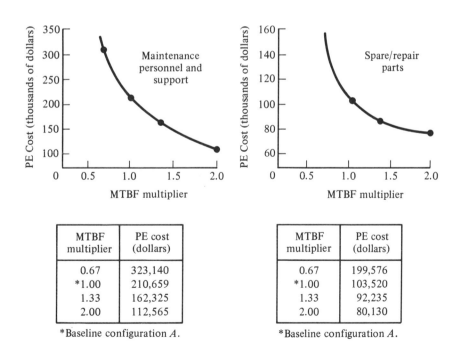

MTBF multiplier	PE cost (dollars)
0.67	323,140
*1.00	210,659
1.33	162,325
2.00	112,565

*Baseline configuration A.

MTBF multiplier	PE cost (dollars)
0.67	199,576
*1.00	103,520
1.33	92,235
2.00	80,130

*Baseline configuration A.

Figure 9.14 Sensitivity analysis to the MTBF multiplier.

tion A. Assuming that the selected maximum payback
the difference in alternatives is equivalent to approxi-
esent equivalent cost difference between the two config-
year point. This indicates the range of input variations
, if design configuration A changes, or if the reliability
resulting in a MTBF as low as 450 hours (the specified
the maintenance personnel and support cost will in-
crease to approximately $324,000. This is an increase of about $113,340 above
the baseline value. Thus, although the system reliability is within the specified
requirements, the cost increase due to the input MTBF variation causes a decision shift in favor of configuration B. Accordingly, the analyst should always
assess the sensitivity of significant input parameters and determine their impact on the planned decision.

9.5 BREAK-EVEN EVALUATION OF ALTERNATIVES

The break-even economic evaluation technique is useful in relating fixed and
variable costs to the number of hours of operation, the number of units produced, or other measures of operational activity. In each case, the break-even
point is of primary interest in that it identifies the range of the decision variable within which the most desirable economic outcome may occur.

Break-Even Analysis under Certainty

When the cost of two or more alternatives is a function of the same
variable, it is usually useful to find the value of the variable for which the alternatives incur equal cost. Several examples will be presented.

Make-or-buy evaluation.   Often a manufacturing firm has the choice
of making or buying a certain component for use in the product being produced. When this is the case, the firm faces a make-or-buy decision.

Suppose, for example, that a firm finds that it can buy from a vendor the
electric power supply for the system it produces for $8 per unit. Alternatively,
suppose that it can manufacture an equivalent unit for a variable cost of $4 per
unit. It is estimated that the additional fixed cost in the plant would be $12,000
per year if the unit is manufactured. The number of units per year for which
the cost of the two alternatives would be equal (break-even) should help the
firm make the final decision.

First, the total annual cost is formulated as a function of the number of
units for the make alternative. It is

$$TC_M = \$12,000 + \$4N$$

and the total annual cost for the buy alternative is

$$TC_B = \$8N$$

Break-even occurs when $TC_M = TC_B$, or

$$\$12,000 + \$4N = \$8N$$

$$\$4N = \$12,000$$

$$N = 3,000 \text{ units}$$

These cost functions and the break-even point are shown in Figure 9.15. For requirements in excess of 3,000 units per year, the make alternative would be more economical. If the rate of use is likely to be less than 3,000 units per year, the buy alternative should be chosen. If the production requirement changes during the course of the production program, the break-even choice in Figure 9.15 can be used to guide the decision of whether to make or to buy the power unit. Small deviations below and above 3,000 units per year make little difference.[5] However, the difference can be significant when the production requirement is well above or below 3,000 units per year.

Lease-or-buy evaluation.   As another example of break-even analysis, consider the decision to lease or buy a piece of equipment. Assume that a small electronic computer is needed for data processing in an engineering

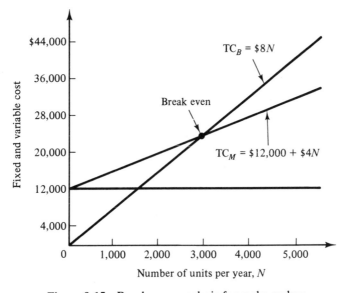

Figure 9.15   Break-even analysis for make or buy.

[5] Sometimes it is not economically feasible to produce a component, but to ensure continuation of vital activities, components may be produced in-house.

office. Suppose that the computer can be leased for $50 per day for the days used, which includes the cost of maintenance. Alternatively, the computer can be purchased for $25,000.

The computer is estimated to have a useful life of 15 years with a salvage value of $4,000 at the end of that time. It is estimated that annual maintenance costs will be $2,800. If the interest rate is 9% and it costs $50 per day to operate the computer, how many days of use per year are required for the two alternatives to break even?

First, the annual cost if the computer is leased is

$$TC_L = (\$50 + \$50)N$$

$$= \$100N$$

and the annual equivalent total cost if the computer is bought is

$$\overset{A/P,9,15}{TC_B = (\$25,000 - \$4,000)(\,0.1241\,) + \$4,000(0.09) + \$2,800 + \$50N}$$

$$= \$2,606 + \$360 + \$2,800 + \$50N$$

$$= \$5,766 + \$50N$$

The first three terms represent the fixed cost and the last term is the variable cost. Break-even occurs when $TC_L = TC_B$ or

$$\$100N = \$5,766 + \$50N$$

$$\$50N = \$5,766$$

$$N = 115 \text{ days}$$

A graphical representation of this decision situation is shown in Figure 9.16. For all levels of use exceeding 115 days per year, it would be more economical to purchase the computer. If the level of use is anticipated to be below 115 days per year, the computer should be leased.

Equipment selection evaluation. Suppose that a fully automatic controller for a machine center can be fabricated for $140,000 and that it will have an estimated salvage value of $20,000 at the end of four years. Maintenance costs will be $12,000 per year, and the cost of operation will be $85 per hour.

As an alternative, a semiautomatic controller can be fabricated for $55,000. This device will have no salvage value at the end of a four-year service life. The cost of operation and maintenance is estimated to be $140 per hour.

With an interest rate of 10%, the annual equivalent total cost for the automatic attachment as a function of the number of hours of use per year is

$$\overset{A/P,10,4}{TC_A = (\$140,000 - \$20,000)(\,0.3155\,) + \$20,000(0.10) + \$12,000 + \$85N}$$

$$= \$51,800 + \$85N$$

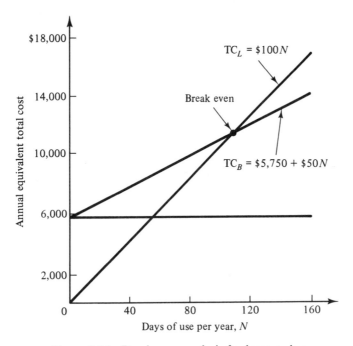

Figure 9.16   Break-even analysis for lease or buy.

and the annual equivalent total cost for the semiautomatic controller as a
function of the number of hours of use per year is

$$\overset{A/P,\,10,\,4}{TC_S = \$55,000(\ 0.3155\ ) + \$140N}$$

$$= \$17,400 + \$140N$$

Break even occurs when $TC_A = TC_S$, or

$$\$51,800 + \$85N = \$17,400 + \$140N$$

$$\$55N = \$34,400$$

$$N = 625 \text{ hours}$$

Figure 9.17 shows the two cost functions and the break-even point. For
rates of use exceeding 625 hours per year, the automatic controller would be
more economical. However, if it is anticipated that the rate of use will be less
than 625 hours per year, the semiautomatic controller should be fabricated.

Evaluation involving learning.   Consider the economic evaluation of
manufacturing costs for an identical item to be produced by two different
firms. Firm A takes a proactive approach to manufacturing improvement and
has devoted resources "up-front" to minimize the direct labor required to

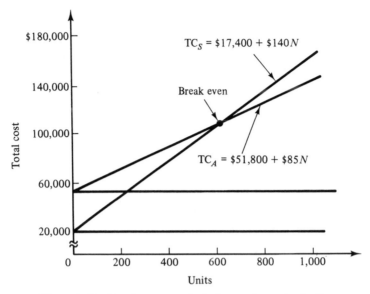

Figure 9.17 Break-even analysis for equipment selection.

produce the first unit. Firm B takes an expedient approach to manufacturing improvement. Firm B is more concerned with building the first unit and improving the process based on this experience. A summary of the comparative startup and manufacturing costs of the firms is given in Table 9.8.

The average item cost for various size production programs for each firm may be determined from the information in Table 9.8. Utilizing Equation 7.5, the average item cost for the 4,000-unit program for firm A is

$$C_i = \frac{12(4,000)^{-0.152}}{0.848} (\$7.50)(1.90) + \$45$$

$$= \$57.16 + \$45.00 = \$102.16$$

In a similar manner, the average item cost can be found for firm B for a 4,000 unit production program. These results, along with results for other unit pro-

TABLE 9.8 Manufacturing Information for Two Firms

Item	Firm A	Firm B
Planning and investment	$15,000	$3,500
Capital expenditure	$25,000	$25,000
Slope parameter of progress function, ϕ	0.9	0.8
Number of direct labor hours required for first unit, K	12	40
Direct labor hourly rate, LR	$7.50	$8.00
Direct material cost per unit, DM	$45	$45
Factory burden rate as a percent of DL	90	110

TABLE 9.9 Average Item Cost for Manufacturing

Size of Production Program, N	Firm A	Firm B
4,000	$102.16	$113.63
6,000	98.74	105.20
8,000	96.44	99.87
10,000	94.73	96.09
12,000	93.37	93.16
14,000	92.25	90.82
16,000	91.30	88.89
18,000	90.48	87.26
20,000	89.76	85.85

duction programs for each firm, are given in Table 9.9. By repeating the calculations for a range of production program sizes, the point of indifference (break-even) is found to be approximately 12,000 units, as shown in Figure 9.18. Above this program size, firm B's policy is preferable, and below it, firm A's policy is best.

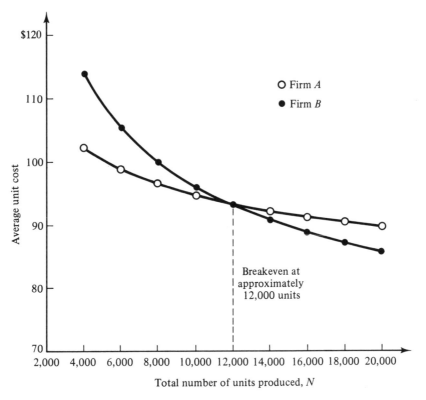

Figure 9.18 Break-even analysis for two firms involving learning.

TABLE 9.10 Item Cost Including Initial Investment

	Firm A	Firm B
Total initial investment	$40,000	$28,500
Investment cost per unit, $N = 4,000$	$ 10.00	$ 7.12
Average item cost for manufacturing	102.16	113.63
Cost per item, including initial investment	$112.16	$120.75
Investment cost per unit, $N = 10,000$	$ 4.00	$ 2.85
Average item cost for manufacturing	94.73	96.09
Cost per item, including initial investment	$ 98.73	$ 98.94

When planning and investment costs are considered at a 0% interest rate, it is necessary to spread these costs over the number of units produced. Firm A retains its advantage, even though the difference is negligible at 10,000 units of production as shown in Table 9.10.

The effect of a positive interest rate should be considered in the evaluation. If it is assumed that the production rate will be 2,000 units per year, the present equivalent item cost for a 4,000-unit production program is as given in Table 9.11 for each firm. For a 10,000-unit production program, the present equivalent item cost as a function of the interest rate is given in Table 9.12.

Firm A continues to maintain its advantage. When $N = 4,000$, firm A's advantage appears to be slowly narrowing in terms of relative dollars; however, in terms of percent difference firm A's advantage is slowly growing as interest rates increase. When $N = 10,000$ this is more obvious since firm A's advantage is apparent in terms of relative dollars and percent difference.

TABLE 9.11 Item Cost For Various Interest Rates ($N = 4,000$)

Interest Rate, i (%)	Firm A	Firm B
8	$91.30	$101.90
10	88.91	99.31
12	86.63	96.84
14	84.45	94.47
20	78.48	87.99
30	70.08	78.84

TABLE 9.12 Item Cost For Various Interest Rates ($N = 10,000$)

Interest Rate, i (%)	Firm A	Firm B
10	$72.51	$74.52
12	69.09	71.17
15	64.42	66.60
20	57.73	60.02

Percent difference is expressed as firm B's unit cost in terms of a percentage of firm A's unit cost.

Break-Even Analysis under Risk

In Section 9.5 the make-or-buy analysis was aided by Figure 9.15, showing the break-even point on which a make-or-buy decision is based. The analysis was based on certainty about the demand for the electric power supply. Ordinarily, the decision maker does not know with certainty what the demand level will be.

Consider demand ranging from 1,500 units to 4,500 units with probabilities as given in Table 9.13. Entries for the cost to make and the cost to buy are calculated from the equations exhibited in Figure 9.15.

TABLE 9.13   Demand and Probabilities for Make or Buy

	Demand (Units)						
	1500	2000	2500	3000	3500	4000	4500
Probability	0.05	0.10	0.15	0.20	0.25	0.15	0.10
Cost to make	$18,000	20,000	22,000	24,000	26,000	28,000	30,000
Cost to buy	$12,000	16,000	20,000	24,000	28,000	32,000	36,000

The expected demand may be calculated from the probabilities associated with each demand level as given in Table 9.13:

$$1,500(0.05) + 2,000(0.10) + 2,500(0.15) + 3,000(0.20) + 3,500(0.25)$$
$$+ 4,000(0.15) + 4,500(0.10) = 3,175$$

From the equations for this situation, the expected total cost to make is

$$TC_M = \$12,000 + \$4(3,175)$$
$$= \$24,700$$

and the expected total cost to buy is

$$TC_B = \$8(3,175)$$
$$= \$25,400$$

Accordingly, the power supply should be made. Alternatively, this decision might be based on the most probable future criterion. From Table 9.13 it is evident that a demand level of 3,500 is most probable. Therefore, the cost to make of $26,000 is compared with cost to buy of $28,000 and the decision would be to make the item. This is the same decision as for the expected demand approach.

9.6 EVALUATING ALTERNATIVES WITH MULTIPLE FUTURES

An engineering firm is engaged in the design of a unique machine tool. Since the new machine tool is technologically advanced, the firm is considering setting up a new production facility separate from its other operations.

Since the firm's own finances are not adequate to set up this new facility, there is a need to borrow capital from one of several financial sources. The firm has identified three sources, A, B, and C, which would lend money for this venture.

Each of these financial sources will lend money based on the anticipated sales of the product and will use a varying interest rate based on the anticipated demand for the product. If the product demand is anticipated to be low over the next few years, the financial backers will charge a high interest rate. This is because the backers feel that the firm may not borrow money in the future if the product fails due to low demand.

On the other hand, if the financial sources feel that the demand will be high, they will be willing to lend the money at a lower interest rate. This is because of the possibility of future business with the firm, owing to its present product being in high demand.

The engineering firm has fairly accurate knowledge of the receipts and disbursements associated with each demand level and the financial sources under consideration. The firm has knowledge about the initial outlay and anticipated receipts over three years for each demand level, as summarized in Table 9.14. The interest rates quoted by each financial source are summarized in Table 9.15.

The engineering firm wishes to select a financing source in the face of three demand futures, not knowing which demand future will occur. Accordingly, a decision evaluation matrix is developed as a first step. Using the present equivalent approach, nine evaluation values are derived and displayed in Table 9.16, one for each financing source for each demand level. For example, if financing comes from source A, and the demand level is low, the present equivalent payoff is

$$PE(15) = \$-500,000 + \$400,000(\overset{P/A,15,3}{2.2832}) = \$413,000$$

TABLE 9.14 Anticipated Disbursements and Receipts for Machine Tool Production (Thousands of Dollars)

Demand Level	Initial Outlay	Annual Receipts
Low	$ 500	$400
Medium	1,300	700
High	2,000	900

TABLE 9.15 Anticipated Interest Rates for Production Financing

Financing Source	Demand Level	Interest Rate (%)
A	Low	15
	Medium	13
	High	7
B	Low	14
	Medium	12
	High	8
C	Low	15
	Medium	11
	High	6

TABLE 9.16 Present Equivalent Payoffs for Three Financing Sources

Source	Demand Level		
	Low	Medium	High
A	$413	$353	$362
B	429	382	320
C	343	411	406

If the firm applied probabilities to each of the demand futures, the financing decision becomes one under risk. If the probability of a low demand is 0.3, the probability of a medium demand is 0.2, and the probability of a high demand is 0.5, the expected present equivalent amount for each financing source is calculated as follows:

Source A: $413,000(0.3) + \$353,000(0.2) + \$362,000(0.5) = \$376,000$
Source B: $429,000(0.3) + \$382,000(0.2) + \$320,000(0.5) = \$365,000$
Source C: $343,000(0.3) + \$411,000(0.2) + \$406,000(0.5) = \$388,000$

Accordingly, financing source C is selected by this decision rule.

In the event the firm has no basis for assigning probabilities to demand futures, the financing decision must be made under uncertainty. Under Laplace criterion, each future is assumed to be equally likely and the present equivalent payoffs are calculated as follows:

Source A: $\$(413,000 + 353,000 + 362,000) \div 3 = \$376,000$
Source B: $\$(429,000 + 382,000 + 320,000) \div 3 = \$377,000$
Source C: $\$(343,000 + 411,000 + 406,000) \div 3 = \$386,000$

Financing Source *C* would be selected by this decision rule.

By the maximin rule, the firm calculates the minimum present equivalent amount that could occur for each financing source and then selects the source that provides a maximum. The minimums for each source are:

Source *A*: $353,000
Source *B*: $320,000
Source *C*: $343,000

Financing source *A* would be selected by this decision rule as the one that will maximize the minimum present equivalent amount.

By the maximax rule, the firm calculates the maximum present equivalent amount that could occur for each financing source and then selects the source that provides a maximum. The maximums for each course are

Source *A*: $413,000
Source *B*: $429,000
Source *C*: $411,000

Financing source *B* would be selected by this decision rule as the one that will maximize the present equivalent amount.

A summary of the sources selected by each decision rule is given in Table 9.17. The basis for decision now depends on which criterion is used as well as upon intangeable factors.

TABLE 9.17 Summary of Financing Source Selections

	Financing Source		
Decision Rule	*A*	*B*	*C*
Expected value			×
Laplace			×
Maximax	×		
Maximin		×	

QUESTIONS AND PROBLEMS

1. A transportation firm plans to purchase a bus for $75,000 which will have a capacity of 80 passengers. As an alternative, a larger bus can be purchased for $95,000 which will have a capacity of 100 passengers. The salvage value of either bus is estimated to be $8,000 after a 10 year life. If an annual net profit of $200 can

be realized per passenger, which alternative should be adopted using an interest rate of 12%?

2. The annual heat loss cost in a chemical processing plant is estimated to be $60,000. Two feasible alternatives for reducing this loss are under consideration. Proposal *A* will reduce the heat loss cost by 60% and is estimated to cost $30,000. Proposal *B* will reduce the heat loss cost by 55% and is estimated to cost $25,000. If the cost of money is 11%, and the plant will benefit from the saving for 10 years, which proposal should be accepted?

3. A firm is considering the purchase of high technology diagnostic equipment to decrease the time required to isolate faults. Three equipment configurations have been identified as follows:

Configuration	First Cost	Operating Cost
A	$60,000	$20,500
B	75,000	17,000
C	80,000	15,400

There is no real difference in the service to be performed by the equipment configurations. If the cost of money is 10% and the diagnostic equipment is to be used for 8 years, which configuration should be specified?

4. A firm is considering the possibility of introducing a new product. A market analysis indicates that the firm could sell over 500 of these products per year (if available) at a price of $60 each for at least 10 years in the future. The product is not repairable and is discarded at failure. To manufacture the product, the corporation needs to procure some flexible automation equipment. Based on a survey of potential sources, there are two alternatives considered feasible to meet the need.

(1) Configuration *A* includes equipment that is automatic, will produce up to 350 products per year, and can be purchased at a price of $14,500. The expected reliability (MTBF) of this equipment is 210 hours, and the anticipated cost per corrective maintenance action is $75. Preventive maintenance is required every six months, and the cost per maintenance action is $50. The average operation cost is $0.50 per hour, and the estimated salvage value after 10 years of operation is $500.

(2) Configuration *B* includes equipment that is also automatic, will produce 440 products per year, and can be purchased at a price of $13,000. The expected reliability (MTBF) of this equipment is 385 hours, and the anticipated cost per corrective maintenance action is $100. Preventive maintenance is required every six months, and the cost per maintenance action is $60. The average operating cost is $0.65 per hour, and the estimated salvage value after 10 years of operation is $400.

The expected utilization of the equipment will be 8 hours per day and 260 days per year. Output is expected to be one-half (0.5) during the first year of operation, at full capacity during year 2, and on. The manufacturing cost (materials and labor associated with material procurement, material handling, quality control, inspection and test, and packaging) for product *X* is $20 using configura-

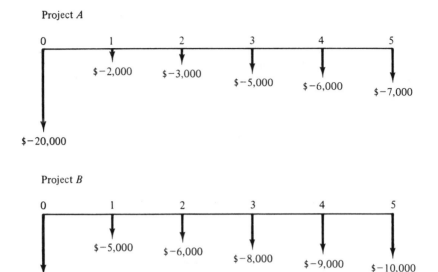

tion A and $30 using configuration B. The expected allocated distribution cost (transportation, warehousing, etc.) is $5 per item. The cost of money is 10%.
(a) Evaluate each equipment configuration and select one on the basis of life-cycle cost.
(b) Construct break-even curves showing the preferences in terms of time.
5. Two different projects are identified by the cost streams illustrated above. Using an 11% interest rate, determine which project is preferred. At what point in time does the preferred project assume a favorable position? Illustrate by a break-even analysis.
6. Based on the information provided below, compute the life-cycle cost in terms of present equivalent using a 10% interest rate for system XYZ. Indicate the total value at the start of the program (decision point) and plot the cost stream or profile.

System XYZ is installed in an aircraft that will be deployed at five operational bases. Each base will have a maximum force level of 12 aircraft, with the bases being activated in series (e.g., base 1 at the end of year 3, base 2 in year 5, etc.). The total number of system XYZs in operation are

Year	1	2	3	4	5	6	7	8	9	10
Number of system XYZs	0	0	0	10	20	40	60	55	35	25

System XYZ is a newly designed configuration packaged in three units (unit A, unit B, and unit C) with the following specified requirements for each unit.

The average system XYZ use is 4 hours per day and units A, B, and C are operating 100% of the time when system XYZ is on. One of the aircraft crew

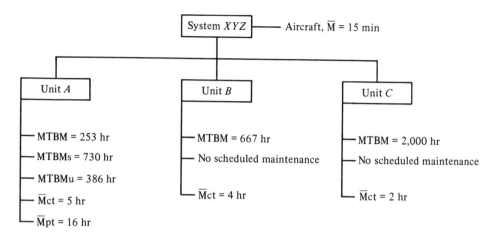

members will be assigned to operate several different systems throughout flight and it is assumed that 10% of his time is allocated to system *XYZ*.

Relative to the maintenance concept, system *XYZ* incorporates a built-in self-test that enables rapid system checkout and fault isolation to the unit level. No external support equipment is required at the aircraft. In the event of a *no-go* condition, fault isolation is accomplished to the unit and the applicable unit is removed, replaced with a spare, and sent to an intermediate-level maintenance shop (located at the operational base) for corrective maintenance. Unit repair is accomplished through module replacement, with the modules being discarded at failure. Scheduled (preventive) maintenance is accomplished on unit A in the intermediate shop every six months. No depot maintenance is required; however, the depot does provide backup supply and support functions as required. The requirements for system *XYZ* dictate the program profile shown. Assume that life-cycle costs are broken down into three categories, represented by the blocks in the program profile.

In an attempt to simplify the problem, the following additional factors are provided.

(1) RDT&E costs for system *XYZ* (to include labor and material) are $100,000 for year 1, $200,000 for year 2, and $250,000 for year 3.

(2) RDT&E costs for special support equipment are $50,000 in year 2 and $10,000 in year 3.

(3) System *XYZ* operational models are produced, delivered, and purchased in the year prior to the operational deployment need. System unit costs are unit *A* = $6,000, unit *B* = $3,000, and unit *C* = $1,000. Recurring and nonrecurring manufacturing costs are amortized on a unit basis.

(4) Support equipment is required at each intermediate maintenance shop at the start of the year when system *XYZ* operational models are deployed. In addition, a backup support equipment set is required at the depot when the first operational base is activated. The cost per set of support equipment is $20,000. Support equipment maintenance is based on a burden rate of $0.50 per direct maintenance labor hour for the prime equipment.

(5) Spares units are required at each intermediate maintenance shop at the time of base activation. Assume that two unit *A*s, one unit *B*, and one unit *C* are provided at each shop as safety stock. Also, assume that one spare system *XYZ* is stocked at the depot for backup support. Additional spares constitute modules. Assume that material costs are $100 per corrective maintenance action and $50 per preventive maintenance action. This includes inventory maintenance costs. In the interests of simplicity, the effects of the total logistics pipeline and shop turnaround time on spares are ignored in this problem.

(6) For each maintenance action at the system level, one low-skilled technician at $9.00 per direct maintenance labor-hour is required on a full-time basis. $\overline{M}$ is 15 minutes. For each corrective maintenance action involving unit *A*, unit *B*, or unit *C*, two technicians are required on a full-time basis. One technician is low-skilled at $9.00 per hour and one technician is high-skilled at $11.00 per hour. Direct and indirect costs are included in these rates. For each preventive maintenance action, one high-skilled technician at $11.00 per hour is required on a full-time basis.

(7) System operator personnel costs are $12.00 per hour.

(8) Facility costs are based on a burden rate of $0.20 per direct maintenance labor hour associated with the prime equipment.

(9) Maintenance data costs are assumed to be $20 per maintenance action.

Assume that the design-to-unit-acquisition cost (i.e., unit flyaway cost) requirement is $15,000. Has this requirement been met? Assume that the design-to-unit-O&M cost requirement is $20,000. Has this requirement been met?

7. A manufacturer can buy a required component from a supplier for $96 per unit delivered. Alternatively, the firm can manufacture the component for a variable cost of $46 per unit. It is estimated that the additional fixed cost would be $8,000 per year if the part is manufactured. Find the number of units per year for which the cost of the two alternatives will break even.

8. A marketing company can lease a fleet of automobiles for its sales personnel for $35 per day plus $0.09 per mile for each vehicle. As an alternative, the company can pay each salesperson $0.30 per mile to use his or her own automobile. If these

are the only costs to the company, how many miles per day must a salesperson drive for the two alternatives to break even?

9. An electronics manufacturer is considering the purchase of one of two types of laser trimming machines. The sales forecast indicated that at least 8,000 units will be sold per year. Machine A will increase the annual fixed cost of the plant by $20,000 and will reduce variable cost by $5.60 per unit. Machine B will increase the annual fixed cost by $5,000 and will reduce variable cost by $3.60 per unit. If variable costs are now $20 per unit produced, which machine should be purchased?

10. Machine A costs $20,000, has zero salvage value at any time, and has an associated labor cost of $1.14 for each piece produced on it. Machine B costs $36,000, has zero salvage value at any time and has an associated labor cost of $0.85. Neither machine can be used except to produce the product described. If the interest rate is 10% and the annual rate of production is 20,000 units, how many years will it take for the cost of the two machines to break even?

11. An electronics manufacturer is considering two methods for producing a circuit board. The board can be hand-wired at an estimated cost of $0.98 per unit and an annual fixed equipment cost of $1,000. A printed equivalent can be produced using equipment costing $18,000 with a service life of nine years and salvage value of $1,000. It is estimated that the labor cost will be $0.32 per unit and that the processing equipment will cost $450 per year to maintain. If the interest rate is 13%, how many circuit boards must be produced each year for the two methods to break even?

12. It is estimated that the annual sales of a new product will be 2,000 the first year and increased by 1,000 per year until 5,000 units are sold during the fourth year. Proposal A is to purchase equipment costing $12,000 with an estimated salvage value of $2,000 at the end of four years. Proposal B is to purchase equipment costing $28,000 with an estimated salvage value of $5,000 at the end of four years. The variable cost per unit under proposal A is estimated to be $0.80, but is estimated to be only $0.25 under proposal B. If the interest rate is 9%, which proposal should be accepted for a four-year production period?

13. The fixed cost of a machine (capital recovery, interest, maintenance, space charges, supervision, insurance, and taxes) is F dollars per year. The variable cost of operating the machine (power, supplies, and other items, but excluding direct labor) is V dollars per hour of operation. If N is the number of hours the machine is operated per year, TC the annual total cost of operating the machine, TC_h the hourly cost of operating the machine, t the time in hours to process 1 unit of product, and M the machine cost of processing 1 unit of product per year, write expressions for:
   (a) TC.
   (b) TC_h.
   (c) M.

14. In Problem 13, $F = $600 per year, $t = 0.2$ hour, $V = $0.50 per hour, and N varies from 0 to 10,000 in increments of 1,000.
   (a) Plot values of M as a function of N.
   (b) Write an expression for the total cost of direct labor and machine cost per unit, TC_u, using the symbols in Problem 13 and letting H equal the hourly cost of direct labor.

15. A certain firm has the capacity to produce 800,000 units per year. At present it is operating at 75% of capacity. The income per unit is $0.10 regardless of output. Annual fixed costs are $28,000 and the variable cost is $0.06 per unit. Find the annual profit or loss at this capacity and the capacity for which the firm will break even.

16. An arc welding machine that is used for a certain joining process costs $10,000. The machine has a life of five years and a salvage value of $1,000. Maintenance, taxes, insurance, and other fixed costs amount to $500 per year. The cost of power and supplies is $3.20 per hour of operation and the operator receives $15.80 per hour. If the cycle time per unit of product is 60 min and the interest rate is 8%, calculate the cost per unit if (a) 200, (b) 600, (c) 1,200, (d) 2,500 units of product are made per year.

17. A certain firm has the capacity to produce 650,000 units of product per year. At present, it is operating at 65% of capacity. The firm's annual income is $416,000. Annual fixed costs are $192,000 and the variable costs are $0.38 per unit of product.
    (a) What is the firm's annual profit or loss?
    (b) At what volume of sales does the firm break even?
    (c) What will be the profit or loss at 70, 80, and 90% of capacity on the basis of constant income per unit and constant variable cost per unit?

18. A chemical company owns two plants, A and B, that produce an identical product. The capacity of plant A is 60,000 gallons while that of B is 80,000 gallons. The annual fixed cost of plant A is $260,000 per year and the variable cost is $3.20 per gallon. The corresponding values for plant B are $280,000 and $3.90 per gallon. At present, plant A is being operated at 35% of capacity and plant B is being operated at 40% of capacity.
    (a) What would be the total cost of production of plant A and plant B?
    (b) What is the total cost and the average cost of the total output of both plants?
    (c) What would be the total cost to the company and cost per gallon if all production were transferred to plant A?
    (d) What would be the total cost to the company and cost per gallon if all production were transferred to plant B?

10

Life-Cycle Optimization of Alternatives

There are a number of economic decision situations in design and operations to which optimization approaches must be applied before alternatives can be compared equivalently. Many economic decisions are characterized by two or more cost factors that are affected differently by common design or policy variables. Certain costs may vary directly with an increase in the value of a variable while others may vary inversely. When the total cost of an alternative is a function of increasing and decreasing cost components, a value may exist for the common variable, or variables, which will result in a minimum cost for the alternative. In this chapter we present selected examples from classical situations that illustrate the application of optimization in economic analysis.

10.1 OPTIMIZING INVESTMENT OR FIRST COST

Investment (or first cost) has a significant effect on the equivalent life-cycle cost of an undertaking. Accordingly, it is important that investment cost be minimized before a life-cycle cost analysis is performed. In this section the classical situation of bridge design will be used to illustrate the appropriate approach.

Bridge Design Evaluation Model

Before engaging in detail design, it is important to optimally allocate the anticipated capital investment to superstructure and to piers. This can be accomplished by recognizing that there exists an inverse relationship between the cost of superstructure and the number of piers. As the number of piers increases, the cost of superstructure decreases. Conversely, the cost of superstructure increases as the number of piers decreases. Pier cost for the bridge is directly related to the number specified. This is a classical design situation involving increasing and decreasing cost components, the sum of which will be a minimum for a certain number of piers. Figure 10.1 illustrates two bridge superstructure designs with the span between piers indicated by S.

A general mathematical model may be derived for the evaluation of investment in superstructure and piers. The decision evaluation function of Equation 5.2 applies as

$$E = f(X, Y)$$

where

E = evaluation measure (total first cost)

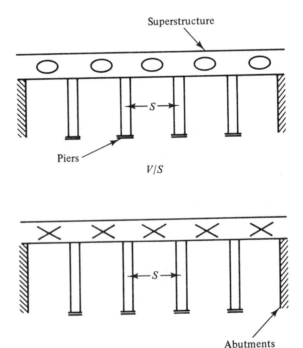

Figure 10.1 Two bridge superstructure design alternatives.

X = design variable of the span between piers

Y = system parameters of the bridge length, the superstructure weight, the erected cost of superstructure per pound, and the cost of piers per pier

Equation 5.3 is the design evaluation function applicable to the evaluation of alternative design configurations, where design-dependent parameters arise in selecting the best alternative. Let

L = bridge length (feet)

W = superstructure weight (pounds per foot)

S = span between piers (feet)

C_S = erected cost of superstructure (dollars per pound)

C_P = installed cost of piers (dollars per pier)

Assume that the weight of the superstructure is linear over a certain span range, $W = AS + B$, with the parameters A and B having been established by a sound statistical procedure. Accordingly, the superstructure cost, SC, will be

$$SC = (AS + B)(L)(C_S) \qquad (10.1)$$

The total cost of piers, PC, will be

$$PC = \left(\frac{L}{S} + 1\right)(C_P) \qquad (10.2)$$

where two abutments are included as though they were piers.

The total first cost of the bridge is expressed as

$$TFC = SC + PC$$

$$= (AS + B)(L)(C_S) + \left(\frac{L}{S} + 1\right)(C_P)$$

$$= ASLC_S + BLC_S + \frac{LC_P}{S} + C_P \qquad (10.3)$$

To find the optimum span between piers, differentiate Equation 10.3 with respect to S and equate the result to zero as follows:

$$\frac{d(TFC)}{dS} = ALC_S - \frac{LC_P}{S^2} = 0$$

$$S^* = \sqrt{\frac{C_P}{AC_S}} \qquad (10.4)$$

The minimum total first cost for the bridge is found by substituting Equation 10.4 for S in Equation 10.3 to obtain

$$TFC^* = 2\sqrt{AC_P L^2 C_S} + BLC_S + C_P \qquad (10.5)$$

Equation 10.4 can be used to find the optimal pier spacing for a given bridge design. However, to evaluate alternative bridge designs, Equation 10.5 would be utilized first followed by a single application of Equation 10.4 to the best alternative. This procedure is illustrated by examples in the following sections.

Single Design Alternative

Assume that a bridge to serve a 1,000-foot crossing is to be fabricated from steel with a certain girder design configuration. For this design alternative, the weight of the superstructure in pounds per foot is estimated to be linear (over a limited span range) and is expressed as

$$W = 16S + 600$$

Also, assume that the superstructure is expected to cost $0.65 per pound erected. Piers are anticipated to cost $80,000 each in place, and this amount will also be used as the estimated cost for each abutment.

From Equation 10.4, the optimum span between piers is found to be

$$S^* = \sqrt{\frac{\$80,000}{16 \times \$0.65}} = 87.7 \text{ feet}$$

This result is a theoretical spacing and must be adjusted to obtain an integer number of piers. The required adjustment gives 12 piers (11 spans) for a total cost from Equation 10.3 of $2,295,454. The span will be 90.9 feet, slightly greater than the theoretical minimum. A check can be made by considering 13 piers (12 spans) with each span being 83.3 feet. In this case, the total cost is higher ($2,296,667), so the 12-pier design would be adopted.

Total cost as a function of the pier spacing (and the number of piers) is summarized in Table 10.1. Note that a minimum occurs when 12 piers are

TABLE 10.1 TFC as a Function of the Span between Piers

Span (feet)	Number of Piers	Pier Cost	Superstructure Cost	Total First Cost
142.8	8	$ 640,000	$1,875,714	$2,515,714
111.1	10	800,000	1,545,555	2,345,555
100.0	11	880,000	1,430,000	2,310,000
90.9	12	960,000	1,335,454	2,295,454
83.3	13	1,040,000	1,256,666	2,296,667
76.9	14	1,120,000	1,190,000	2,310,000
71.4	15	1,200,000	1,132,857	2,332,857
66.6	16	1,280,000	1,083,333	2,363,333
58.8	18	1,440,000	1,001,765	2,441,765

specified; actually, 10 piers and two abutments. The optimal pier spacing is 90.9 feet.

Multiple Design Alternatives

To introduce optimal design for multiple alternatives, assume that there is another superstructure configuration under consideration for the bridge design described in the preceding section. The weight in pounds per foot for the alternative configuration is estimated from parametric methods to be

$$W = 22S + 0$$

Assume that all other factors are the same as for the previous design.

A choice between the design alternatives is made by finding the optimum total cost for each alternative utilizing Equation 10.5. This gives $2,294,280 for design A and $2,219,158 for design B. Thus design B would be chosen.

For design B, the optimum span between piers is found from Equation 10.4 to be

$$S^* = \sqrt{\frac{\$80,000}{22 \times \$0.65}} = 74.8 \text{ feet}$$

and the lowest-cost integer number of piers is found to be 14 (13 spans) with a span of 76.9 feet.

Table 10.2 summarizes this design decision by giving the total cost as a function of the number of piers for each alternative. The theoretical total cost function for each alternative is exhibited in Figure 10.2 along with an indication of the number of piers.

TABLE 10.2   TFC for Two Bridge Design Alternatives

Number of Piers	Pier Cost	Superstructure Cost		Total First Cost	
		Design A	Design B	Design A	Design B
8	$ 640,000	$1,875,714	$2,042,857	$2,515,714	$2,682,857
10	800,000	1,545,555	1,588,889	2,345,555	2,388,889
11	880,000	1,430,000	1,430,000	2,310,000	2,310,000
12	960,000	1,335,454	1,300,000	2,295,454	2,260,000
13	1,040,000	1,256,666	1,191,666	2,296,667	2,231,666
14	1,120,000	1,190,000	1,100,000	2,310,000	2,220,000
15	1,200,000	1,132,857	1,021,438	2,332,857	2,221,438
16	1,280,000	1,083,333	953,333	2,363,333	2,233,333
18	1,440,000	1,001,765	841,176	2,441,765	2,281,176

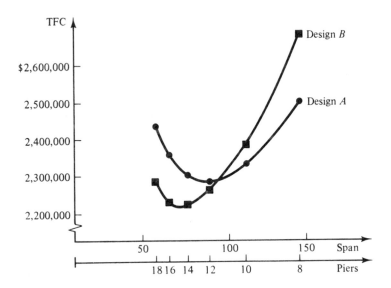

Figure 10.2   Total first cost for two bridge design alternatives.

10.2 OPTIMIZING LIFE-CYCLE COST

Investment cost was optimized in the derivations and example applications presented in Section 10.1. When the annual cost of maintenance or operations differs between design alternatives, it is important to formulate a life-cycle cost function including both first cost and operating cost as a basis for choosing the best alternative.

Bridge Evaluation Including Maintenance

Equation 10.5 gave the total first cost of the bridge. It can be augmented by Equation 3.14 to give the present equivalent life-cycle cost as follows:

$$\text{PELCC} = [2\sqrt{AC_PL^2C_S} + BLC_S + C_P] + M\left[\frac{(\overset{P/A,g',n}{})}{1+g}\right] \qquad (10.6)$$

where

n = anticipated service life of the bridge (years)

M = maintenance cost of the bridge in the first year

g = percent increase in maintenance cost in each subsequent year

As an example of the application of Equation 10.6, assume that the two bridge design alternatives differ in the maintenance cost to be experienced. Design A is estimated to cost \$100,000 the first year with a 5% increase in each subsequent year. Design B will cost \$90,000 to maintain in the first year with a 7% increase each subsequent year. If the interest rate is 10%, the PELCC for design A as a function of its life, n, is

$$\text{PELCC}_A = [2\sqrt{16(\$80,000)(1,000)^2(\$0.65)} + 600(1,000)(\$0.65) + \$80,000]$$

$$+ \$100,000\left[\frac{\overset{P/A,g',n}{(\qquad)}}{1+0.05}\right]$$

where

$$g' = \frac{1+i}{1+g} - 1 = \frac{1+0.10}{1+0.05} - 1 = 4.76\%$$

The PELCC for Design B as a function of n is

$$\text{PELCC}_B = [2\sqrt{22(\$80,000)(1,000)^2(\$0.65)} + \$80,000] + \$90,000\left[\frac{\overset{P/A,g',n}{(\qquad)}}{1+0.07}\right]$$

$$g' = \frac{1+i}{1+g} - 1 = \frac{1+0.10}{1+0.07} - 1 = 2.80\%$$

Assuming a service life of 40 yrs (n = 40), the present equivalent cost for Design A is

$$\text{PELCC}_A = \$2,294,281 + \$100,000\left[\frac{\overset{P/A,4.76,40}{(\ 17.7382\ )}}{1.05}\right] = \$3,983,633$$

And, for Design B it is

$$\text{PELCC}_B = \$2,219,159 + \$90,000\left[\frac{\overset{P/A,2.80,40}{(\ 23.8807\ )}}{1.07}\right] = \$4,227,816$$

From this, it appears that design A is best.

A break-even illustration of the present equivalent life-cycle cost of design A and design B is exhibited in Figure 10.3. From this illustration, it is evident that design A becomes better than design B after 21 years. Thus the choice of design A is confirmed.[1]

---

[1] Note that Design B was preferred when only investment cost is considered (see Figure 10.1 and Table 10.2). The inclusion of maintenance cost leads to a clear preference for Design A, illustrating the importance of life-cycle thinking.

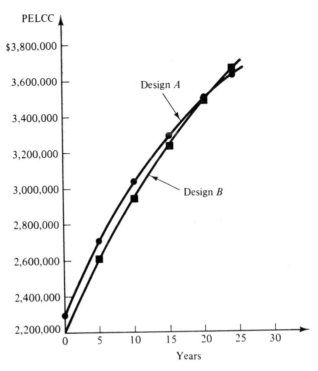

Figure 10.3 Cumulative present equivalent life-cycle cost for two bridge design alternatives.

Conductor Design Evaluation Model

Another classical situation illustrating life-cycle cost optimization is the design of an electrical conductor. The design variable of interest is the cross-sectional area, with increasing and decreasing cost components related thereto. As the area increases, so does the installed cost of the conductor. However, the power-loss cost is inversely proportional to the area. The sum of these costs will be a minimum at the optimum value for the cross-sectional area.

An evaluation model may be derived for determining total cost as a function of the cross-sectional area of a conductor. The decision evaluation function of Equation 5.2 applies as

$$E = f(X, Y)$$

where

E = evaluation measure (life-cycle cost)

X = design variable of the cross-sectional area

Y = system parameters of the conductor length, the electrical load, the resistivity of the conductor material, the cost of energy, the cost of the conductor, and the cost of money

If alternative designs (material types) are under consideration, then Equation 5.3 is the applicable design evaluation function. Design-dependent parameters arise from the material choice and are key to the selection from among design alternatives. Let

A = conductor cross-sectional area (in^2)

L = length of the conductor (feet)

I = transmission load through the conductor (amperes)

H = number of hours conductor is utilized per year

i = interest rate (%)

n = conductor useful life

C_e = cost of electricity ($/kWh)

C_i = fixed installation cost ($)

C_m = unit cost of the conductor ($/lb)

R_m = resistance of the conductor (ohms)

D_m = density of the conductor material (lb/ft^3)

W_m = weight of the conductor material (lb)

F_m = salvage value of the conductor material ($/lb)

In the notation above, the subscript m will designate the material selected for a given design alternative.

The annual equivalent life-cycle cost (AELCC) is composed of the cost due to power loss and the capital investment cost as

$$\text{AELCC} = \text{power loss cost} + \text{investment cost} \tag{10.7}$$

The power loss in dollars per year is

$$\text{power loss cost} = C_e I^2 R_m \frac{H}{1000A} \tag{10.8}$$

The annual equivalent capital investment cost (capital recovery) is

$$\text{investment cost} = C_i(\overset{A/P,i,n}{\quad}) + (C_m - F_m)(\overset{A/P,i,n}{\quad})W_m + F_m W_m i \tag{10.9}$$

where

$$W_m = \frac{LAD_m}{144} \tag{10.10}$$

Therefore, the annual equivalent life-cycle cost is

$$
\text{AELCC} = C_i(\overset{A/P,i,n}{\quad}) + (C_m - F_m)(\overset{A/P,i,n}{\quad})\frac{LAD_m}{144}
$$

$$
+ F_m \frac{LAD_m}{144} i + C_e I^2 R_m \frac{H}{100A} \tag{10.11}
$$

To optimize the equation above, the minimum cross-sectional area must be found. Taking the derivative of Equation 10.11 with respect to A and setting the result equal to zero gives

$$
\frac{d(\text{AELCC})}{dA} = (C_m - F_m)(\overset{A/P,i,n}{\quad})\frac{LD_m}{144}
$$

$$
+ F_m \frac{LD_m}{144} i - C_e I^2 R_m \frac{H}{1000A^2} = 0 \tag{10.12}
$$

from which

$$
C_e I^2 R_m \frac{H}{1000A^2} = (C_m - F_m)(\overset{A/P,i,n}{\quad})\frac{LD_m}{144} + F_m \frac{LD_m}{144} i \tag{10.13}
$$

$$
A^2 = \frac{C_e I^2 R_m \dfrac{H}{1000}}{(C_m - F_m)(\overset{A/P,i,n}{\quad})\dfrac{LD_m}{144} + F_m \dfrac{LD_m}{144} i} \tag{10.14}
$$

$$
A^* = \sqrt{\frac{C_e I^2 R_m \dfrac{H}{1000}}{(C_m - F_m)(\overset{A/P,i,n}{\quad})\dfrac{LD_m}{144} + F_m \dfrac{LD_m}{144} i}} \tag{10.15}
$$

By substituting Equation 10.15 into Equation 10.11, the minimum AELCC is found as

$$
\text{AELCC}^* = C_i(\overset{A/P,i,n}{\quad})
$$

$$
+ (C_m - F_m)(\overset{A/P,i,n}{\quad})\frac{LD_m}{144}\sqrt{\frac{C_e I^2 R_m \dfrac{H}{1000}}{(C_m - F_m)(\overset{A/P,i,n}{\quad})\dfrac{LD_m}{144} + F_m \dfrac{LD_m}{144} i}}
$$

$$
+ F_m i \frac{LD_m}{144}\sqrt{\frac{C_e I^2 R_m \dfrac{H}{1000}}{(C_m - F_m)(\overset{A/P,i,n}{\quad})\dfrac{LD_m}{144} + F_m \dfrac{LD_m}{144} i}}
$$

$$
+ C_e I^2 R_m \frac{H}{1000}\sqrt{\frac{(C_m - F_m)(\overset{A/P,i,n}{\quad})\dfrac{LD_m}{144} + F_m \dfrac{LD_m}{144} i}{C_e I^2 R_m \dfrac{H}{1000}}} \tag{10.16}
$$

To ensure that Equation 10.16 is truly a minimum, the second derivative test is applied. Taking the second derivative of Equation 10.16 yields

$$\frac{d^2(\text{AELCC})}{dA^2} = 2C_e I^2 R_m \frac{H}{1000A^3}$$

Since the second derivative is positive, A is a minimum and Equation 10.16 provides an optimal solution.

Single Design Alternative

Assume that a copper conductor is being designed to transmit 2,000 amperes continuously throughout the year for 10 years over a distance of 120 feet. The resistivity of a copper conductor is 0.000982 ohms, and copper has a density of 555 pounds per cubic foot. The interest rate is 15%. Other parameters are

$C_i = \$300$
$C_c = \$1.30$ per lb
$F_c = \$0.78$ per lb
$C_e = \$0.052$ per kWh

Using Equations 10.8, 10.9, and 10.11, Table 10.3 is obtained. Next, using Equations 10.15 and 10.16, the optimal cross-sectional area is found to be 4.19 in.^{2} at an AELCC* of $914.39 as shown in Figure 10.4. At this point, design alternative 1 is considered to be the current best (or baseline design).

TABLE 10.3   AETC for Design Alternative 1 as a Function of a Cross-Sectional Area

Cost	Cross-Sectional Area (in.^{2})					
	2	4	6	8	10	12
Investment cost	$ 263.88	$467.97	$672.05	$ 876.14	$1,080.23	$1,284.32
Power loss cost	894.64	447.32	298.21	223.66	178.93	149.11
Annual equivalent cost	$1,158.52	$915.29	$970.27	$1,099.80	$1,259.13	$1,433.43

Multiple Design Alternatives

Conductors can be fabricated from materials other than copper. Assume that aluminum is being considered as an alternative to the copper choice in the previous section. The resistivity of an aluminum conductor is 0.001498 ohms, and aluminum has a density of 168 pounds per cubic foot. Other parameters are

$C_i = \$300$
$C_a = \$1.10$ per lb

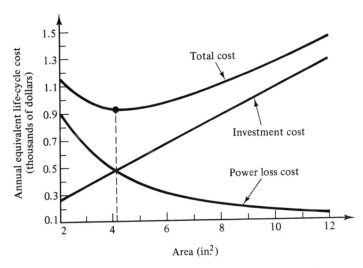

Figure 10.4   AELCC and cost components for copper conductor.

$F_a = \$0.66$ per lb
$C_e = \$0.052$ per kWh

The optimal cross-sectional area is found from Equation 10.15 to be 10.22 in.^{2}. This occurs at an AELCC* of \$593.98 from Equation 10.16. At this point the designer is ready to make a decision. The annual equivalent cost curves for both the copper design alternative and the aluminum design alternative are presented graphically in Figure 10.5. Clearly, the aluminum design, with an equivalent annual cost of \$593.98, provides the lower-cost alternative. Therefore, design alternative 2 is the best and should be selected.

Design Decision Reversal

The designer might like to know how much the price of copper would have to drop in order for copper to become the preferred conductor material. Holding the price of aluminum at \$1.10 per pound and varying the cost of copper, the annual equivalent life-cycle cost (AELCC) in Table 10.4 is obtained. In each case the salvage value is assumed to be in the same proportion to the price of copper as the original estimate, that is, 0.60 (\$0.78/\$1.3). The optimal cross-sectional area and the corresponding annual equivalent total costs (AETC) are provided in Table 10.4.

The results of Table 10.4 show the point of design decision reversal as the price of copper changes. As the price of copper decreases, the annual equiva-

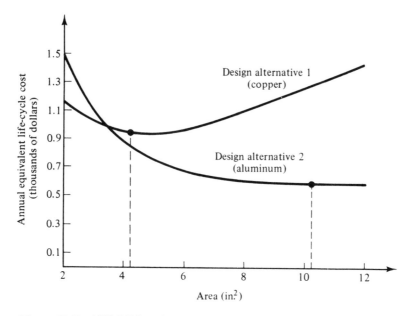

Figure 10.5   AELCC functions for two conductor design alternatives.

TABLE 10.4   Optimal A and AELCC for Various Prices of Copper

Price of Copper ($/lb)	Optimum Area (in.^{2})	AELCC* ($/yr)
1.30	4.19	914.39
1.00	4.77	809.32
0.70	5.71	686.90
0.50	6.75	589.79[a]
0.40	7.55	533.84

[a] Decision reversal occurs at $593.98.

lent life-cycle cost curves shift downward, indicating lower optimal costs (AELCC*). For copper to become the preferred material selection, its price must be approximately $0.50/lb or lower. That is, at a price less than $0.50/lb the AELCC* of copper becomes lower than that of aluminum. The point at which the copper conductor becomes the lower-cost alternative is defined as a decision reversal point. If

$C_c > \$0.50/\text{lb}$ select aluminum

$C_c < \$0.50/\text{lb}$ select copper

$C_c = \$0.50/\text{lb}$ use either

10.3 OPTIMUM EQUIPMENT LIFE

The optimum service life of an asset may be projected from knowledge of its first cost and by estimating maintenance and operation cost. Generally, the objective is to minimize the annual equivalent cost over the service life. This optimum life is also known as the minimum cost service life or the optimum replacement interval.

In this section, a general model is developed for finding the optimum life of an asset. This model is then applied to a determination of the economic life of an existing asset and the selection of an asset from among competing design alternatives. In each case, the life-cycle cost provides the basis for decision.

Equipment Life Evaluation by Mathematical Approach

Operating and maintenance costs generally increase with an increase in the age of equipment. This rising trend is offset by a decrease in the annual equivalent cost of capital recovery with return. Thus, for some age, there will be a minimum life-cycle cost or a minimum-cost life.

If the time value of money is neglected, the average annual life-cycle cost of an asset with constantly increasing maintenance cost is

$$\text{ALCC} = \frac{P}{n} + O + (n - 1)\frac{M}{2} \qquad (10.17)$$

where

ALCC = average annual life-cycle cost
P = first cost of the asset
O = annual constant portion of operating cost (equal to first-year operation cost, of which maintenance is a part),
M = amount by which maintenance costs increase each year,
n = life of the asset (years)

The minimum-cost life can be found mathematically using differential calculus as

$$\frac{d\,\text{ALCC}}{dn} = \frac{P}{n^2} + \frac{M}{2} = 0$$

$$n^* = \sqrt{\frac{2P}{M}} \qquad (10.18)$$

Therefore, minimum average life-cycle cost is given by

$$\text{ALCC}^* = P\sqrt{\frac{M}{2P}} + O + \left(\sqrt{\frac{2P}{M}} - 1\right)\frac{M}{2}$$

$$= \sqrt{\frac{PM}{2}} + O + \sqrt{\frac{PM}{2}} - \frac{M}{2}$$

$$= 2\sqrt{\frac{PM}{2}} + O - \frac{M}{2}$$

$$= \sqrt{2PM} + O - M/2 \qquad (10.19)$$

As an example of the application of Equation 10.19, consider an asset with a first cost of $18,000, a salvage value of zero at any age, a first year operating and maintenance cost of $4,000, and with maintenance costs increasing by $1,000 in each subsequent year. The minimum-cost life from Equation 10.18 is

$$n^* = \sqrt{\frac{2(\$18,000)}{\$1,000}} = 6 \text{ years.}$$

And, the minimum total cost at this life is found from Equation 10.19 as

$$\text{ALCC}^* = \sqrt{2(\$18,000)(\$1,000)} + \$4,000 - \$500 = \$9,500$$

This situation can also be seen by tabulating the cost components and the average life-cycle cost as shown in Table 10.5. The minimum life-cycle cost occurs at a life of six years. Figure 10.6 illustrates the nature of the increasing and decreasing cost components and the optimum life of six years.

Consider an alternative equipment configuration which is more reliable than the previous configuration, leading to operating and maintenance costs in the first year of $3,200, and with an increase each subsequent year equal to $800. This configuration has a first cost of $25,600. The optimum cost from

TABLE 10.5   Average Annual Life-Cycle Cost of an Asset
(First Configuration)

End of Year	Maintenance Cost at End of Year	Cumulative Maintenance Cost	Average Maintenance Cost	Average Capital Cost	Average Life-Cycle Cost
A	B	$C = \Sigma B$	$D = C/A$	$E = \$18,000/A$	$F = D + E$
1	$4,000	$4,000	$4,000	$18,000	$22,000
2	5,000	9,000	4,500	9,000	13,500
3	6,000	15,000	5,000	6,000	11,000
4	7,000	22,000	5,500	4,500	10,000
5	8,000	30,000	6,000	3,600	9,600
6	9,000	39,000	6,500	3,000	9,500
7	10,000	49,000	7,000	2,571	9,571
8	11,000	60,000	7,500	2,250	9,750
9	12,000	72,000	8,000	2,000	10,000

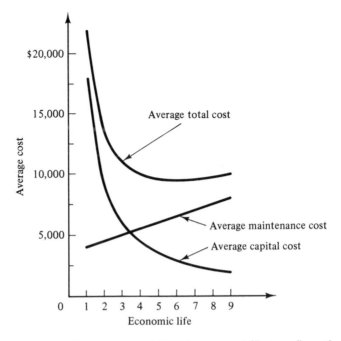

Figure 10.6 Component and LCC for an asset (first configuration).

Equation 10.18 is

$$n^* = \sqrt{\frac{2(\$25,600)}{\$800}} = 8 \text{ years.}$$

And, the optimum life-cycle cost at this age is found from Equation 10.19 as

$$\text{ALCC}^* = \sqrt{2(\$25,600)(\$800)} + \$3,200 - \$400 = \$9,200$$

This situation can be tabulated as before to illustrate the cost components and the average life-cycle cost. This is shown in Table 10.6. The minimum total cost occurs at a life of eight years and is $9,200. Figure 10.7 illustrates the nature of the increasing and decreasing cost components and the optimum life of eight years. This is the preferred configuration from an average life-cycle cost standpoint and from the standpoint of service life.

Equipment Life Evaluation by Tabular Approach

Often it is not possible to find the minimum-cost life mathematically. When nonlinearaties enter and the time value of money is taken into consideration, a tabular approach must be used. Consider the following example. The economic future of an asset with a first cost of $15,000, with linearly decreasing salvage values and with operating costs beginning at $1,000, increas-

TABLE 10.6 Average Annual Life-Cycle Cost of an Asset
(Alternative Configuration)

End of Year	Maintenance Cost at End of Year	Cumulative Maintenance Cost	Average Maintenance Cost	Average Capital Cost	Average Life-Cycle Cost
A	B	$C = \Sigma B$	$D = C/A$	$E = \$25{,}600/A$	$F = D + E$
1	$3,200	$3,200	$3,200	$25,600	$28,800
2	4,000	7,200	3,600	12,800	16,400
3	4,800	12,000	4,000	8,533	12,533
4	5,600	17,600	4,400	6,400	10,800
5	6,400	24,000	4,800	5,120	9,920
6	7,200	31,200	5,200	4,267	9,467
7	8,000	39,200	5,600	3,657	9,257
8	8,800	48,000	6,000	3,200	9,200
9	9,600	57,600	6,400	2,844	9,244
10	10,400	68,000	6,800	2,560	9,360
11	11,200	79,200	7,200	2,327	9,527
12	12,000	91,200	7,600	2,133	9,733

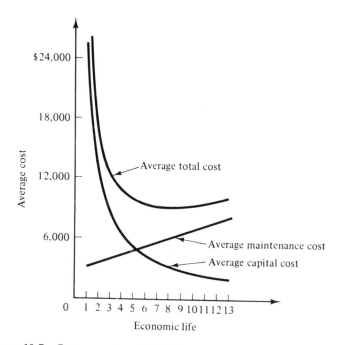

Figure 10.7 Component and LCC for an asset (alternative configuration).

ing by $300 in the second year and thereafter (the increase each year is $55 more than the increase in the preceding year), and with an interest at a rate of 12%, is shown in Table 10.7. To find the asset's optimum life, it is necessary to identify the relevant money flows associated with retaining the asset one, two, three, four, or five years. These flows are depicted in Figure 10.8 and are the basis for the annual equivalent life-cycle cost calculations shown in Table 10.7.

Table 10.7 illustrates the tabular method for determining the economic life of an asset. If the asset were retired after three years, it would have a minimum annual equivalent life-cycle cost of $5,762, and this is the life most favorable for comparison purposes. Suppose that the need for the asset discussed and tabulated in Table 10.7 can be met by an alternative physical configuration. The initial investment needed for the alternative asset is $12,500, again with linearly decreasing salvage values and with operating costs beginning at $1,600, increasing by $200 in the second year and thereafter the increase each year is $100 more than the increase in the preceding year, and

TABLE 10.7 Tabular Calculations for Optimum Life (first case)

End of Year	Salvage Value When Asset Retired	Operating Costs	Annual Equivalent Cost of Asset	Annual Equivalent Operating Cost	Annual Equivalent LCC
1	$12,000	$1,000	$4,800	$1,000	$5,800
2	9,000	1,300	4,630	1,142	5,772
3	6,000	1,655	4,468	1,294	5,762[a]
4	3,000	2,065	4,310	1,455	5,765
5	0	2,530	4,161	1,624	5,785

[a]Optimum.

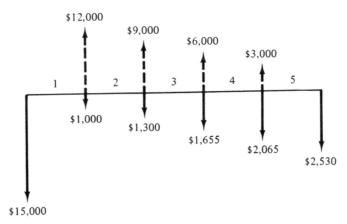

Figure 10.8 Money flows for an asset.

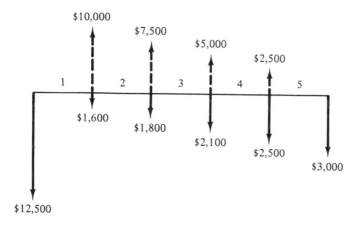

Figure 10.9 Money flows for an alternative asset.

with an interest rate of 12%. To find this asset's optimum life, it is necessary to identify, as before, the relevant money flows. These money flows are depicted in Figure 10.9 and are the basis for the annual equivalent life-cycle cost calculations shown in Table 10.8.

TABLE 10.8 Tabular Calculations for Optimum Life (alternative)

End of Year	Salvage Value When Asset Retired	Operating Costs	Annual Equivalent Cost of Asset	Annual Equivalent Operating Cost	Annual Equivalent LCC
1	$10,000	$1,600	$4,000	$1,600	$5,600
2	7,500	1,800	3,859	1,694	5,553
3	5,000	2,100	3,723	1,815	5,538[a]
4	2,500	2,500	3,592	1,958	5,550
5	0	3,000	3,468	2,122	5,590

[a] Optimum.

In this example, both the first case and the alternative have an optimum life of three years. However, the alternative is to be preferred in that the annual equivalent life-cycle cost is lower by $5,762 - $5,538 = $224.

QUESTIONS AND PROBLEMS

1. The cost of producing and selling a certain item is $220x + $15,000$ for the first 1,000 units, $120x + $115,000$ for a production range between 1,000 and 2,500 units, and $205x - $97,500$ for more than 2,500 units, where x is the number of units produced. If the selling price is $200 per unit, and all units produced are sold, find the level of production that will maximize profit.

2. What is the profit attainable at the optimum level of production and the profit 10% on either side of this optimum for the production situation in Problem 1?

3. Ethyl acetate is made from acetic acid and ethyl alcohol. Let x = pounds of acetic acid input, y = pounds of ethyl alcohol input, and z = pounds of ethyl acetate output. The relationship of output to input is

$$\frac{z^2}{(1.47x - z)(1.91y - z)} = 3.9$$

  (a) Determine the output of ethyl acetate per pound of acetic acid, where the ratio of acetic acid of ethyl alcohol is 2.0, 1.0, and 0.67, and graph the result.
  (b) Graph the cost of material per pound of ethyl acetate for each of the ratios given and determine the ratio for which the material cost per pound of ethyl acetate is a minimum if acetic acid costs $0.80 per pound and ethyl alcohol costs $0.92 per pound.

4. It has been found that the heat loss through the ceiling of a building is 0.13 Btu per hour per square foot of area per degree Fahrenheit. If the 2,200-ft^2 ceiling is insulated, the heat loss in Btu per hour per degree temperature difference per square foot of area is taken as

$$\frac{1}{(1/0.13) + (t/0.27)}$$

where t is the thickness in inches. The in-place cost of insulation 2, 4, and 6 in. thick is $0.18, $0.30, and $0.44 per square foot, respectively. The building is heated to 75°F 3,000 hours per year by a gas furnace with an efficiency of 50%. The mean outside temperature is 45°F and the natural gas used in the furnace costs $4.40 per 1,000 ft^3 and has a heating value of 2,000 Btu per 1,000 ft^3. What thickness of insulation, if any, should be used if the interest rate is 10% and the resale value of the building six years hence is enhanced $850 if insulation is added, regardless of the thickness?

5. An overpass is being considered for a certain crossing. The superstructure design under consideration will be made of steel and will have a weight per foot depending on the span between piers in accordance with $W = 32(S) + 1,850$. Piers will be made of concrete and will cost $185,000 each. The superstructure will be erected at a cost of $0.70 per pound. If the number of piers required is to be one less than the number of spans, find the number of piers that will result in a minimum total cost for piers and superstructure if $L = 1,250$ feet.

6. Two girder designs are under consideration for a bridge for a 1,200-foot crossing. The first is expected to result in a superstructure weight per foot of $22(S) + 800$, where S is the span between piers. The second should result in superstructure weight per foot of $20(S) + 1,000$. Piers and two required abutments are estimated to cost $220,000 each. The superstructure will be erected at a cost of $0.55 per pound. Choose the girder design that will result in a minimum cost and specify the optimum number of piers.

7. What is the cost advantage of choosing the best girder design for the bridge described in Problem 6? If the number of piers is determined from the best girder design alternative, but the other design alternative is adopted, what cost penalty is incurred?

8. Refer to Problem 6. If the annual maintenance cost for the first girder design is $400,000 and is $410,000 for the second girder design, find the number of years in the bridge life cycle for which the annual equivalent costs would be equal. The cost of money is taken to be 12%.

9. If the span between piers in Problem 5 must be at least 200 feet, what lost penalty is incurred for this constraint?

10. Suppose that no more than six piers can be utilized in the bridge design of Problem 5. What is the cost penalty incurred for this constraint if the piers cost $210,000 each?

11. An hourly electric load of 1,600 amperes is to be transmitted from a generator to a transformer in a certain power plant. A copper conductor 150 ft long can be installed for $380 + $1.15 per pound, will have an estimated life of 20 years, and can be salvaged for $0.96 per pound. Power loss from the conductor will be a function of the cross-sectional area and may be expressed as $25,875 \div A$ kilowatt-hours per year. Energy lost is valued at $0.06 per kilowatt-hour, taxes, insurance, and maintenance are negligible, and the interest rate is 8%. Copper weighs 555 lb per ft^3.

(a) Plot the total annual cost of capital recovery with a return and power loss cost for conductors for cross sections of 1, 2, 3, 4, and 5 in.^{2}.

(b) Find the minimum-cost cross section mathematically and check the result against the minimum point found in part (a).

12. The daily electrical load to be transmitted by a conductor in a laboratory is 1,900 amperes per day for 365 days per year. Two conductor materials are under consideration, copper and aluminum. The information listed in the table is available for the competing materials.

	Copper	Aluminum
Length	120 ft	120 ft
Installed cost	$410 + $0.88	$410 + $0.48
Estimated life	10 yr	10 yr
Salvage value	$0.72	$0.40
Electrical resistance of conductor		
120 ft by 1 in.^{2} cross section	0.000982 Ω	0.001498 Ω
Density	555 lb/ft^3	168 lb/ft^3

The energy loss in kilowatt-hours in a conductor due to resistance is equal to I^2R times the number of hours divided by 1,000, where I is the current flow in amperes and R is the resistance in the conductor in ohms. The electrical resistance is inversely proportional to the area of the cross section. Lost energy is valued at $0.048 per kilowatt-hour.

(a) Plot the total annual cost of capital recovery and return plus power loss cost for each material for cross sections of 3, 4, 5, 6, 7, and 8 in.^{2} if the interest rate is 12%.

(b) Recommend the minimum-cost conductor material and specify the cross-sectional area.

13. A used automobile can be purchased by a student to provide transportation to and from school for $5,500 as is (i.e., the auto will have no warranty). First-year maintenance cost is expected to be $350 and the maintenance costs will increase by $100 per year thereafter. Operation costs for the automobile will be $1,200 for every year the auto is used and its salvage value decreases by 15% per year.

    (a) What is the economic life without taking into account the time value of money?

    (b) With interest at 16%, what is the economic life?

14. As an alternative to the used automobile in Problem 13, the student can purchase a new "utility" model for $6,800 with a three-year warranty. First-year maintenance cost is expected to be $50 and the maintenance cost will increase by $50 per year thereafter. Operation costs for this new automobile are expected to be $850 for each year of use and its salvage value decreases by 20% per year. What is the economic advantage of the new automobile without interest; with interest at 16%?

15. Special equipment can be designed and built for $80,000. This equipment will have a salvage value of $70,000 in year 1, and decrease by $10,000 through year 8. Operation and maintenance costs will start at $18,000 in year 1, and increase by 5% per year through year 8. The organization proposing this design can borrow money with a 10% annual interest rate. Using the tabular approach, find the economic life of this equipment.

16. Company X is considering using an impact wrench with a torque-sensitive clutch to fasten bolts on one of their assembly lines. The impact wrench, which can be purchased for $950, has a maximum life of four years. The impact wrench will have a salvage value of $600 in year 1, and will decrease in value by $200 through year 4. The impact wrench will have operation and maintenance costs of $100 in year one, $250 in year 2, $325 in year 3, and $400 in year 4. Company X has an MARR of 25%. Using the tabular approach, find the impact wrench's economic value. Show the impact wrench's economic value graphically.

11

Life-Cycle Cost in Program Evaluation

Large projects such as the acquisition of an airplane, the construction and operation of a processing plant, the development of a computer installation, and so on, consume enormous quantities of resources. The potential for savings through the application of life-cycle cost and economic analysis methods is great. However, it is recognized that the basic principles of life-cycle costing should also be accepted at the consumer level or by groups of individuals procuring relatively small products such as an automobile, an electrical appliance, and so on. This chapter addresses the management and program evaluation aspects of life-cycle costing as applied to a typical medium or large-scale program. Although much of the discussion is oriented in this direction, one can "tailor" the various concepts presented to the specific situation.

11.1 PROGRAM REQUIREMENTS AND PLANNING

The need for life-cycle costing has evolved as a result of the current economic dilemma discussed in Chapters 1 and 6. To attain the total cost visibility desired requires that emphasis be placed on life-cycle cost at program inception. Thus, market analyses, technical feasibility studies, and early program planning activities must consider life-cycle cost as a major criterion factor in decision making. This is particularly essential since decisions early in the life cycle have the greatest impact on life-cycle cost, as emphasized in Figure 1.5.

Setting Cost Requirements

Life-cycle cost emphasis can best be applied by initially setting realistic quantitative cost targets for the system or product at the start of a program. Such quantitative factors may be assigned to both material items and program activities, and should be allocated to the level necessary to ensure adequate cost monitoring and control. The system/product cost allocation process was illustrated in Figure 6.3. Note that these cost targets include not only acquisition cost, but life-cycle cost. As these cost values are assigned, they should be included in the appropriate system/product specifications in the form of required "design to" criteria (e.g., design to a unit life-cycle cost of $15,000). This is particularly applicable in the preparation of product specifications for the procurement of inventoried items from potential suppliers, and in system specifications covering the development and acquisition of new systems.

Concurrent with the consideration of life-cycle cost as a system design parameter, early planning data must include a formal program effort that identifies and provides the necessary tasks required in establishing the cost targets; accomplishing life-cycle cost analyses on a continuing basis; generating cost estimating data; measuring and reporting life-cycle cost analysis results; participating in design reviews and periodic program reviews; initiating the necessary corrective action when intolerable situations develop; and so on. In other words, a formal program effort must be planned and implemented to ensure that the desired cost targets or goals are met. This activity need not be extensive, but must be at a level that will provide the necessary management emphasis to produce a cost-effective output. The formal life-cycle cost task level of effort should be included in the program plan, and should be scheduled and organized in a manner similar to any other program activity. Further, this activity should be completely *integrated* into the overall management approach implemented for the program or project.

Program Planning

Program planning includes (1) defining the tasks required to implement life-cycle costing activities; (2) scheduling and organizing these tasks to produce the desired results in a timely manner; (3) determining the resources required to accomplish life-cycle analyses for a given program; and (4) establishing the methods by which task accomplishment can be measured and evaluated.

Figure 6.2 illustrated the application of life-cycle costing throughout the various program phases, and Figure 6.4 showed the process in accomplishing a life-cycle cost analysis. These figures, combined with the application examples in Chapter 8 and the case studies in Part III, indicate the detailed tasks

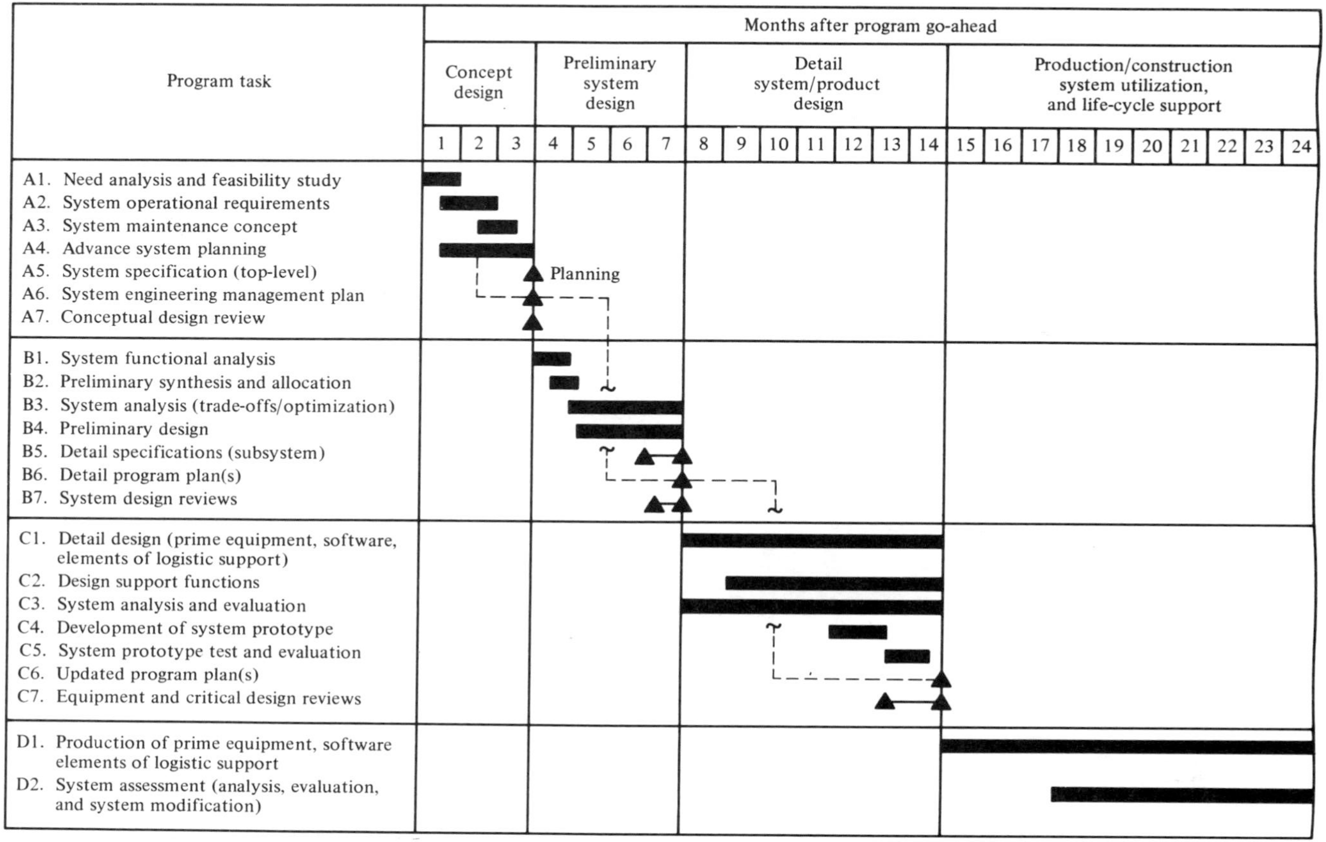

Months after program go-ahead

	Concept design	Preliminary system design	Detail system/product design	Production/construction system utilization, and life-cycle support
	1 2 3	4 5 6 7	8 9 10 11 12 13 14	15 16 17 18 19 20 21 22 23 24

Program task

A1. Need analysis and feasibility study
A2. System operational requirements
A3. System maintenance concept
A4. Advance system planning
A5. System specification (top-level)
A6. System engineering management plan
A7. Conceptual design review

Planning

B1. System functional analysis
B2. Preliminary synthesis and allocation
B3. System analysis (trade-offs/optimization)
B4. Preliminary design
B5. Detail specifications (subsystem)
B6. Detail program plan(s)
B7. System design reviews

C1. Detail design (prime equipment, software, elements of logistic support)
C2. Design support functions
C3. System analysis and evaluation
C4. Development of system prototype
C5. System prototype test and evaluation
C6. Updated program plan(s)
C7. Equipment and critical design reviews

D1. Production of prime equipment, software elements of logistic support
D2. System assessment (analysis, evaluation, and system modification)

Figure 11.1 Program milestone chart showing LCC reporting requirements as ▲.

259

required in this area. If one were to group these tasks into functional categories, the significant functions would probably include the following:

1. Development of system/product operational requirements and the maintenance concept
2. Development of economic factors to include the cost breakdown structure, cost category descriptions, cost estimating relationships, and individual cost factors
3. Development of program planning information to include the identification of design functions, production functions, distribution functions, operational and support functions, and so on
4. Development of reliability, maintainability, and logistic support factors
5. Development of the analytical methods to facilitate the life-cycle cost analysis process (e.g., models)

The functions required for life-cycle costing are inherent within the spectrum of activities for a typical program. Figure 11.1[1] illustrates system design and development activities, along with selected major milestones. While life-cycle cost analyses are important in the definition of operational requirements (A.2), the maintenance concept (A.3), and so on, life-cycle cost analysis reports are prepared and evaluated as an integral part of scheduled program and design reviews. Accordingly, life-cycle cost analyses are performed on a continuing basis throughout all program phases, and the results are provided in the form of special cost reports prepared at designated review points.

Figure 11.2 illustrates the concept of review and evaluation, The program reviews should be tied in with the conceptual, system, equipment/software, and critical design reviews as identified in Figure 11.1. At these points the life-cycle cost estimates and projections are compared with the initially established targets. Areas of noncompliance are investigated and corrective action is initiated as appropriate.

Success in the accomplishment of life-cycle cost analyses depends directly on the availability of good data from a wide range of program activities. Life-cycle cost analysis is based on product design data, manufacturing data, reliability data, maintainability data, human factors data, logistics data, and so on. The activity interfaces are numerous, and it is important for these activities and related tasks to be integrated into the overall planning for a comprehensive life-cycle costing effort.

---

[1] Figure 11.1 conveys a relatively comprehensive program, and is applicable to medium-sized and large-scale systems of products. Obviously, the planning requirements for small products, or those items already developed, are considerably less than that illustrated in the figure. In such instances, the required functions and milestones are tailored accordingly.

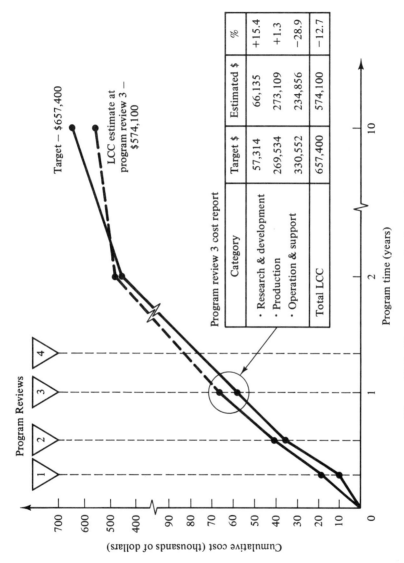

Figure 11.2 Program cost projections and reviews.

Program review 3 cost report

Category	Target $	Estimated $	%
· Research & development	57,314	66,135	+15.4
· Production	269,534	273,109	+1.3
· Operation & support	330,552	234,856	−28.9
Total LCC	657,400	574,100	−12.7

261

11.2 ORGANIZATION FOR LIFE-CYCLE COSTING

As conveyed earlier, life-cycle costing is a technique employed by managers and engineers primarily for decision-making purposes. Life-cycle cost analyses must be objective, comprehensive in scope, responsive to specific problem-oriented needs, and accomplished in a timely manner. The allotted time for completing a life-cycle cost analysis is often limited to a few days, and response to the "what if" questions may result in an overnight requirement.

Thus the organizational component necessary for accomplishing a life-cycle costing must be relatively small and versatile. The people within the organization should be thoroughly familiar with the process discussed in Chapter 1, the data requirements covered in Chapter 6, and the analytical techniques available. It is recognized that no one person will possess all of the skills required. However, a team of specialists with the proper backgrounds and experience can be assigned to accomplish the analysis activity itself, with supporting organizations providing the appropriate data as required. This team should include some expertise in the area of computer applications and modeling; experience in system/product operations and logistic support; experience in reliability and maintainability; knowledge of internal producer and supplier activities; and experience in cost estimating and cost analysis.

In some instances, the data requirements for a given analysis may be rather extensive and the need for detailed reliability and maintainability predictions, comprehensive cost estimates, design drawings, and so on, is valid. The participation by supporting organizations is necessary and should be encouraged as long as the data requirements are precisely defined, the costs of data preparation are minimal, and the data are available in a timely manner. It is relatively easy to misjudge actual needs and ask for too much data, which may turn out to be quite costly and ineffective.

On the other hand, the nature of the problem may allow for the analysis effort to be accomplished on a relatively independent basis by the assembled team of specialists. In such cases, the operational requirements, maintenance concept, reliability estimates, logistic support factors, cost values, and so on, must be developed by the team, and the team members should have prior experience in these areas if they are to produce effective results. Occasionally, additional expertise may be necessary, and selected personnel are assigned to the team on a temporary basis in order to complete the task.

The provisions for accomplishing life-cycle cost analyses will vary, and the organized team must be able to quickly assess the situation. The decision on whether to perform the analysis independently or with outside assistance is a function of the nature of the problem, the required analysis scope and depth, and the time allowed for analysis completion. In any event, the analysis effort must be responsive to management needs.

As a final point, there are certain organizational operating conditions that must exist if the life-cycle cost analysis effort is to be successful. These are summarized below.

1. The analysis activity must have direct access to all levels of program management. A *staff* function is usually preferred over a *line* function, since the staff function is not likely to be assigned other concurrent activities of a possible conflicting nature and is more apt to be objective in performing the analysis.

2. The analysis activity must not be constrained by any individual manager or organization in such a way that will cause incomplete, inaccurate, or untimely reporting. Changing the data or influencing the results to support a personal "cause" is self-defeating.

3. The analysis activity must have direct access to all program cost data and applicable design data, reliability and maintainability prediction data, production data, and logistics support data.

4. The analysis effort must be an inherent part of the program review function. Design decisions should be supported by life-cycle cost data in the formal design reviews, and life-cycle cost projections should be evaluated as a part of the periodic program management reviews (refer to Figure 11.1).

11.3 PROGRAM REVIEW AND CONTROL

Once that system design and program requirements have been established, it is essential that an ongoing review, evaluation, and control function be initiated. Management must conduct a periodic assessment to compare current life-cycle cost estimates with the specified requirements. The selected review points should either be a part of or tied directly to the normally scheduled program reviews. Usually, major reviews occur after a significant stage or level of activity in the program and prior to entering the next phase. Figure 11.1 identifies the major reviews for one type of program.

In preparation for each individual program review, a life-cycle cost analysis is accomplished for the system/product configuration as it exists at that time. The cost breakdown structure (CBS) in Appendix B may serve as the basis for cost collection and the latest design data, production data, reliability and maintainability predictions, logistic support analyses, and so on, are employed to the extent possible in developing the required cost projections.

Figure 11.2 identifies the various program review points, and shows a comparison between the target life-cycle cost and the estimated value at the third formal review scheduled one year after program start. The projections convey expected cumulative expenditures. Note that the illustration indicates that actual research and development costs did exceed the initial projection (i.e., the costs in the first year); the expected cost at the end of production will exceed the anticipated value; and the life-cycle cost at the end of the 10-year life period will be less than the target due to a reduction in operation and support cost.

If the projected life-cycle cost at any given program review exceeds the target value, one should evaluate the different categories of cost in the CBS and identify the high-cost contributors. Also, one should determine the relative relationships of these costs, with each other and with the overall life-cycle cost figure, to see if any significant changes have occurred since the previous review (i.e., unusual trends). Areas of concern should be investigated in terms of the possible cause(s) for the high cost, and recommendations for corrective action should be initiated where appropriate. Such recommendations may take the form of design changes, production or process changes, logistic support policy revisions, and/or changes involving the management of resources. Recommendations where significant life-cycle cost reduction can be realized should be documented and submitted for management action.

The program review and control function is an iterative process of life-cycle cost assessment. Inherent in this process is not only the accomplishment of life-cycle cost analyses, but the feedback and corrective action that is required when problems occur and requirements are not being met. Management emphasis is necessary in both areas. It is not sufficient merely to review and assess a system/product in terms of life-cycle cost unless corrective measures can be taken when required.

11.4 CONSUMER/PRODUCER/SUPPLIER INTERFACES

The major interfaces that exist between the producer (i.e., contractor), the supplier of components for the system or product (i.e., subcontractor), and the consumer (i.e., customer) are depicted in Figure 11.3. The initiation of life-cycle costing activities begins with the definition of requirements. Consumer requirements are imposed on the producer, and producer requirements are allocated to each supplier as appropriate. Subsequently, there are supplier proposals, contractual agreements, life-cycle cost reporting, and cost measurement and evaluation activity of one type or another. These activities create many interfaces between the consumer, producer, and supplier throughout a program.

Of particular concern when dealing with life-cycle costing are the quantitative cost figures of merit that are proposed and reported through a period of time. All affected organizations (or levels of activity) must be thoroughly familiar with each figure of merit in terms of what is and is not included, how the figure is derived, and the data base used in deriving the figure. This is particularly true when various potential suppliers submit proposals to the producer that include life-cycle costing information. In each instance, the

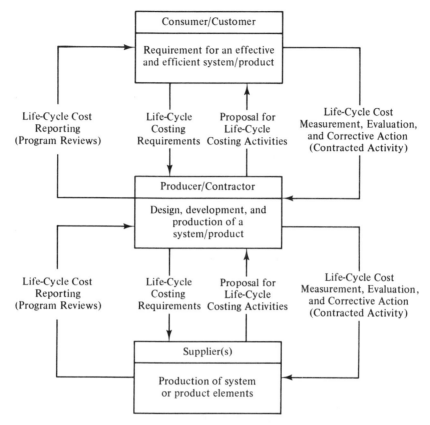

Figure 11.3   Major consumer/producer/supplier interfaces.

supplier in all probability has developed a cost structure peculiar to his own interests and organization, individual cost estimating relationships, and cost model. These activities, which vary from one supplier to the next, result in proposed life-cycle cost figures of merit which the producer must evaluate objectively and in a consistent manner. In other words, the producer is often faced with the task of evaluating alternative supplier proposals, including life-cycle cost information, on an equivalent basis. This is extremely difficult to accomplish (if not impossible) unless the producer is thoroughly familiar with the factors and procedures employed by the supplier in developing his life-cycle cost figures.

As an alternative, the producer may develop his/her own cost breakdown structure, estimating relationships, cost model, and so on, and employ these tools in evaluating various supplier proposals. Each supplier, in turn, is requested to provide specific cost data in a prescribed format and the producer uses this information in the evaluation process. The producer is familiar with the analysis process and the techniques employed, and the various suppliers may be evaluated on an equivalent basis. This approach is generally preferred when there are a number of suppliers being considered for program support.

Given that contractual agreements exist and there are program requirements for life-cycle cost reporting, measurement, and evaluation, the problem of proper communication once again becomes significant. The consumer, producer, and supplier(s) alike must be thoroughly familiar with the content and relevance of the information reported and the techniques used in measurement and evaluation. It is relatively easy to accept life-cycle cost figures at "face value," but the risks are extremely high unless one knows and understands the bases for such figures. The objective, of course, is to minimize this risk through a better understanding of life-cycle cost analysis and its implications.

11.5 CONTRACTUAL IMPLICATIONS

There are many different applications of contracts used in the acquisition of systems, products, services, and so on.[2] Also, the type of contract imposed will vary depending on the phase of system/product development and the anticipated risks in procurement. For instance, when system/product design is fairly well established, or in the acquisition of items already in the inventory, fixed-price contracts are usually effective. On the other hand, cost-reimbursement type contracts are relatively flexible and more appropriate for newly designed items where frequent changes are likely to occur. In essence, the methods of contracting between the consumer, producer, and/or supplier are tailored to the specific program and the related risks.

Associated with each major type of contract is the method and schedule of payments, incentive and penalty clauses, warranty and guarantee provisions, and so on. For relatively large programs, progress payments are often made by the contractor on the successful completion and acceptance of each significant line item specified in the contract. If incentive contracting is used, and incentive/penalty plan is often developed and implemented as a supplement to the schedule for progress payments. Additionally, as a condition in contracting, many systems and products are procured with the assumption that the contractor will guarantee the item(s) for a designated period of time after purchase (i.e., the contractor will accomplish any necessary maintenance and support at no cost to the consumer).

When addressing life-cycle costing in the overall contractual process, the necessary steps must be taken to ensure that the life-cycle cost activities

---

[2] Contract types include: firm-fixed-price; fixed-price-with-escalation; fixed-price-incentive; cost-plus-fixed-fee; cost-plus-incentive-fee; cost-sharing; time and material; and letter agreements. For a discussion of contract types, applications, and negotiations, see B. S. Blanchard, *Engineering Organization and Management* (Englewood Cliffs, NJ: Prentice-Hall, Inc., 1976).

discussed earlier receive the proper emphasis, and that the results of life-cycle cost analyses are in some manner tied directly to the contractual payment structure. The objective is to convey that life-cycle costing is important and should be taken seriously, and an approach used in attaining the objective is to positively identify life-cycle costing milestones as part of the contract negotiations between the consumer, producer, and/or supplier (as applicable). Three areas of consideration are noted below.

The first area of consideration includes the application of *progress payments* directly to the successful completion of life-cycle costing activities, and contingent on meeting the anticipated life-cycle cost target requirements at that stage in the program. Referring to Figure 11.1, a progress payment of sufficient magnitude to be meaningful could be applied to the conceptual design review (task A.7) if life-cost analyses have been completed, and if the projected life-cycle cost estimate at that stage is less than the specified target value. On the other hand, if the life-cycle cost estimate does not reflect compliance with the target value, the progress payment may be withheld until such time that the producer (or supplier) implements corrective action that will cause the necessary reduction in life-cycle cost.

A second consideration relates to *incentive contracting* where an incentive/penalty plan is established as in Figure 11.4. Such a plan will specify the application of incentive and penalty payments at a designed point in the program when there is adequate assurance that the requirements have been met. For life-cycle costing, it is believed that the application of an incentive/penalty plan would be appropriate at a point in time after the system or product has acquired some field experience and realistic life-cycle cost projections can be accomplished using some "real-world" data. Although this specific point in time will vary with the type of system or product, two to three years of experience seems appropriate.

Referring to Figure 11.4, the illustrated plan indicates proposed incentive/penalty values along the ordinate values and negotiated sharing ratios (SRs). A target life-cycle cost value of $800,000 is assumed, and different sharing ratios are developed around this value. Nearly all incentive plans assume the form of a sharing arrangement, generally expressed as a percentage ratio. For instance, the 30/70 SR indicates that if the estimated life-cycle cost is significantly less than the target value (i.e., $600,000 or less), the value of dollars indicated on the ordinate would be split, with 30% going to the customer and 60% being paid to the producer. Conversely, if the estimated life-cycle cost is between $800,000 and $1,000,000, a penalty payment of 40% of the indicated ordinate value would be paid by the producer.

The aspect of incentive/penalty plan development and implementation is a comprehensive subject. There are all kinds of variations, and the approach selected is highly dependent on the type of system, the program functions, development risks, budget limitations, and the formal negotiated contractual structure.

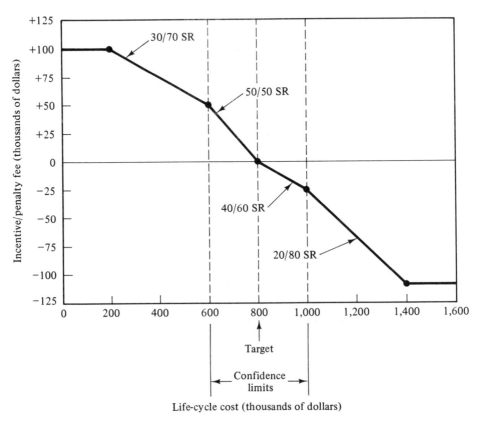

Figure 11.4   Example of contractual incentive/penalty plan.

A third area of consideration involves *warranties*. For systems or products where the configuration is relatively "fixed," it may be appropriate to control operation and support costs through a firm maintenance and support agreement. At this stage, the producer (or supplier) has established MTBF or MTBM targets and specific logistic support requirements. As illustrated in Chapter 1, these factors have a significant impact on life-cycle cost, particularly operation and support cost. Thus it may be feasible to negotiate a fixed-price contract where the producer or supplier provides a designated level of sustaining support for a system/product being utilized by the consumer. This level of support is based on the frequency of maintenance (e.g., the reciprocal of the MTBM), and the logistic support resources required when maintenance actions occur. If the level of support is higher than anticipated, the additional costs are borne by the producer. On the other hand, if the level is less than predicted, the producer should realize some savings. In essence, a contract of this type is basically a warranty established by the producer using reliability, maintainability, and logistic support data to determine the provisions of the warranty.[3]

11.6 MANAGERIAL IMPLICATIONS

With the limitation of resources, emphasis must be applied toward increasing productivity. Productivity relates to the effective and efficient utilization of resources. Increased productivity is attained by ensuring that each current and potential program is planned and implemented with the best allocation of resources possible. The life-cycle cost analysis technique is an excellent tool for assessing resource allocation and for identifying areas where a shift in resources could result in improvement(s).

Life-cycle costing theory, methodology, and applications were discussed thoroughly in earlier chapters. However, the ultimate benefits of life-cycle costing are entirely dependent on management acceptance and the proper use of this approach. One can accomplish the best possible analysis, but the effort is of little value unless the activity is taken seriously and the results are effectively utilized in the decision-making process. Thus the successful implementation of life-cycle cost analyses is a direct function of management awareness, interest, and emphasis.

In performing any life-cycle-oriented analysis, there are many factors to be considered, assumptions to be made, data to collect and evaluate, parameter relationships to establish, and so on. The process allows for the introduction of a great deal of error if management is not careful. Although it is obviously impossible to eliminate all error (and risk in terms of using the analysis in decision making), management should take every precaution to validate the analysis to the extent possible. In making a final recommendation to management as to a proposed course of action (based on analysis results), the analyst should review the overall analysis process in terms of problem definition, validity of stated assumptions, model parameter relationships, inclusions/exclusions, adequacy of data input, and stated conclusions. The main question is: Does the preferred configuration clearly have the advantage over other alternative considerations? In response, the analyst may wish to pose a number of specific questions in the form of a checklist as an aid in assessing the final output results. Figure 11.5 presents a sample checklist, including some basic but significant questions that may pertain to any type of analysis.

Management considerations pertaining to life-cycle costing are numerous and varied. Some of the highlights are noted in this chapter, and many related implications are included in previous chapters. Life-cycle costing con-

---

[3] Contractual provisions of a similar nature include reliability improvement warranties (RIWs), which are being applied in many programs today.

A. *Assumptions*

1. Are all assumptions adequately identified?
2. Do any of the specified assumptions treat quantitative uncertainties as facts?
3. Do any of the specified assumptions treat qualitative uncertainties as facts?
4. Are major assumptions reasonable?

B. *Alternatives*

1. Are current capabilities adequately considered among alternatives?
2. Are mixtures of system components considered among the alternatives?
3. Are any feasible and significant alternatives omitted?

C. *Documentation*

1. Is the study adequately documented?
2. Are the facts stated correctly?
3. Are the facts stated with proper qualification?
4. Are the applicable reference sources listed?

D. *Model relationships*

1. Does the model adequately address the problem?
2. Are cost and effectiveness parameters linked logically?
3. Does the model allow for a timely response?
4. Does the model provide valid (comprehensive) and reliable (repeatable) results?

E. *Effectiveness parameters*

1. Are the measures of effectiveness identified?
2. Is the effectiveness measure appropriate to the mission function? Are operational and maintenance concepts adequately defined?
3. Do the effectiveness measures employed ignore some objectives and concentrate on others?
4. Are performance measures mistaken for effectiveness measures?
5. Does the effectiveness of a future system take into account the time dimension?
6. Are expected and average values used correctly to measure effectiveness?
7. If quantitative measures of effectiveness are unattainable, is a qualitative comparison feasible?
8. Is the effectiveness measure sensitive to changes in assumptions?
9. In the event that two or more effectiveness measures are appropriate, are the measures properly weighted (the relative weighting in terms of significance or level of importance of each applicable criterion factor employed)?

F. *Cost*

1. Is the cost model employed adequately described?
2. Are cost categories adequately defined?
3. Are cost estimates relevant?
4. Are incremental and marginal costs considered?
5. Are variable and fixed costs separately identifiable?
6. Are escalation factors specified and employed?
7. Is the discount rate specified and employed?
8. Are all costs elements considered?
   (a) Feasibility studies
   (b) Design and development
   (c) Production and test
   (d) Installation and checkout
   (e) Personnel and training
   (f) Technical data
   (g) Facility construction and maintenance
   (h) Spare/repair parts
   (i) Support equipment/tools
   (j) Inventory maintenance
   (k) Customer support (field service)
   (l) Program management
9. Are the cost aspects of all alternatives treated in a consistent and comparable manner?
10. Are the cost estimates (cost estimating relationships) reasonably accurate? Are areas of risk and uncertainty identified?
11. Is cost amortization employed? If so, how?
12. Has the sensitivity of cost estimates been properly addressed through a sensitivity analysis?

G. *Conclusions and recommendations*

1. Are the conclusions and recommendations logically derived from the material contained in the study?
2. Have all the significant ramifications been considered in arriving at the conclusions and recommendations presented?
3. Are the conclusions and recommendations really feasible in light of political, cultural, policy or other considerations?
4. Do the conclusions and recommendations indicate bias?
5. Are the conclusions and recommendations based on external considerations?
6. Are the conclusions and recommendations based on insignificant differences?

Figure 11.5 Sample checklist of questions for assessing life-cycle analysis.

stitutes an approach to the management decision-making process, and must be an integral part of all program activities. As such, it is impossible to cover the entire spectrum of management as it applies to life-cycle costing within the confines of this book. However, it is hoped that the points discussed herein will be beneficial in establishing life-cycle cost and economic analysis requirements for future programs.

QUESTIONS AND PROBLEMS

1. Identify a system or product of your choice and assume that new design and development is required. Prepare a life-cycle cost implementation plan to include activities, schedules, organization, resource needs, and output requirements.

2. Within an organization, describe in detail how you would fulfill the objectives of life-cycle costing.

3. Identify the organizations or groups within a company (or agency) where support is required in the accomplishment of life-cycle cost analysis.

4. What individual skills are required to accomplish life-cycle cost analyses? Be specific in your discussion.

5. What specific steps would you take to ensure that life-cycle costing is being implemented in a program?

6. How can life-cycle cost analysis be employed successfully as a management tool in system/product planning, development, production, operational use, and logistic support?

PART III
Case Studies

12

Communication System Procurement

A large metropolitan area plans to upgrade its overall communications capability by procuring new communication equipment for installation in patrol aircraft, helicopters, ground vehicles, certain designated ground facilities, and in a central communications control facility. Two alternative system configurations are being considered and evaluated. The objective is to define system operational requirements, the maintenance concept, and required program planning information so that the system configuration with the lowest life-cycle cost can be acquired.[1]

12.1 CASE STUDY INTRODUCTION

The communication system network is shown in Figure 12.1. There is an overall requirement for 80 equipment installations. Proposed maintenance and support facilities are also shown. The new communication equipment should be adaptable for use in all designated installations. The only configuration difference should be in the interface connections, mounting fixtures, and so on.

---

[1] A version of this case study first appeared in B. S. Blanchard, *Design and Manage to Life-Cycle Cost* (Forest Grove, OR: M/A Press, 1978). Also see Chapter 19 in B. S. Blanchard and W. J. Fabrycky, *Systems Engineering and Analysis*, 2nd ed. (Englewood Cliffs, NJ: Prentice-Hall, Inc., 1990).

272

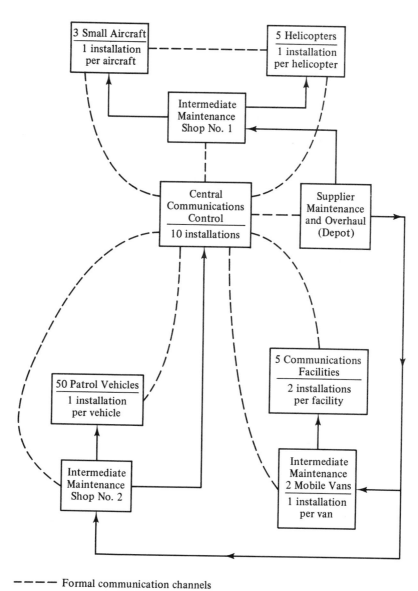

Figure 12.1   Communication system network.

Communication System Objectives

System planning activity has identified six operational objectives to be met by the new equipment. Although these objectives pertain largely to the equipment, the communication system is composed of the equipment packages collectively, together with the proposed maintenance support capability. The six objectives are:

Objective 1.   The equipment is to be installed in three low-flying light aircraft (10,000 ft or less) in quantities of one per aircraft. This will enable communication with loitering helicopters dispersed within a 200-mile radius and with the central communication control facility. It is anticipated that each aircraft will fly 15 times per month with an average flight duration of 3 hours. The equipment utilization requirement is 1.1 hours of operation for every hour of aircraft operation, which includes air time plus some ground time. It is assumed that all functions are fully operational throughout this time period. The equipment must exhibit a MTBM of at least 500 hours and a $\overline{M}$ct not to exceed 15 minutes.[2]   *Ang 45*

Objective 2.   The equipment is to be installed in each of five helicopters and will enable communication with patrol aircraft within a 200-mile range, other helicopters within a 50-mile radius and with the central communications control facility. It is anticipated that each helicopter will fly 25 times per month, with an average flight duration of 2 hours. The utilization requirement is 0.9 hour of equipment operation for every flight hour of helicopter operation. The equipment must meet a 500-hour MTBM requirement and a $\overline{M}$ct of 15 minutes or less.   *50*

Objective 3.   The equipment is to be installed in each of 50 police patrol vehicles (one per vehicle) and will enable communication with other vehicles within a range of 25 miles, and with the central communications control facility from a range of 50 miles or less. Each vehicle will be in operation on the average of 5 hours per day, 5 days per week, and will be utilized 100% during that time. The required MTBM is 400 hours, and the $\overline{M}$ct should be less than 30 minutes.   *100*

Objective 4.   Two installations are to be made in each of five fixed communications facilities optimally located throughout the metropolitan geographical area. This will enable communication with patrol vehicles within a range of 25 miles and the central communications control facility from a range of up to 50 miles. Equipment utilization requirements are 120 hours per month, the required MTBM is 200 hours, and the $\overline{M}$ct should not exceed 60 minutes.

---

[2]MTBM, $\overline{M}$ct, and other factors are defined in Appendix C.

Objective 5.   Ten installations are to be made in the central communications control facility and will enable communication with patrol aircraft and loitering helicopters within a range of 400 miles, the five fixed communication facilities within a range of 50 miles, and with patrol vehicles within a 50-mile radius. In addition, each will be able to communicate with the intermediate maintenance facilities. The average equipment utilization requirement is 3 hours per day for 360 days per year. The MTBM requirement is 200 hours and the $\overline{M}ct$ should not exceed 45 minutes.

Objective 6.   Two mobile vans will be used to support intermediate-level maintenance at the five fixed communications facilities. Each van will incorporate one communication package, which will be used an average of 2 hours per day for a 360-day year. The required MTBM is 400 hours, and the $\overline{M}ct$ is 15 minutes.

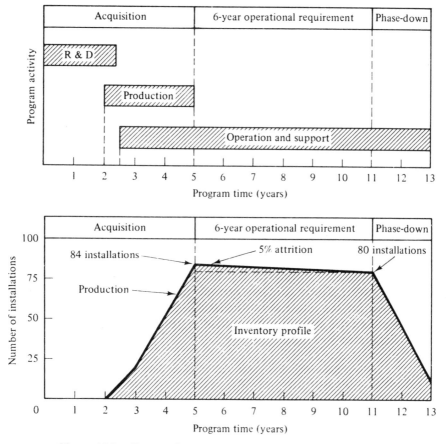

Figure 12.2 Communication system program plan and profile.

Performance and Effectiveness Requirements

To achieve the stated operational objectives, there is a need to acquire equipment that will meet certain performance and effectiveness requirements (e.g., voice transmission range, clarity of message, MTBM, $\overline{\text{M}}$ct, etc.). Further, budget limitations require that the cost of development and production (over the first five years of the program) not exceed $6,000,000 in inflated dollars. Advanced program planning indicates that a full complement of units must be in operation five years after the start of the program, and that this capability must be maintained through the eleventh year. The significant program milestones and projected number of units in operational use are presented in Figure 12.2. This forms the basis for defining the unit life cycle, the major life-cycle functions, and the life-cycle cost.

Based on a review of the available sources of supply, there is no known existing system that will completely fulfill the need; but there are two new candidate design configurations that should suffice, assuming that all design goals are met. The objective is to evaluate each configuration in terms of its life-cycle cost and to recommend the preferred configuration.

12.2 THE ANALYSIS APPROACH

Prior to the identification of a cost breakdown structure (CBS) and the development of cost elements, the baseline configuration for the communication equipment and its maintenance concept should be described in detail. As a start, an assumed packaging scheme is developed as shown in Figure 12.3. This configuration (including units, assemblies, and modules) is developed from conceptual design considerations to be fairly representative of each candidate being considered.[3] The maintenance concept can be defined as a series of statements and/or illustrations that include criteria covering maintenance levels, support policies, effectiveness factors (e.g., maintenance time constraints, turnaround times, transportation times), and basic logistic support requirements. The maintenance concept is a prerequisite to the system or product design, whereas a detailed maintenance plan reflects the results of design and is used for the acquisition of the logistics elements required for the sustaining life-cycle support of the system in the field. The maintenance concept is illustrated by Figure 12.4.[4]

---

[3]The configuration reflected in Figure 12.3 obviously does not represent *final* design but is close enough for life-cycle purposes (particularly for analyses accomplished in the early stages of a program). Further design definition will occur as the program progresses.

[4]The quantitative support factors presented in Figure 12.4 are minimum design requirements. For each alternative configuration being evaluated in a life-cycle cost analysis, the support factors may vary somewhat as a function of the specific design characteristics. However, the minimum requirements still must be met.

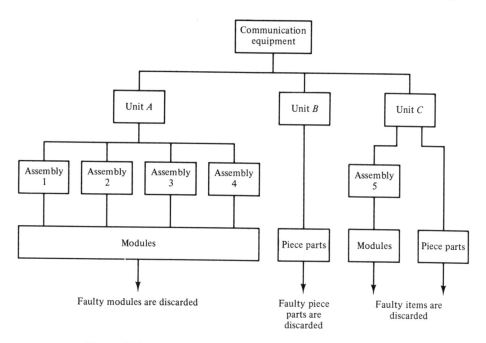

Figure 12.3 Communication equipment packaging (baseline configuration).

There are three levels of maintenance to consider. *Organizational maintenance* is performed in the aircraft or helicopters, in the patrol vehicles, or in various communication facilities (as applicable) by user or operator personnel. *Intermediate maintenance*, or the second level of maintenance, is accomplished in a remote shop facility by trained personnel possessing the skills necessary to perform the assigned functions. *Depot maintenance*, the highest level of maintenance, constitutes the specialized repair or overhaul of complex components at the supplier's facility by highly skilled supplier maintenance personnel.

The specific functions scheduled to be accomplished on the equipment at each level of maintenance are noted. In the event of a malfunction, fault isolation is performed to the applicable unit by using the built-in test capability (i.e., unit A, B, or C). Units are removed and replaced at the organizational level and sent to the intermediate maintenance shop for corrective maintenance. At the intermediate shop, units are repaired through assembly and/or part replacement, assemblies are repaired through module replacement. In case of fault isolation to assembly 5 in unit C, the faulty assembly is sent to the depot, where repair is accomplished through module replacement.

The maintenance concept illustrated in Figure 12.4 identifies the functions that are anticipated for each level of maintenance, the effectiveness re-

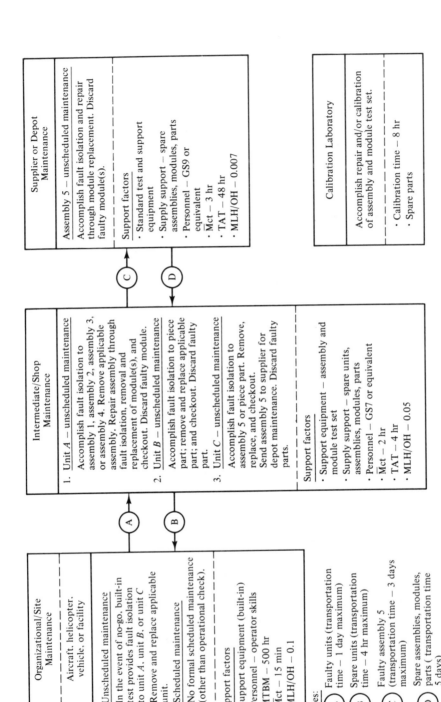

Figure 12.4 Communication system maintenance concept (repair policy).

Organizational/Site Maintenance

Aircraft, helicopter, vehicle, or facility.

1. Unscheduled maintenance

   In the event of no-go, built-in test provides fault isolation to unit *A*, unit *B*, or unit *C*. Remove and replace applicable unit.

2. Scheduled maintenance

   No formal scheduled maintenance (other than operational check).

Support factors

- Support equipment (built-in)
- Personnel – operator skills
- MTBM – 500 hr
- $\overline{M}ct$ – 15 min
- MLH/OH – 0.1

Intermediate/Shop Maintenance

1. Unit *A* – unscheduled maintenance

   Accomplish fault isolation to assembly 1, assembly 2, assembly 3, or assembly 4. Remove applicable assembly. Repair assembly through fault isolation, removal and replacement of module(s), and checkout. Discard faulty module.

2. Unit *B* – unscheduled maintenance

   Accomplish fault isolation to piece part; remove and replace applicable part; and checkout. Discard faulty part.

3. Unit *C* – unscheduled maintenance

   Accomplish fault isolation to assembly 5 or piece part. Remove, replace, and checkout. Send assembly 5 to supplier for depot maintenance. Discard faulty parts.

Support factors

- Support equipment – assembly and module test set
- Supply support – spare units, assemblies, modules, parts
- Personnel – GS7 or equivalent
- $\overline{M}ct$ – 2 hr
- TAT – 4 hr
- MLH/OH – 0.05

Supplier or Depot Maintenance

Assembly 5 – unscheduled maintenance

Accomplish fault isolation and repair through module replacement. Discard faulty module(s).

Support factors

- Standard test and support equipment
- Supply support – spare assemblies, modules, parts
- Personnel – GS9 or equivalent
- Mct – 3 hr
- TAT – 48 hr
- MLH/OH – 0.007

Calibration Laboratory

Accomplish repair and/or calibration of assembly and module test set.

- Calibration time – 8 hr
- Spare parts

Notes:

(A) Faulty units (transportation time – 1 day maximum)

(B) Spare units (transportation time – 4 hr maximum)

(C) Faulty assembly 5 (transportation time – 3 days maximum)

(D) Spare assemblies, modules, parts (transportation time 5 days)

quirements in terms of maintenance frequency and times, and the major elements of logistic support to include personnel skill levels, test and support equipment, supply support requirements, and facilities. This information is not only required as an input to the system design process, but serves as the basis for determining operation and support costs.

12.3 LIFE-CYCLE COST ANALYSIS

With the problem (or need) defined, and with a description of the system operation requirements and maintenance concept, it is now appropriate to proceed with the specific steps involved in the life-cycle cost analysis of the proposed alternative configurations. These steps, leading to the generation of cost data, are presented in this section.

Development of the Cost Breakdown Structure

The CBS assumed for the purpose of this evaluation is presented in Figure 12.5 (also refer to Appendix B). Although not all of the cost categories may be relevant or significant in terms of the magnitude of cost as a function of total life-cycle cost, this CBS does serve as a good starting point. Initially, all costs must be considered, with the subsequent objective of concentrating on those cost categories reflecting the high contributors. The evaluation of two alternative communication equipment configurations, and the selection of a preferred approach, is required. There will be activities involving planning, management, engineering design, test and evaluation, production, distribution, system operation, maintenance and logistic support, and ultimate equipment disposal for each alternative. In an attempt to be more specific for the life-cycle cost analysis, the analyst should consider the following steps:

1. Identify all anticipated program activities that will generate costs over the life cycle for each of the two alternatives.
2. Relate each identified activity to a specific cost category in the CBS. Each activity should fall into one or more of the categories. If it does not, the CBS should be expanded or revised as appropriate to cover the activity.
3. Develop a matrix-type worksheet for the purpose of recording costs for each applicable category by year in the life cycle.[5]
4. Generate cost input data for each applicable activity listed in the matrix and record the results in Table 12.1.

---

[5]The matrix desired could be a direct printout from the life-cycle cost model. Model design must consider the various data output requirements in terms of both content and format.

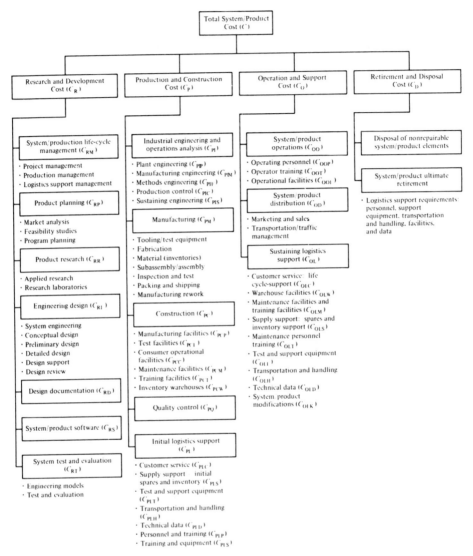

Figure 12.5 Cost breakdown structure (CBS).

Generation of Input Cost Data[6]

For the communication system, the major cost categories are C_R, C_P, and C_O in the CBS of Figure 12.5. It is assumed that C_D will be negligible in this instance. The following paragraphs present an overview of the major sources supporting these relevant cost categories.

[6]The material covered here is presented in enough detail to convey the overall approach used in the evaluation of the two alternative configurations. An in-depth discussion of each cost input factor would be rather extensive.

TABLE 12.1 Cost Collection Worksheet

Program Activity	Cost Category Designation	Cost by Program Year (dollars) 1 2 3 4 5 6 7 8 9 10 11 12 13	Total Cost (constant dollars)	Total Cost (actual dollars)	Percent Contribution
Alternative A					
1. Research and development	C_R				
a. Life-cycle management	C_{RM}				
b. Product planning	C_{RP}				
(1) Feasibility studies	—				
(2) Program planning					
2.					
3.					
Others					
Alternative B					
1. Research and development	C_R				
2.					

Research and development cost (C_R).   Research and development costs include those early life-cycle costs that will be incurred by the metropolitan agency responsible for the procurement of the communication system (i.e., the customer or consumer), and those costs incurred by the supplier in the development of the system (i.e., the contractor). There will be some common costs to the customer associated with both alternatives and relating to initial program planning, the accomplishment of feasibility studies, the development of operational requirements and the maintenance concept, the preparation of top-level system specifications, and general management activities. Also, there will be supplier costs that are peculiar to each alternative and that are included in the supplier's proposal.

Although the analyst may ultimately wish to evaluate only delta or incremental costs (i.e., those costs peculiar to one alternative or the other), the approach used here is to address total life-cycle cost.[7] In determining such costs, the analyst uses a combination of customer cost projections and the proposals submitted by each of two potential suppliers as source data for the life-cycle cost analysis.

Table 12.2 presents a summary of research and development costs. These costs are primarily nonrecurring, constituting management and engineering labor with inflationary factors included. Labor costs are developed from personnel projections indicating the class of labor (i.e., manager, supervisor, senior engineer, engineer, technician, etc.) and the labor hours of effort required by class per month for each functional activity. The labor hours per month are then converted to dollars by applying standard cost factors. Both indirect and direct costs are included, along with a 5% per year inflation factor. Material costs are included in test and evaluation (category C_{RT}), since engineering prototype models must be produced to verify performance, effectiveness, and supportability characteristics.

The supplier costs for alternatives A and B in Table 12.2 are derived directly from the individual supplier proposals. Direct costs, indirect costs, inflation factors for both labor and material, general and administrative expenses, and projected supplier profits are included.

Production and construction cost (C_P).   This category includes the recurring and nonrecurring costs associated with the production of the required 80 operational packages plus four additional packages intended to compensate for possible attrition. Referring to Figure 12.2, the leading edge of the inventory profile represents production requirements. The analyst must convert the projected population growth to a specific production profile, as shown in Figure 12.6. This profile becomes the basis for determining production costs. If permitted the option, each of the two potential suppliers may propose an entirely different production scheme while still meeting the inven-

---

[7]It is important to look at total life-cycle cost in order to assess major cost drivers properly.

TABLE 12.2 Research and Development Cost Summary

Program Activity[a]	Cost Category Designator	Cost by Program Year (inflated dollars)			Total Actual Cost (dollars)
		Year 1	Year 2	Year 3	
A. Customer costs: alternative A					
1. System/product management	C_{RM}	115,256	121,019	137,069	373,344
2. Product planning	C_{RP}	45,704	0	0	45,704
B. Supplier costs: alternative A					
1. System/product management	C_{RM}	101,957	107,055	112,407	321,419
2. Product planning	C_{RP}	28,814	30,255	0	59,069
3. Engineering design	C_{RE}	186,692	221,887	239,396	647,975
4. Design documentation	C_{RD}	28,951	49,517	52,707	131,175
5. System test and evaluation	C_{RT}	0	0	176,509	176,509
Total research and development cost for alternative A	C_R	507,374	529,733	718,088	1,755,195
A. Customer costs: alternative B					
1. System/product management	C_{RM}	115,256	121,019	137,069	373,344
2. Product planning	C_{RP}	45,704	0	0	45,704
B. Supplier costs: alternative B					
1. System/product management	C_{RM}	93,091	97,746	102,634	293,471
2. Product planning	C_{RP}	0	0	0	0
3. Engineering design	C_{RE}	145,267	152,530	160,156	457,953
4. Design documentation	C_{RD}	34,976	36,724	39,921	111,621
5. System test and evaluation	C_{RT}	0	0	157,939	157,939
Total research and development cost for alternative B	C_R	434,294	408,019	597,719	1,440,032

[a] Only applicable cost categories are listed. There are no costs associated with product research (C_{RR}) and system software (C_{RS}).

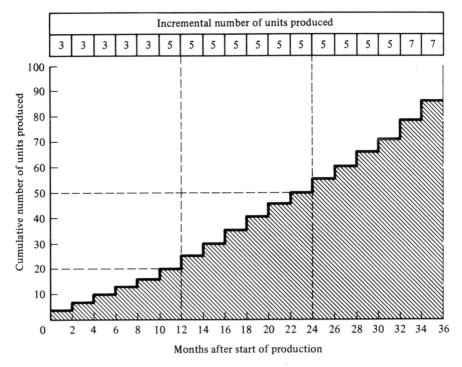

Figure 12.6 Equipment production requirements.

tory requirements illustrated in Figure 12.2. This would probably create a significant variation in the input planning factors and cost. However, in this instance the specified production scheme in Figure 12.6 is assumed for both alternatives.[8]

Production and construction cost considers the appropriate factors indicated in Figure 12.5, and the results are given in Table 12.3.[9] A description of these costs follows:

1. *System or product management cost* (C_{RM}): includes the ongoing management activity required throughout the production phase. Costs in this category are a continuation of the system or product management cost stream reflected in the R&D cost summary in Table 12.2.

---

[8]It is this "investment" cost that should be the budget constraint to be designed within. If the final production profile differs significantly, the budget constraint may be violated.

[9]The results in Tables 12.2, 12.3, and 12.5 include inflationary effects. Costs given in the written text are not adjusted for inflation.

2. *Industrial engineering and operations analysis cost* (C_{PI}): includes the functions of production planning, manufacturing engineering, methods engineering, and so on. A minimal level of effort is shown in Table 12.3.

3. *Manufacturing recurring cost* (C_{PMR}): includes those activities related directly to the fabrication, assembly, inspection, and test of the 84 packages being produced. Each of the two potential suppliers submitted a proposal covering functions compatible with and in direct support of the production scheme illustrated in Figure 12.6. Since the majority of such activities are repetitive in nature, each supplier estimated the cost of the first package and then projected a learning curve to reflect the cost of subsequent packages. The proposed learning curves for alternatives *A* and *B* are illustrated in Figure 12.7. These curves support the recurring manufacturing costs given in Table 12.3.

4. *Manufacturing nonrecurring cost* (C_{PMN}): includes all costs associated with the acquisition and installation of special tooling, fixtures and jigs, and factory test equipment. These costs, included in the supplier's proposal, are basically a one-time expenditure during year 2 in anticipation of the production requirements beginning in year 3.

5. *Quality control cost* (C_{PQ}): includes the category of quality assurance, which is a sustaining level of activity required to ensure that good overall product quality exists throughout the production process, and the category of qualification testing, which constitutes the testing of a representative sample to verify that the level of quality inherent in the items being produced is adequate. The costs for each supplier's proposal are included.

6. *Initial spares and inventory cost* (C_{PLS}): includes the acquisition of major units to support organizational maintenance, and a few assemblies plus parts to provide support at the intermediate level of maintenance. These items represent the inventory safety stock factor and are located at the intermediate maintenance shops and the supplier facility identified in Figure 12.1. Replenishment spares for the sustaining support of the system in operational use throughout the life cycle are covered in category C_{OLS}. This category covers an initial limited procurement, whereas the replenishment spares are based on realistic consumption and demand factors. The assumptions used in determining costs are as follows:

a. *Alternative A.* One complete set of units (unit *A*, unit *B*, and unit *C*) are required for shop 1, shop 2, each of the two mobile vans, and for the supplier facility as a backup. The acquisition price for unit *A* is $11,400, unit *B* is $6,450, and unit *C* is $7,950. Five sets are equivalent to $129,000, with $25,800 in year 3, $51,600 in year 4, and $51,600 in year 5. The cost of assemblies and parts is $15,000 ($3,000 in year 3, $6,000 in year 4, and $6,000 in year 5).

TABLE 12.3 Production/Construction Costs

Program Activity	Cost Category Designator	Cost by Program Year (inflated dollars)				Total Actual Cost (dollars)
		Year 2	Year 3	Year 4	Year 5	
A. Customer costs: alternative A						
1. System/product management	C_{RM}	0	0	146,824	154,080	300,904
B. Supplier costs: alternative A						
1. Industrial engineering and operations analysis	C_{PI}	30,082	51,679	54,816	57,525	194,102
2. Manufacturing						
a. Recurring cost	C_{PMR}	0	499,567	620,790	613,421	1,733,778
b. Nonrecurring cost	C_{PMN}	147,100	0	0	0	147,100
3. Quality control	C_{PQ}	0	72,925	76,578	74,782	224,285
4. Initial logistics support						
a. Supply support	C_{PLS}	0	33,350	70,041	73,503	176,894
b. Test and support equipment	C_{PLT}	16,545	225,810	0	0	242,355
c. Technical data	C_{PLD}	16,876	0	0	0	16,876
d. Personnel training	C_{PLP}	54,268	52,110	54,720	0	161,098
Total production and construction cost for alternative A	C_P	264,871	935,441	1,023,769	973,311	3,197,392

	Symbol					
A. Customer costs: alternative B						
1. System/product management	C_{RM}	0	0	146,824	154,080	300,904
B. Supplier costs: alternative B						
1. Industrial engineering and operations analysis	C_{PI}	45,123	57,421	60,298	63,277	226,119
2. Manufacturing						
a. Recurring cost	C_{PMR}	0	479,469	645,458	666,762	1,791,689
b. Nonrecurring cost	C_{PMN}	165,751	0	0	0	165,751
3. Quality control	C_{PQ}	0	56,847	60,572	81,293	198,712
4. Initial logistics support						
a. Supply support	C_{PLS}	0	63,712	70,554	74,039	208,305
b. Test and support equipment	C_{PLT}	16,545	225,810	0	0	242,355
c. Technical data	C_{PLD}	17,703	0	0	0	17,703
d. Personnel training	C_{PLP}	54,268	52,110	54,720	0	161,098
Total production and construction cost for alternative B	C_P	299,390	935,369	1,038,426	1,039,451	3,312,636

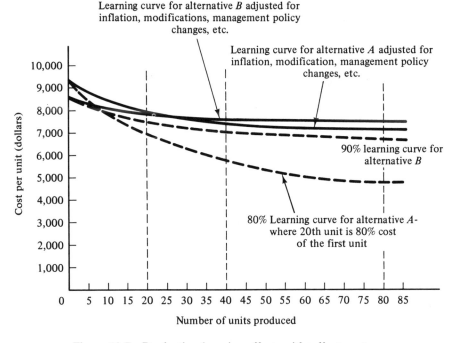

Figure 12.7 Production learning effects with adjustments.

b. *Alternative B.* Six sets of units (unit *A*, unit *B*, and unit *C*) are required. The additional unit (above and beyond the requirements for alternative *A*) is to be located at shop 2 to cover the anticipated increased number of maintenance actions. The acquisition price for unit *A* is $10,590, unit *B* is $6,180, and unit *C* is $7,740. Six sets are equivalent to $147,060, with $49,020 in each of the years 3, 4, and 5. The cost of assemblies and parts is $24,000 ($6,000 in year 3, $9,000 in year 4, and $9,000 in year 5).

7. *Test and support equipment acquisition cost* (C_{PLT}): includes the assembly and module test set located in each intermediate maintenance facility, and several items of commercial and standard equipment located at the supplier facility to support depot maintenance (refer to Figures 12.1 and 12.4). The design cost associated with the test set is $15,000 expended in year 2. The production acquisition price of each test set is $45,000 and there are four test sets required. Referring to Table 12.4, there are packages being introduced into operational use in year 3 at all locations; thus the four test sets must be available in year 3. The commercial and standard equipment needed for depot maintenance requires no additional design effort, and can be acquired for $15,000. Thus the costs for year 3 are $195,000. The test and support equipment requirements for each alternative are considered to be comparable. The

TABLE 12.4 Communication Packages in Use and Operating Times

Category	Program Year												
	1	2	3	4	5	6	7	8	9	10	11	12	13
Communication packages in use	—	—	20	50	80	80	80	80	80	80	80	29	10
1. Aircraft application (3)													
a. Number of packages	—	—	1	3	3	3	3	3	3	3	3	3	1
b. Operating time (hr)	—	—	594	1,782	1,782	1,782	1,782	1,782	1,782	1,782	1,782	1,782	594
2. Helicopter application (3)													
a. Number of packages	—	—	2	5	5	5	5	5	5	5	5	5	3
b. Operating time (hr)	—	—	1,080	2,700	2,700	2,700	2,700	2,700	2,700	2,700	2,700	2,700	1,620
3. Patrol vehicles (50)													
a. Number of packages	—	—	7	22	50	50	50	50	50	50	50	10	2
b. Operating time (hr)	—	—	9,100	28,600	65,000	65,000	65,000	65,000	65,000	65,000	65,000	13,000	2,600
4. Communication facilities (5)													
a. Number of packages	—	—	5	10	10	10	10	10	10	10	10	5	—
b. Operating time (hr)	—	—	7,200	14,400	14,400	14,400	14,400	14,400	14,400	14,400	14,400	7,200	—
5. Central communications control (1)													
a. Number of packages	—	—	4	8	10	10	10	10	10	10	10	4	—
b. Operating time (hr)	—	—	4,320	8,640	10,800	10,800	10,800	10,800	10,800	10,800	10,800	5,400	3,240
6. Mobile vans (2)													
a. Number of packages	—	—	1	2	2	2	2	2	2	2	2	2	1
b. Operating time (hr)	—	—	720	1,440	1,440	1,440	1,440	1,440	1,440	1,440	1,440	1,440	720

sustaining annual maintenance and logistics requirements for test equipment are included in cost category C_{OLE}.

8. *Technical data cost* (C_{PLD}): includes the preparation and publication of system installation and test instructions, operating procedures, and maintenance procedures. These data are required to operate and maintain the system in the field throughout its programmed life cycle. The acquisition cost of this data is $15,300 for alternative A and $16,050 for alternative B. These costs are applicable in year 2.

9. *Personnel training cost* (C_{PLP}): includes the initial cost of training system operators and maintenance technicians. For operator training, it is assumed that 20 operators are trained in year 2, 30 operators in year 3, and 30 operators in year 4. The cost of training is $1,500 per technician (for each alternative configuration). In the maintenance area, formal training will be given to two technicians assigned to each of the four intermediate maintenance facilities. These technicians will accomplish on-the-job training for the additional personnel in the shops and vans. The cost of maintenance training is $2,400 per student week, or $19,200 in year 2.

Operation and support cost (C_O).   This category includes the cost of operating and supporting the system throughout its programmed life cycle. These costs primarily constitute user costs and are based on the program planning information in Figure 12.2. The inventory profile in the figure is expanded as shown in Table 12.4 to indicate the number of systems in use and the total operating time (in hours) for all systems in each applicable year of the life cycle.

System use is based on the individual operating times stated in the six objectives described as part of the problem definition, and is determined from Equations 12.1 through 12.6 as follows:

operating time for aircraft application (hours)
$$= \text{(number of units in aircraft)(15 flights/month)(12)} \qquad (12.1)$$
$$\times \text{(3 hours/flight)(1.1)}$$

operating time for helicopter application (hours)
$$= \text{(number of units in helicopters)(25 flights/month)} \qquad (12.2)$$
$$\times \text{(12 months)(2 hours/flight)(0.9)}$$

operating time for patrol vehicle application (hours)
$$= \text{(number of units in patrol vehicles)(5 hours/day)} \qquad (12.3)$$
$$\times \text{(5 days/week)(52 weeks/year)(1.0)}$$

operating time for communication facility application (hours)
$$= \text{(number of units in facilities)(120 hours/month)(12)} \qquad (12.4)$$

operating time for central communication control application (hours)
= (number of units)(3 hours/day)(360 days/year) $\qquad$ (12.5)

operating time for mobile van application (hours)
= (number of units in vans)(2 hours/day)(360 days/year) $\qquad$ (12.6)

    Although the actual utilization of the equipment will vary from operator to operator, from organization to organization, from one geographical area to the next, and so on, the factors included in Table 12.4 are average values and are employed in the baseline example. Also, it is assumed that each alternative configuration being evaluated will be operated in the same manner.

    Operation and support cost includes those individual costs associated with operations, distribution, and sustaining logistic support. Only those significant costs that are applicable to the communication system are discussed below.

    1. *Operating personnel cost* (C_{OOP}) covers the total costs of operating the communication system for the various applications. Since the operator is charged with a number of different duties, only that allocated portion of time associated with the direct operation of the communication system is counted. Operating personnel cost is determined from Equation 12.7 using the data in Table 12.4 as a base.

C_{OOP} = (number of units)(hours of system operation)

$\qquad\qquad$ (% allocation)(labor cost) $\qquad$ (12.7)

    In determining operator costs, different hourly rates are applied for the various applications (e.g., \$43.50 per hour for the aircraft and helicopter application, \$37.50 per hour for the facility application, etc.) and varied allocation factors are applied because of a personnel workload different from one application to the next (e.g., 1%, 2%). The resulting costs, adjusted for inflation, are given in Table 12.5.

    2. *Dstribution and transportation cost* (C_{ODT}) covers the initial transportation and installation cost (i.e., the packing and shipping of equipment from the supplier's manufacturing facility to the point of application, and installation of equipment for operational use). Equation 12.8 is used to determine total cost in this category.

C_{ODT} = (cost of packing) + (cost of transportation)

$\qquad\qquad$ + (cost of system installation) $\qquad$ (12.8)

where transportation and packing costs are based on dollars per hundredweight (cwt) (i.e., \$90 per cwt for transportation and \$120 per cwt for pack-

TABLE 12.5   Operation and Support Cost Summary

Program Activity	Cost Category Designation	Cost by Program Year (dollars)				
		1	2	3	4	5
A. Alternative A						
1. Operating personnel	C_{OOP}	—	—	2,990	9,423	9,894
2. Transportation	C_{ODT}	—	—	27,783	72,930	122,523
3. Unscheduled maintenance	C_{OLA}	—	—	12,902	32,403	56,939
4. Maintenance facilities	C_{OLM}	—	—	483	1,218	2,140
5. Supply support	C_{OLS}	—	—	23,170	77,890	136,919
6. Maintenance personnel training	C_{OLT}	—	—	0	0	4,978
7. Test and support equipment	C_{OLE}	—	—	11,291	11,856	12,443
8. Transportation/ handling	C_{OLH}	—	—	584	1,378	2,412
Total operation and support cost for alternative A	C_O	—	—	79,203	207,098	348,248
B. Alternative B						
1. Operating personnel	C_{OOP}	—	—	2,990	9,423	9,894
2. Transportation	C_{ODT}	—	—	27,783	72,930	122,523
3. Unscheduled maintenance	C_{OLA}	—	—	16,355	39,678	70,152
4. Maintenance facilities	C_{OLM}	—	—	587	1,491	2,642
5. Supply support	C_{OLS}	—	—	37,507	95,393	169,081
6. Maintenance personnel training	C_{OLT}	—	—	0	0	4,978
7. Test and support equipment	C_{OLE}	—	—	16,936	17,784	18,662
8. Transportation/ handling	C_{OLH}	—	—	730	1,684	2,895
Total operation and support cost for alternative B	C_O	—	—	102,888	238,383	400,827

ing), and installation costs are a function of labor cost in dollars per labor-hour and the number of labor hours required.

Costs in this category are based on the number of packages indicated in Table 12.4, and on the appropriate transportation rate structures. The analyst should review the latest Interstate Commerce Commission (ICC) documentation on rates in order to determine the proper transportation costs. The figures used in this life-cycle cost analysis are presented in Table 12.5.

TABLE 12.5 Operation and Support Cost Summary (continued)

Cost by Program Year (dollars)								Total Actual Cost (dollars)
6	7	8	9	10	11	12	13	
10,388	10,908	11,453	12,026	12,627	13,258	13,291	4,871	111,759
128,649	135,082	141,817	148,927	156,374	164,192	36,000	6,364	1,140,641
59,786	62,775	65,914	69,209	72,671	76,303	26,377	8,689	543,968
2,247	2,360	2,478	2,602	2,732	2,868	991	317	20,436
143,765	150,954	158,501	166,426	174,748	183,485	63,358	20,365	1,299,581
5,226	5,488	5,762	6,050	6,353	6,670	0	0	40,527
13,066	13,719	14,405	15,125	15,882	16,676	17,510	18,194	160,167
2,533	2,659	2,792	2,932	3,079	3,233	1,131	870	23,603
365,660	383,945	403,122	423,297	444,466	466,685	159,288	59,670	3,340,682
10,388	10,908	11,453	12,026	12,627	13,258	13,921	4,871	111,759
128,649	135,082	141,817	148,927	156,374	164,192	36,000	6,364	1,140,641
73,660	77,343	81,210	85,270	89,534	94,010	32,740	10,251	670,203
2,774	2,913	3,058	3,211	3,372	3,540	1,234	385	25,207
177,536	186,413	195,733	205,520	215,796	226,586	78,874	24,438	1,612,877
5,226	5,488	5,762	6,050	6,353	6,670	0	0	40,527
19,598	20,577	21,601	22,683	23,824	25,009	26,267	27,290	240,231
3,039	3,192	3,351	3,519	3,695	3,879	1,358	475	27,817
420,870	441,916	463,985	487,206	511,575	537,144	190,394	74,074	3,869,262

3. *Unscheduled maintenance cost* (C_{OLA}) covers the personnel activity costs associated with the accomplishment of *unscheduled* or corrective maintenance on the communication system. Specifically, this includes the direct and indirect cost in the performance of maintenance actions (a function of maintenance labor-hours and the cost per labor-hour), the material handling cost associated with given maintenance actions, and the cost of documentation for each maintenance action. These costs for the two alternative communication system configurations being evaluated are summarized in Table 12.6. Determining unscheduled maintenance cost is dependent on predicting the number of maintenance actions that are likely to occur throughout the life cycle (i.e., the expected frequency of unscheduled maintenance, or the reciprocal of the MTBM). Since there is no *scheduled* maintenance permitted in this instance, the MTBM factor assumed here is directly equated with unscheduled maintenance actions. The frequency of maintenance is usually based on the failure rates for individual components of the system and is derived from reliability prediction data, maintainability prediction data, logistic support analysis data, or a combination thereof.

Review of the objectives in the problem definition indicates that the need relative to MTBM requirements differs from one application to the next. Since it is the goal to design a single system configuration for use in all applications (to the maximum extent practicable), the most stringent conditions must be met. Thus the new system is required to exhibit a MTBM of 500 hours or greater. Response to this requirement by the two suppliers is illustrated in Figure 12.8. Note that the predicted MTBM for alternative *A* is 650 hours and for alternative *B* is 525 hours. These values are further broken down to unit levels compatible with the system packaging scheme in Figure 12.4 and illustrated maintenance concept in Figure 12.3. Although failures are randomly distributed in general, these values are used to determine an average factor for the frequency of maintenance.

Figure 12.8 represents the final results of an iterative design process that trades off the life-cycle cost of the system with its MTBM. The MTBMs shown are optimal values. Using the information in Figure 12.8, the next step is to calculate the average number of maintenance actions for each system (and unit-level) configuration by year through the life cycle. This is accomplished by dividing the operating time in Table 12.4 by the MTBM. The results (rounded off to the nearest whole number) are presented in Table 12.6.[10]

Personnel labor cost covering the accomplishment of unscheduled maintenance is a function of maintenance labor hours and the cost per labor hour. Maintenance labor-hour and labor-cost factors in this instance are based on the number of technicians (with specific skill levels) assigned to a given maintenance action and the length of time that the technicians are assigned. The assumed factors are:

Organizational maintenance: 0.25 MLH per maintenance action at a cost of $33.00 per MLH.

Intermediate maintenance: 3 MLH per maintenance action at a cost of $39.00 per MLH.

[10] A more precise method is to use Monte Carlo analysis to determine the number of maintenance actions and then to assess each individual anticipated maintenance action in terms of expected logistic support resource requirements. The analyst should adapt to the needs of the analysis.

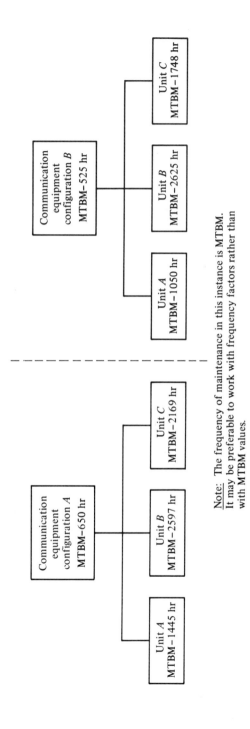

Note: The frequency of maintenance in this instance is MTBM. It may be preferable to work with frequency factors rather than with MTBM values.

Figure 12.8 Equipment maintenance factors.

295

TABLE 12.6 Unscheduled Maintenance Costs (dollars)

Program Activity		Program Year			
		1	2	3	4
A. Alternative *A*					
1. Organizational	Total labor hours	—	—	9.25	22.25
maintenance	Personnel cost	—	—	306	735
	Material handling cost	—	—	1,110	2,670
	Documentation cost	—	—	1,110	2,670
2. Intermediate	Total labor hours	—	—	111	267
maintenance	Personnel cost	—	—	4,329	11,223
	Material handling cost	—	—	1,110	2,670
	Documentation cost	—	—	2,220	5,340
3. Depot	Total labor hours	—	—	16	36
maintenance	Personnel cost	—	—	720	1,620
	Material handling cost	—	—	120	270
	Documentation cost	—	—	120	270
Total unscheduled maintenance cost		—	—	11,145	27,468
Total cost (adjusted for inflation)		—	—	12,906	33,401
B. Alternative *B*					
1. Organizational	Total labor hours	—	—	11.25	27.25
maintenance	Personnel cost	—	—	372	900
	Material handling cost	—	—	1,350	3,270
	Documentation cost	—	—	1,350	3,270
2. Intermediate	Total labor hours	—	—	135	327
maintenance	Personnel cost	—	—	5,265	12,753
	Material handling cost	—	—	1,350	3,270
	Documentation cost	—	—	2,700	6,540
3. Depot	Total labor hours	—	—	20	44
maintenance	Personnel cost	—	—	900	1,980
	Material handling cost	—	—	150	330
	Documentation cost	—	—	150	330
Total unscheduled maintenance cost		—	—	13,587	32,643
Total cost (adjusted for inflation)		—	—	15,734	39,694

Supplier (or depot) maintenance: 4 MLH per maintenance action at a cost of $45.00 per MLH.

The labor-hour factors used are related to personnel requirements for direct maintenance where the elapsed times are indicated by the $\overline{M}$ct values. The hourly rates include direct dollars plus a burden or overhead rate. Labor-hour calculations, personnel cost, material handling cost (i.e., $30 per mainte-

TABLE 12.6 Unscheduled Maintenance Costs (dollars) (continued)

			Program Year					
5	6	7	8	9	10	11	12	13
37.35	37.35	37.35	37.35	37.35	37.35	37.35	12.25	3.75
1,230	1,230	1,230	1,230	1,230	1,230	1,230	405	123
4,470	4,470	4,470	4,470	4,470	4,470	4,470	1,470	450
4,470	4,470	4,470	4,470	4,470	4,470	4,470	1,470	450
447	447	447	447	447	447	447	147	45
17,433	17,433	17,433	17,433	17,433	17,433	17,433	5,733	1,755
4,470	4,470	4,470	4,470	4,470	4,470	4,470	1,470	450
8,940	8,940	8,940	8,940	8,940	8,940	8,940	2,940	900
60	60	60	60	60	60	60	20	8
2,700	2,700	2,700	2,700	2,700	2,700	2,700	900	360
450	450	450	450	450	450	450	150	60
450	450	450	450	450	450	450	150	60
44,613	44,613	44,613	44,613	44,613	44,613	44,613	14,688	4,608
56,926	59,781	62,770	65,893	69,195	72,675	76,288	26,380	8,599
46	46	46	46	46	46	46	15.25	4.5
1,518	1,518	1,518	1,518	1,518	1,518	1,518	504	150
5,520	5,520	5,520	5,520	5,520	5,520	5,520	1,830	540
5,520	5,520	5,520	5,520	5,520	5,520	5,520	1,830	540
552	552	552	552	552	552	552	183	54
21,528	21,528	21,528	21,528	21,528	21,528	21,528	7,137	2,106
5,520	5,520	5,520	5,520	5,520	5,520	5,520	1,830	540
11,040	11,040	11,040	11,040	11,040	11,040	11,040	3,660	1,080
72	72	72	72	72	72	72	24	8
3,240	3,240	3,240	3,240	3,240	3,240	3,240	1,080	360
540	540	540	540	540	540	540	180	60
540	540	540	540	540	540	540	180	60
54,966	54,966	54,966	54,966	54,966	54,966	54,966	18,231	5,436
70,137	73,654	77,337	81,185	85,252	89,540	93,992	32,743	10,144

nance action), and documentation cost (i.e., $30 per maintenance action at the depot level, $60 at the intermediate level, and $30 at the organizational level) are noted in Table 12.6 for each of the configurations being evaluated. The total cost factors are also included in Table 12.5.

4. *Maintenance facilities cost* (C_{OLM}) is based on the occupancy, utilities, and facility maintenance costs as prorated to the communication system.

Facilities cost in this instance is primarily related to the intermediate level of maintenance.

5. *Supply support cost* (C_{OLS}) includes the cost of spare parts required as a result of system failures; spare parts required to fill the logistics pipeline to compensate for delays due to active repair times, turnaround times, and supplier lead times; spare parts required to replace repairable items which are condemned or phased out of the inventory for one reason or another (e.g., those items that are damaged to the extent beyond which it is not economically feasible to accomplish repair); and the cost of maintaining the inventory throughout the designated period of support.

Referring to the illustrated maintenance concept in Figure 12.4, spare units are required in the intermediate maintenance shops to support unit replacements at the organizational level. Spare assemblies, modules, and certain designated piece parts are required to support intermediate maintenance actions, and some assemblies and parts are required to support supplier repair activities or depot maintenance. In other words, the maintenance concept indicates the type of spares required at each level of maintenance, and the system network in Figure 12.1 (with specific geographical locations defined) conveys the quantity of maintenance facilities providing overall system support. A logistic support analysis is accomplished to provide additional maintenance data as required.

The next step is to determine the number of spare parts required at each location. Too many spares, or a large inventory, could be extremely costly in terms of investment and inventory maintenance. On the other hand, not enough spares could result in a stock-out condition, which will in turn cause systems to be inoperative, and the defined objectives of the communication network will not be met. This condition may also be quite costly. The goal is to analyze the inventory requirements and obtain a balance between the cost of acquiring spares and the cost of maintaining inventory. The critical factor constitutes consumption of demand and the probability of having the right type of spare part available when required. Relative to this analysis, demand rates are a function of unit, assembly, module, or part reliability and are based on the Poisson distribution.

Another consideration is the turnaround time (TAT) and the transportation time between facilities for repairable items (i.e., the total time from the point of failure until the item is repaired and recycled back into the inventory and ready for use, or the time that it takes to acquire an item from the source of supply). These time factors, identified in Figure 12.4, have a significant impact on spare-part requirements.

The process employed for determining the costs associated with supply support is fairly comprehensive, and all of the specific detailed steps used in this analysis are not included here. However, the concepts used are discussed. In essence, inventory requirements are covered in two categories. An initial procurement of spare units and assemblies, basically representing safety stock, is reflected under initial logistics support cost (i.e., category C_{PLS}). The spares required for sustaining support, to include both repairable and non-repairable items, are covered in this category. These items are directly related to consumption and the quantity of unscheduled maintenance actions identified in Table 12.7. The associated costs include both material costs and the cost of maintaining the inventory. Annual inventory holding cost is assumed to be 20% of the inventory value.

6. *Maintenance personnel training cost* (C_{OLT}) is covered in two categories. Initially, when the system is first introduced, there is a requirement to train operators and maintenance technicians. The cost for this initial training is included in category C_{PLP}. Subsequently, the cost of training relates to personnel attrition and the addition of new operators and/or maintenance technicians. A cost of $2,600 per year is assumed for formal sustaining training until that point in time when system phaseout commences.

7. *Test and support equipment cost* (C_{OLE}) is presented in two categories. Category P_{PLT} includes the design and acquisition of the test and support equipment required for the intermediate and depot levels of maintenance. This category includes the sustaining support of these items on a year-to-year basis (i.e., the unscheduled and scheduled maintenance actions associated with the test equipment). Unscheduled maintenance is a function of the use of the test equipment, which in turn relates directly to the unscheduled maintenance actions noted in Table 12.7. In addition, the reliability and maintainability characteristics of the test equipment itself will significantly influence the cost of supporting that test equipment. Scheduled maintenance constitutes the periodic 180-day calibration of certain elements of the test equipment in the calibration laboratory (refer to Figure 12.4). Calibration is required to maintain the proper test traceability to primary and secondary standards. The costs associated with test equipment maintenance and logistic support can be derived through an in-depth logistic support analysis (described in Appendix C). However, the magnitude of the test equipment required in this case is relatively small when compared to other systems. Based on past experience with comparable items, a factor of 5% of the acquisition cost ($9,750) is considered to be appropriate for the annual maintenance and logistics cost for the test equipment associated with alternative *A*. A factor of 7.5% ($14,625) is assumed for alternative *B*, since the test equipment use requirements will be greater.

8. *Transportation and handling costs* (C_{OLH}) includes the annual costs associated with the movement of materials among the organizational, intermediate, and depot levels of maintenance. This is in addition to the costs of initial distribution and system installation covered in category C_{ODT}.

For the system being analyzed, the movement of materials between the organizational and intermediate levels of maintenance is considered insignif-

TABLE 12.7 Number of Unscheduled Maintenance Actions

Alternative	Application	Equipment or Unit	1	2	3	4	5	6	7	8	9	10	11	12	13
Alternative A	Aircraft application	System	—	—	1	3	3	3	3	3	3	3	3	3	1
		Unit A	—	—	1	1	1	1	1	1	1	1	1	1	1
		Unit B	—	—	—	1	1	1	1	1	1	1	1	1	—
		Unit C	—	—	—	1	1	1	1	1	1	1	1	1	3
	Helicopter application	System	—	—	2	4	4	4	4	4	4	4	4	4	3
		Unit A	—	—	1	2	2	2	2	2	2	2	2	2	1
		Unit B	—	—	—	1	1	1	1	1	1	1	1	1	1
		Unit C	—	—	1	1	1	1	1	1	1	1	1	1	1
	Patrol vehicle application	System	—	—	14	44	100	100	100	100	100	100	100	20	4
		Unit A	—	—	6	20	45	45	45	45	45	45	45	9	2
		Unit B	—	—	4	11	25	25	25	25	25	25	25	5	1
		Unit C	—	—	4	13	30	30	30	30	30	30	30	6	1
	Communications facilities	System	—	—	11	22	22	22	22	22	22	22	22	11	—
		Unit A	—	—	5	10	10	10	10	10	10	10	10	5	—
		Unit B	—	—	2	5	5	5	5	5	5	5	5	2	—
		Unit C	—	—	4	7	7	7	7	7	7	7	7	4	—
	Central communications control	System	—	—	7	13	17	17	17	17	17	17	17	8	5
		Unit A	—	—	3	6	8	8	8	8	8	8	8	4	2
		Unit B	—	—	2	3	4	4	4	4	4	4	4	2	1
		Unit C	—	—	2	4	5	5	5	5	5	5	5	2	2
	Mobile vans	System	—	—	2	3	3	3	3	3	3	3	3	3	2
		Unit A	—	—	1	1	1	1	1	1	1	1	1	1	1
		Unit B	—	—	—	1	1	1	1	1	1	1	1	1	—
		Unit C	—	—	1	1	1	1	1	1	1	1	1	1	1

Alternative B

Category	Unit											
Aircraft application	System	—	2	4	4	4	4	4	4	4	4	2
	Unit A	—	1	2	2	2	2	2	2	2	2	1
	Unit B	—	—	1	1	1	1	1	1	1	1	—
	Unit C	—	1	1	1	1	1	1	1	1	1	1
Helicopter application	System	—	2	5	5	5	5	5	5	5	5	3
	Unit A	—	1	2	2	2	2	2	2	2	2	1
	Unit B	—	—	1	1	1	1	1	1	1	1	1
	Unit C	—	1	2	2	2	2	2	2	2	2	1
Patrol vehicle application	System	—	17	54	124	124	124	124	124	124	25	5
	Unit A	—	9	27	62	62	62	62	62	62	12	2
	Unit B	—	3	11	25	25	25	25	25	25	5	1
	Unit C	—	5	16	37	37	37	37	37	37	8	2
Communications facilities	System	—	14	27	27	27	27	27	27	27	14	—
	Unit A	—	7	14	14	14	14	14	14	14	7	—
	Unit B	—	3	5	5	5	5	5	5	5	3	—
	Unit C	—	4	8	8	8	8	8	8	8	4	—
Central communications control	System	—	8	16	21	21	21	21	21	21	10	6
	Unit A	—	4	8	11	11	11	11	11	11	5	3
	Unit B	—	2	3	4	4	4	4	4	4	2	1
	Unit C	—	2	5	6	6	6	6	6	6	3	2
Mobile vans	System	—	1	3	3	3	3	3	3	3	3	2
	Unit A	—	—	1	1	1	1	1	1	1	1	1
	Unit B	—	—	1	1	1	1	1	1	1	1	—
	Unit C	—	1	1	1	1	1	1	1	1	1	1

icant in terms of relative cost. However, the shipment of materials between the intermediate maintenance facilities and the supplier or depot maintenance is considered significant, and can be determined from

$$C_{OLH} = (\text{cost of packing}) + (\text{cost of transportation})$$

$$\times (\text{number of one-way shipments})$$

where transportation and packing costs are $90 per cwt and $120 per cwt, respectively. The material being moved between the intermediate maintenance facilities and the supplier includes assembly 5 of unit C, which is supported at the depot level of maintenance (refer to Figure 12.4). The estimated number of one-way trips is given in Table 12.8.

TABLE 12.8   Trips between Maintenance
Facilities and Supplier

	Alternative A	Alternative B
Year 3	8	10
Year 4	18	22
Years 5–11	30 per year	36 per year
Year 12	10	12
Year 13	4	4

12.4   EVALUATION OF ALTERNATIVES

The problem is to select the best of the two alternatives on the basis of present equivalent total life-cycle cost. A comparison of alternatives A and B using this criterion is presented in Table 12.9. The costs are listed for those major categories of the cost breakdown structure that are relevant to this analysis. The other categories of cost that are included in Figure 12.5, and not here, are considered unapplicable to this case study. Referring to Figure 12.9, the initial concern is to determine whether the candidates meet the specified requirements (i.e., performance, the budget constraint of $5.0 million for the first five years, the MTBM of 500 hours, etc.). In this instance, both alternatives meet the requirements and fall within the trade-off area identified in Figure 12.9.

When evaluating two or more alternatives on a relative basis, the future cost estimations for each alternative must be reduced to their present equivalent amounts. The present equivalent costs for alternatives A and B are presented in Table 12.10, and the cost profiles are illustrated in Figure 12.10 based on an interest rate of 10%. The present equivalent cost for alternative A is

$$PE = \$507,734(\overset{P/F,10,1}{0.9091}) + \$794,604(\overset{P/F,10,2}{0.8265})$$

$$+ \cdots + \$59,670(\overset{P/F,10,13}{0.2897}) = \$5,255,036$$

TABLE 12.9 Life-Cycle Cost Breakdown

Cost Category	Alternative A		Alternative B	
	Cost	Percent of Total	Cost	Percent of Total
1. Research and development cost (C_R)				
(a) System/product management (C_{RM})	$ 573,392	11.0	$ 550,296	10.4
(b) Product planning (C_{RP})	92,748	1.8	41,549	0.8
(c) Engineering design (C_{RE})	532,959	10.1	378,446	7.1
(d) Design data (C_{RD})	106,841	2.0	92,140	1.7
(e) System test and evaluation (C_{RT})	132,614	2.5	118,662	2.2
Subtotal	$1,438,555	27.4	$1,181,094	22.2
2. Production and construction cost (C_P)				
(a) System/product management (C_{RM})	$ 195,954	3.7	$ 195,954	3.7
(b) Industrial engineering and operations analysis (C_{PI})	136,847	2.6	160,907	3.0
(c) Manufacturing—recurring (C_{PMR})	1,180,226	22.5	1,215,095	22.8
(d) Manufacturing—nonrecurring (C_{PMN})	121,570	2.3	136,984	2.6
(e) Quality control (C_{PQ})	153,527	2.9	134,558	2.5
(f) Initial logistics support (C_{PLS})				
(1) Supply support—initial (C_{PLS})	118,535	2.3	142,030	2.7
(2) Test and support equipment (C_{PLT})	183,328	3.5	183,328	3.4
(3) Technical data (C_{PLD})	13,947	0.3	14,631	0.3
(4) Personnel training (C_{PLP})	121,375	2.3	121,375	2.3
Subtotal	$2,225,310	42.3	$2,304,862	43.2
3. Operation and support cost (C_O)				
(a) Operating personnel (C_{OOP})	$ 52,092	1.0	$ 52,092	1.0
(b) Distribution—transportation (C_{ODT})	549,170	10.5	549,170	10.3
(c) Unscheduled maintenance (C_{OLA})	258,924	4.9	319,134	6.0
(d) Maintenance facilities (C_{OLM})	9,729	0.2	11,994	0.2
(e) Supply support (C_{OLS})	616,532	11.7	767,492	14.4
(f) Maintenance personnel training (C_{OLT})	18,898	0.4	18,898	0.4
(g) Test and support equipment (C_{OLE})	74,674	1.4	112,002	2.1
(h) Transportation and handling (C_{OLH})	11,150	0.2	13,260	0.2
Subtotal	$1,591,170	30.3	$1,844,042	34.6
Grand total	$5,255,036	100.0	$5,329,999	100.0

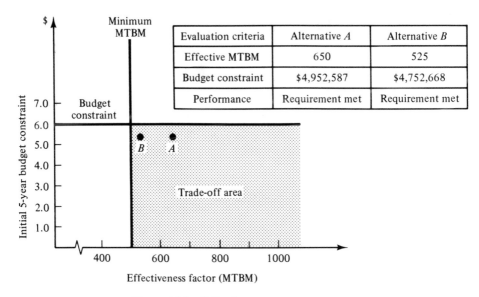

Figure 12.9   Effectiveness versus unit cost.

For alternative B, the present equivalent cost is

$$\text{PE} = \$434,294(\overset{P/F,10,1}{0.9091}) + \$707,409(\overset{P/F,10,2}{0.8265})$$

$$+ \cdots + \$79,074(\overset{P/F,10,13}{0.2897}) = \$5,329,999$$

TABLE 12.10   Cost Allocation by Program Year

Program Activity	Cost Category Designation	Cost by Program Year (dollars)				
		1	2	3	4	5
A. Alternative A						
1. Research and development	C_R	507,374	529,733	718,088		
2. Production and construction	C_P		264,871	935,441	1,023,769	973,311
3. Operation and support	C_O			79,203	207,098	348,248
Total actual cost	C	507,374	794,604	1,732,732	1,230,867	1,321,559
Total present cost	$C(10\%)$	461,254	656,740	1,301,802	840,682	820,556
Cumulative PC		461,254	1,117,994	2,419,796	3,260,478	4,081,034
B. Alternative B						
1. Research and development	C_R	434,294	408,019	597,719		
2. Production and construction	C_P		299,390	935,369	1,038,426	1,039,451
3. Operation and support	C_O			102,888	238,383	400,827
Total actual cost	C	434,294	707,409	1,635,976	1,276,809	1,440,278
Total present cost	$C(10\%)$	394,817	584,674	1,229,109	872,061	894,269
Cumulative PC		394,817	979,491	2,208,600	3,080,661	3,974,930

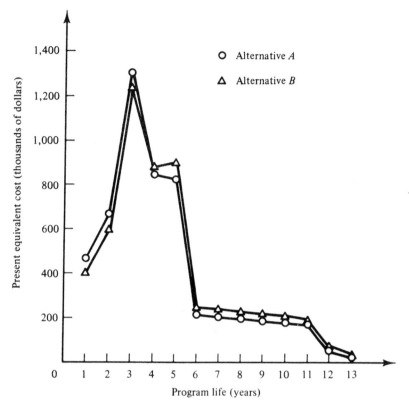

Figure 12.10   Cost profiles for communication system alternatives.

TABLE 12.10   Cost Allocation by Program Year (continued)

Cost by Program Year (dollars)								Total Actual Cost (dollars)
6	7	8	9	10	11	12	13	
								1,755,195
								3,197,392
365,660	383,945	403,122	423,297	444,466	483,355	159,288	59,670	3,340,682
365,660	383,945	403,122	423,297	444,466	483,355	159,288	59,670	8,309,939
206,415	197,041	188,056	179,520	171,386	163,573	50,749	17,286	5,255,036
4,287,449	4,484,490	4,672,546	4,852,066	5,023,452	5,187,025	5,237,774	5,255,036	5,255,036
								1,440,032
								3,312,636
420,870	441,916	463,985	487,206	511,575	537,144	190,394	74,074	3,869,262
420,870	441,916	463,985	487,206	511,575	537,144	190,394	74,074	8,621,930
237,581	226,791	216,449	206,624	197,263	188,269	60,660	21,459	5,329,999
4,212,511	4,439,302	4,655,751	4,862,375	5,059,638	5,247,907	5,308,567	5,329,999	5,329,999

The results of this analysis support alternative *A* as the preferred configuration on the basis of present equivalent life-cycle cost. Note that the research and development (R&D) cost is higher for alternative *A*; however, the overall life-cycle cost is lower, owing to a significantly lower operation and support (O&S) cost. This would tend to indicate that the equipment design for reliability pertaining to alternative *A* is somewhat better. Although this increased reliability results in higher R&D cost, the anticipated number of maintenance actions is lower, resulting in lower O&S costs.

Prior to a final decision on which alternative to select, the analyst should accomplish a break-even analysis to determine the point in time when alternative *A* becomes more economical than alternative *B*. Figure 12.11 indicates that the break-even point, or the point in time when alternative *A* becomes less costly, is approximately four years and three months after the program start. This point is early enough in the life cycle to support the decision. If this crossover point were much further out in time, the decision might be questioned.

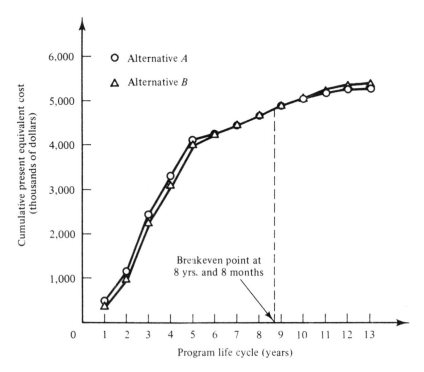

Figure 12.11 Break-even analysis for communication system alternatives.

12.5   SENSITIVITY ANALYSIS

It is noted in considering the analysis results that the delta present equivalent cost between the two alternatives is $74,963 (refer to Table 12.10), and the cost profiles are relatively close to each other (refer to Figure 12.10). These factors do not overwhelmingly support a clear-cut decision in favor of alternative *A* without introducing some risk. In view of the possible inaccuracies associated with the input data, the analyst may wish to perform a sensitivity analysis to determine the effects of input parameter variations on the present life-cycle cost. The analyst should determine how much variation can be tolerated before the decision shifts in favor of alternative *B*.

Referring to Table 12.9, the analyst should select the *high contributors* (those that contribute more than 10% of the total cost), determine the cause-and-effect relationships, and identify the various input data factors that directly affect cost. In instances where such factors are based on highly questionable prediction techniques, the analyst should vary these factors over a probable range of values and assess the results. For instance, key input parameters in this analysis include the system operating time (in hours) and the MTBM factor. Using the life-cycle cost model, the analyst will apply a multiple factor to the operating time values and the MTBM and determine the delta cost associated with each variation. From this, trend curves are projected, as was done in Figure 9.14.

A small variation in operating time and/or MTBM may cause the decision to shift in favor or alternative *B*. This provides an indication that there is a high degree of risk associated with making a wrong decision. Thus the analyst should make every effort to reduce this risk by improving the input data to the greatest extent possible. Also, when the results are particularly close, the magnitude of risk associated with the decision must be determined.

Another area of concern in decision making is the variation in the decision independent parameters such as the interest rate, inflation rate, labor rate, and so on. For example, any variation in interest rate will affect both configurations under study, but the magnitude of the effect will be different, depending on the nature of the money flows. Figure 12.12 shows the change in the life-cycle cost of alternative *A* and alternative *B*. There is an interest rate (16.9%) for which there would be no LCC difference in the alternatives being evaluated.

12.6   CASE STUDY SUMMARY

This case study illustrates the application of a life-cycle cost analysis to support a design decision where two alternative configurations are being evaluated in response to a stated need. The objective was to select the configuration that

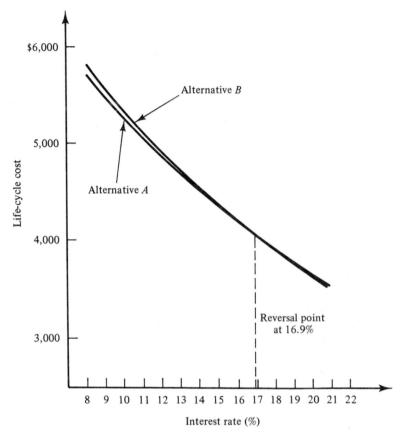

Figure 12.12 Effect of interest rate change on LCC.

will fulfill all system performance and effectiveness requirements, fall within a specified budget constraint, and reflect the lowest life-cycle cost.

Inherent in the process of evaluating the two design alternatives are the initial steps of the system design process illustrated in Figure 1.4. A need is defined through a needs analysis, system operational requirements are identified, and a maintenance concept is described in accordance with the concepts presented in Chapter 1. Based on this information, design requirements are described in terms of a functional packaging approach, and the quantitative effectiveness factors are established in terms of MTBM, $\overline{\text{M}}$ct, MLH/OH, and cost.

The evaluation itself addresses two candidate systems, each of which meets the specified performance and effectiveness requirements and falls within the allocated budget. However, each configuration exhibits different performance and effectiveness, and the objective is to select the best in terms of life-cycle cost.

Accomplishing the life-cycle cost analysis incorporates the steps described in Part II of this book. A cost breakdown structure is developed (refer to Figure 2.5 and Appendix B), cost-generating variables and factors are identified, and costs are summarized year by year. Finally, cost profiles are developed, a break-even analysis is accomplished, and the best configuration is selected using the economic analysis techniques of Chapter 3.

In developing data for the life-cycle cost analysis, many different factors are employed, particularly with regard to the determination of costs for system operation and support. Reliability factors are used in the determination of maintenance frequencies (i.e., the number of unscheduled maintenance actions listed in Table 12.7). These are derived from reliability prediction data described in Appendix C. Maintainability factors ($\overline{M}ct$ and MLH/OH) are employed to determine personnel costs. These factors are developed from maintainability prediction data described in Appendix C. Logistic support requirements include supply support factors, test and support equipment requirements, transportation requirements, and so on, developed through the LSA described in Appendix C. Much of the data developed in this case study utilizes the concepts described in Part I of this book, supported by some of the analysis techniques described in Part II.

A final step in the life-cycle cost analysis involves the application of sensitivity analysis to assess the risk(s) associated with a given decision as presented in Chapter 8. Further, the accomplishment of a sensitivity analysis aids the analyst to evaluate cause-and-effect relationships and the interactions that occur with system parameter variation.

Finally, the equipment considered in this case study is actually one unit in a finite population of similar units. The population is deployed to meet the demand for an improved overall communication capability in a metropolitan area. An optimal population design requires the approach presented in the case study of Chapter 13.

13

Repairable Equipment System Design

A finite population of repairable equipment is to be procured and maintained in operation to meet a demand. As repairable equipment units fail or become unserviceable, they will be repaired and returned to service. As they age, the older units will be removed from the system and replaced with new units. The system design problem is to determine the population size, the replacement age of units, the number of repair channels, the design mean time between failures, and the design mean time to repair, so that design requirements will be met at a minimum life-cycle cost.[1]

13.1 CASE STUDY INTRODUCTION

Two design problems are treated in this case study. The first is to determine the population size, the replacement age of units, and the number of repair channels so that the sum of all costs associated with the system will be minimized. The second design problem is to generate and evaluate candidate systems by specifying the unit mean time between failures, MTBF, and the unit

[1] A version of this case study first appeared in W. J. Fabrycky and J. T. Hart, "Economic Optimization of a Finite Population System Deployed to Meet a Demand," *Proceedings of the Joint Conference,* American Association of Cost Engineers/American Institute of Industrial Engineers, Houston, Texas, 1975. Also see Chapter 20 in B. S. Blanchard and W. J. Fabrycky, *Systems Engineering and Analysis,* 2nd ed. (Englewood Cliffs, NJ: Prentice-Hall, Inc., 1990).

mean time to repair, MTTR, as a function of unit cost, as well as the population size, the replacement age of units, and the number of repair channels.

The Operational System

The repairable equipment population system (REPS) illustrated in Figure 13.1 is designed and deployed to meet a demand, D. Units within the system can be separated into two groups: those in operation and available to meet demand, and those out of operation and hence unavailable to meet demand. It is assumed that units are not discarded upon failure, but are repaired and returned to operation. As units age, they become less reliable and their maintenance costs increase. Accordingly, it is important to determine the optimum replacement age. It is assumed that the number of new units procured each year is constant and that the number of units in each age group is equal to the ratio of the total number required in the population and the desired number of age groups. Although the analysis deals with the life cycle of the units, the objective is to optimize the total system of which the units are a part.

In Design Problem I, the design process consists of specifying a population of units, a number of maintenance channels, and a replacement schedule

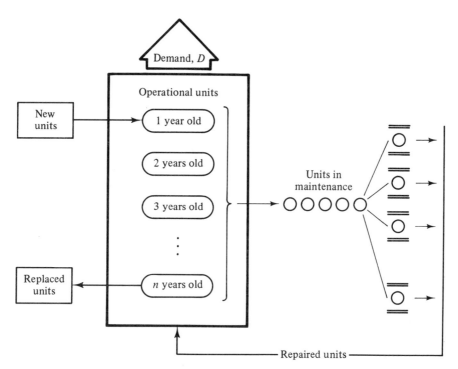

Figure 13.1   Repairable equipment population system.

for bringing new units into the system. For Design Problem II, the design process is extended to include establishing the unit's reliability and maintainability characteristics. In either case the system is to be designed to meet the demand for equipment optimally.

The foregoing paragraphs have described, in general terms, the finite population queuing system under investigation. This model describes the operation of numerous systems. For example, both the airlines and the military operate and maintain aircraft with these system characteristics. In ground transit, vehicles such as rental automobiles, taxis, and commercial trucks constitute repairable equipment populations. Production equipment types such as weaving looms, drill presses, and autoclaves are populations of equipment which fit the repairable classification. But the repairable unit may also be an inventory of components for the larger entities mentioned. For example, aircraft hydraulic pumps, automobile starters and alternators, truck engines, electric motors, and electronic controllers for equipment also constitute repairable equipment population systems.

Scope and Assumptions

Repairable equipment population systems normally come into being over a non-steady-state buildup phase. They then operate over a steady-state interval of years, after which a phaseout period is entered. Only the steady-state mode of operation is considered here.

The following assumptions are adopted in the development of the mathematical model and algorithm for REPS.

1. The interarrival times are exponentially distributed.
2. The repair times are exponentially distributed.
3. The number of units in the population is small such that finite population queuing formulations must be used.
4. The interarrival times are statistically independent of the repair times.
5. The repair channels are parallel and each is capable of similar performance.
6. The population size will always be larger than or at least equal to the number of service channels.
7. Each channel performs service on one unit at a time.
8. MTBF and MTTR values vary for each age group and represent the expected value of these variables for that age group.
9. Units completing repair return to operation with the same operational characteristics as their age group.

System Design Evaluation

Design Problem I may be evaluated by using the decision evaluation function of Equation 5.1. Here the objective is to find optimal values for controllable design variables in the face of uncontrollable system parameters. In Design Problem II, the decision evaluation function of Equation 5.2 is used to seek the best candidate system. This is accomplished by establishing values for controllable design dependent parameters in the face of uncontrollable design independent parameters and optimal values for design variables.

Design variables.   Three design variables are identified in the repairable equipment population system. These controllables are the number of units to deploy, the replacement age of units, and the number of repair channels. Optimal values are sought for these variables so that the sum of all costs associated with the repairable equipment population system will be minimized.

In Design Problem I the focus is entirely on optimizing design variables as the only controllable factors. This situation arises when the system is in existence and the objective is to optimize its operation in the face of uncontrollable system parameters. The focus shifts to seeking the best candidate system in Design Problem II. In this activity, optimal values for design variables are secondary. They are needed as a means for comparing candidate systems equivalently. Then, when the best system is identified, they are used to specify its optimal operation.

System parameters.   Demand is the primary stimulus on the repairable equipment population system and the justification for its existence. This uncontrollable system parameter is assumed to be constant over time. Other uncontrollable system parameters are economic in nature. They include the shortage penalty cost which arises when there are insufficient units operational to meet demand, the cost of providing repair capability, and the time value of money on invested capital.

Some system parameters are uncontrollable in Design Problem I, but controllable in Design Problem II. These are the design MTBF and MTTR, the energy efficiency of equipment units, the design life of units, and the first cost and salvage value of these units. It is through these design dependent system parameters that the best candidate system may be identified.

13.2 EVALUATION FUNCTION FORMULATION

An evaluation function for system design evaluation can be derived using the structure outlined in Section 5.3. The model utilizes annual equivalent life-cycle cost as the evaluation measure expressed as

$$AELCC = PC + OC + RC + SC \tag{13.1}$$

where

AELCC = annual equivalent life-cycle cost
  PC = annual equivalent population cost
  OC = annual operating cost
  RC = annual repair facility cost
  SC = annual shortage penalty cost

Annual Equivalent Population Cost

The annual equivalent cost of a deployed population of N equipment units is

$$PC = C_i N$$

with[2]

$$C_i = P\left(\overset{A|P,i,n}{}\right) - B\left(\overset{A|F,i,n}{}\right) \tag{13.2}$$

Book value, B, in Equation 13.2 is used to represent the original value of a unit minus its accumulated depreciation at any point in time. The depreciation of a unit over its lifetime by the straight-line method gives an expression for book value as

$$B = P - n\frac{P - F}{L} \tag{13.3}$$

where

C_i = annual equivalent cost per unit
P = first or acquisition cost of a unit
F = estimated salvage value of a unit
B = book value of a unit at the end of year n
L = estimated life of the unit
N = number of units in the population
n = retirement age of units, $n > 1$
i = annual interest rate

---

[2] Alternatively, $(P - B)\left(\overset{A|P,i,n}{}\right) + Bi$ could be used as given by Equation 3.33.

Annual Operating Cost

The annual cost of operating a population of N deployed equipment units is

$$OC = (EC + LC + PMC + Other)N \qquad (13.4)$$

where

EC = annual cost of energy consumed
LC = annual cost of operating labor
PMC = annual cost of preventive maintenance

Other annual operating costs may be incurred. These include all recurring annual costs of keeping the population of equipment units in service, such as storage cost, insurance premiums, and taxes.

Annual Repair Facility Cost

The annual cost of providing a repair facility to repair failed equipment units is

$$RC = C_r M \qquad (13.5)$$

where

C_r = annual fixed and variable repair cost per repair channel
M = number of repair channels

If there are a number of repair channel components with different estimated lives, then C_r is the sum of their annual costs. Some of the repair facility cost items that could be included are the cost of the building, maintenance supplies, test equipment, and so on, expressed on a per channel basis. The administrative, maintenance manpower, and other overhead costs would also be computed on a yearly basis and on a per channel basis.

Annual Shortage Penalty Cost

Finite population waiting-line models must be applied to those systems where the population is small relative to the arrival rate. In these systems, units leaving the population significantly affect the characteristics of the population and the arrival probabilities.

In the repairable equipment population system example of this case study, it is assumed that both the time between calls for service for a unit of the finite population and the service times are exponentially distributed. When failed equipment units cause the number in an operational state to fall below the demand, an out-of-operation or shortage cost is incurred. The annual shortage cost is the product of the shortage cost per unit short per year and the expected number of units short expressed as

$$SC = C_S[E(S)] \qquad (13.6)$$

where

     C_S = shortage cost per unit short per year

     $E(S)$ = expected number of units short

The expected number of units short can be found from the probability distribution of n units short, P_n. Let

     N = number of units in the population

     M = number of service channels in the repair facility

     λ = failure rate of a unit, 1/MTBF

     μ = repair rate of a repair channel, 1/MTTR

     n = number of failed units

     P_n = steady-state probability of n failed units

     P_0 = probability that no units failed

     $M\mu$ = maximum possible repair rate

     λ_n = failure rate when n units already failed

     μ_n = repair rate when n units already failed

The failure rate of a unit is expressed as $\lambda = 1/\text{MTBF}$ and the failure rate of the entire population when n units already failed can be expressed as $\lambda_n = (N - n)\lambda$, where $N - n$ is the number of operational units, each of which fails at a rate of λ. Similarly, the repair rate of a repair channel is expressed as $\mu = 1/\text{MTTR}$, and the repair rate of the entire repair facility when n units have already failed can be expressed as

$$\mu_n = \begin{cases} n\mu & \text{if } n \in 1, 2, \ldots, M - 1 \\ M\mu & \text{if } n \in M, M + 1, \ldots, N \end{cases} \qquad (13.7)$$

An analysis using birth–death processes is employed to determine the probability distribution, P_n, for the number of failed units. In the birth–death process, the state of the system is the number of failed units (state $= 0$, 1, 2, ..., N). The rates of change between the states are the breakdown rate, λ_n, and the repair rate, μ_n. This gives

If we assume steady-state operation of the system, this yields

$$N\lambda P_0 = \mu P_1$$

$$N\lambda P_0 + 2\mu P_2 = [\mu + (N-1)\lambda] P_1$$

$$(N-1)\lambda P_1 + 3\mu P_3 = [2\mu + (N-2)\lambda]P_2$$

$$\cdot$$
$$\cdot$$
$$\cdot$$

$$(N-M+2)\lambda P_{M-2} + M\mu P_M = [(M-1)\mu + (N-M+1)\lambda]P_{M-1}$$

$$\cdot$$
$$\cdot$$
$$\cdot$$

$$2\lambda P_{N-2} + M\mu P_N = (M\mu + \lambda)P_{N-1}$$

$$\lambda P_{N-1} = M\mu P_N$$

Additionally,

$$\sum_{n=0}^{N} P_n = 1$$

Solving these balance equations gives

$$P_0 = \left(\sum_{n=0}^{N} C_n\right)^{-1} \tag{13.8}$$

where

$$C_n = \begin{cases} \dfrac{N!}{(N-n)!n!}\left(\dfrac{\lambda}{\mu}\right)^n & \text{if } n = 0, 1, 2, \ldots, M \\[4mm] \dfrac{N!}{(N-n)!M!M^{n-M}}\left(\dfrac{\lambda}{\mu}\right)^n & \text{if } n = M+1, M+2, \ldots, N \end{cases} \tag{13.9}$$

Equations 13.8 and 13.9 can now be used to find the steady-state probability of n failed units as $P_n = P_0 C_n$ for $n = 0, 1, 2, \ldots, N$.

Define the quantity $N - D$ as the number of extra units to be held in the population. For $n = 0, 1, 2, \ldots, N - D$ there is no shortage of units. However, when

$n = N - D + 1$	a shortage of 1 unit exists
$n = N - D + 2$	a shortage of 2 units exists

$$\cdot$$
$$\cdot$$
$$\cdot$$

$n = N$	a shortage of D units exists

The expected number of units short, $E(S)$, can be found by multiplying the number of units short by the probability of that occurrence as

$$E(S) = \sum_{j=1}^{D} jP_{(N-D+j)} \tag{13.10}$$

13.3 SYSTEM DESIGN PROBLEM I

In this REPS design example, the decision maker has no control over system parameters but can only choose the number of equipment units to procure and deploy, the age at which units should be replaced, and the number of channels in the repair facility. Assume that the demand, D, is for 15 identical equipment units. Table 13.1 lists system parameters for this design example. Table 13.2 exhibits a set of design variables for the example under consideration. The example computations that follow are based on these variables and the system parameters in Table 13.2.

TABLE 13.1   System Parameters for Design Problem I Example

Parameter	Value	
Unit acquisition cost	$52,000	
Unit design life	6 years	
Unit salvage value at end of design life	$7,000	
Unit operating cost:		
Energy and fuel	$500	
Operating labor	450	
Preventative maintenance	400	
Other operating costs	400	
Annual repair channel cost	$45,000	
Annual shortage cost	$73,000	
Annual interest rate	10%	
Age cohorts	MTBF	MTTR
0–1	0.20	0.03
1–2	0.24	0.04
2–3	0.29	0.05
3–4	0.29	0.05
4–5	0.26	0.06
5–6	0.22	0.07

TABLE 13.2   Design Variables for Design Problem 1

Population, N	Repair Channels, M	Retirement Age, n
19	3	4

Annual Equivalent Population Cost

First, compute the book value, B, of the units at retirement age after four years using Equation 13.3 as

$$\$52,000 - 4\left(\frac{\$52,000 - \$7,000}{6}\right) = \$22,000$$

The annual equivalent unit cost from Equation 13.2 is

$$C_i = \$52,000\left[\frac{0.10\,(1.10)^4}{(1.10)^4 - 1}\right] - \$22,000\left[\frac{0.10}{(1.10)^4 - 1}\right]$$

$$= \$16,404 - \$4,740 = \$11,664$$

from which the annual equivalent population cost is

$$PC = \$11,664(19) = \$221,616$$

Annual Operating Cost

Annual operating cost for the deployed population is found from Equation 13.4 to be

$$OC = (\$500 + \$450 + \$400 + \$400)(19) = \$33,250$$

Annual Repair Facility Cost

The annual equivalent repair channel cost for three channels from Equation 13.5 is

$$RC = \$45,000(3) = \$135,000$$

Annual Shortage Penalty Cost

Calculation of the shortage cost is based on the MTBF and MTTR values from Table 13.1 for years 1 to 4. From these values, the average MTBF and MTTR for the population can be computed as[3]

$$MTBF = (1/4)(0.20 + 0.24 + 0.29 + 0.29) = 0.2550$$

$$MTTR = (1/4)(0.03 + 0.04 + 0.05 + 0.05) = 0.0425$$

---

[3] Since the units are homogenous, the aggregate MTBF and MTTR for the population can be found as

$$MTBF = \frac{1}{n}\sum_{j=1}^{n} MTBF_j$$

$$MTTR = \frac{1}{n}\sum_{j=1}^{n} MTTR_j$$

where the subscript j represents age groups and n is the number of these age groups. This follows from the superposition of Poisson processes.

The failure rate of a unit and the repair rate at a repair channel are given by

$$= (1/\text{MTBF}) = (1/0.2550) = 3.9215$$

$$= (1/\text{MTTR}) = (1/0.0425) = 23.5294$$

from which $\lambda/\mu = 1/6$. Next, compute C_n for $n = 0, 1, \ldots, 3$ from Equation 13.9 as

$$C_0 = \frac{19!(1/6)^0}{19!0!} = 1$$

$$C_1 = \frac{19!(1/6)^1}{18!1!} = 3.1665$$

$$C_2 = \frac{19!(1/6)^2}{17!2!} = 4.7496$$

$$C_3 = \frac{19!(1/6)^3}{16!3!} = 4.4856$$

Computing C_n for $n = 4, \ldots, 19$, also from Equation 13.9,

$$C_4 = \frac{19!(1/6)^4}{15!3!3!^1} = 3.9813$$

$$C_5 = \frac{19!(1/6)^5}{14!3!3!^2} = 3.3224$$

$$C_6 = \frac{19!(1/6)^6}{13!3!3!^3} = 2.5840$$

$$\vdots$$

$$C_{18} = \frac{19!(1/6)^{18}}{1!3!5!^{15}} = 0.0000$$

$$C_{19} = \frac{19!(1/6)^{19}}{0!3!3!^{16}} = 0.0000$$

Now

$$\sum_{n=0}^{19} C_n = 27.9390$$

and from Equation 13.8,

$$P_0 = \frac{1}{\sum_{n=0}^{19} C_n} = \frac{1}{27.9390} = 0.0358$$

P_n for $n = 1, 2, \ldots, N$ can now be computed from $P_n = P_o C_n = (0.0358)C_n$ as follows:

$$P_0 = 0.0358 \times 1 \qquad = 0.0358$$
$$P_1 = 0.0358 \times 3.1665 = 0.1134$$

.
.
.

$$P_5 = 0.0358 \times 3.3224 = 0.1189$$
$$P_6 = 0.0358 \times 2.5840 = 0.0925$$

.
.
.

$$P_{18} = 0.0358 \times 0.0000 = 0.0000$$
$$P_{19} = 0.0358 \times 0.0000 = 0.0000$$

Now the expected number of units short can be calculated from Equation 13.10 as

$$E(S) = \sum_{j=1}^{D} jP_{(N-D+j)} = \sum_{j=1}^{15} jP_{(4+j)}$$
$$= 1(0.1189) + 2(0.0925) + \cdots + 15(0.0000)$$
$$= 1.00663$$

From Equation 13.6 the annual shortage cost is

$$SC = C_S[E(S)]$$
$$= \$73,000(1.00663) = \$73,484$$

The total system annual equivalent cost may now be summarized as

$$TC = PC + OC + RC + SC$$
$$= \$221,616 + \$33,250 + \$135,000 + \$73,484 = \$463,350$$

As can be seen from Table 13.3, this solution is actually the optimum with neighboring points given for N, M, and n.

TABLE 13.3 Points in the Optimum Region

Retirement Age, n	Number of Units, N	Number of Repair Channels, M		
		2	3	4
3	19	$598,395	$465,985	$469,130
	18	592,920	464,770	465,755
4	19	600,720	463,350[a]	464,295
	20	610,775	466,610	468,755
5	19	643,050	480,375	467,735

[a] Optimum.

The shortage distribution can be calculated from the P_n values and plotted as a histogram of $Pr(S = s) = N - D + s$. In this example, $Pr(S = s) = P_{4+s}$.

$$Pr(S = 0) = 0.622$$

$$Pr(S = 1) = 0.119$$

$$Pr(S = 2) = 0.093$$

$$Pr(S = 3) = 0.067$$

$$Pr(S = 4) = 0.046$$

$$Pr(S = 5) = 0.027$$

$$Pr(S = 6) = 0.015$$

$$Pr(S = 7) = 0.008$$

$$Pr(S = 8) = 0.003$$

[handwritten notes in left margin:] # Shortages $\sum_{n}$ $0 \times .622 + 1(.119) + 2(.093) + 3(.067) + 4(.046) + \ldots$ $.947$

The shortage probability histogram for this example is exhibited in Figure 13.2.

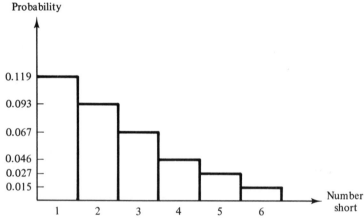

Figure 13.2 Equipment shortage probability histogram.

In the next section the adequacy of this "baseline" design will be considered in the face of design requirements. Additionally, challengers in the form of alternative candidate systems will be presented and evaluated.

13.4 SYSTEM DESIGN PROBLEM II

In Design Problem II, the decision maker has control over a set of design dependent parameters in addition to the set of design variables. Accordingly, the decision evaluation function of Equation 5.3 applies. In this section, design-dependent parameters will be altered in the baseline design of Section 13.3 to seek a REPS candidate more acceptable than the baseline design.

Considering Design Requirements

In the absence of design requirements, the baseline design might be acceptable. However, assume that it is not acceptable due to the existence of the following design requirements:

1. The cost per deployed unit must not exceed $50,000.
2. The probability of no units short of demand must be at least 0.70.
3. The mean MTBF for the unit over its life must be at least 0.20 year.
4. A unit must not be kept in service more than four years.

Note that the baseline design does not meet requirement 1 and 2, but it does meet requirements 3 and 4. Also, its annual equivalent life-cycle cost is noted to be $463,350. Figure 13.3 shows a design evaluation display for this situation. The baseline design is exhibited. A search must now be made to develop one or more candidate systems that will meet all design requirements at an acceptable life-cycle cost.

Generating Candidate Systems

Suppose that two candidate systems are generated in the face of the demand for 15 equipment units and the design-independent parameters of Table 13.1. Design dependent parameters for these candidates are given in Table 13.4. Optimization over the design variables for each set of design-dependent

TABLE 13.4 Design-Dependent Parameters for Candidate Systems

Parameter	Candidate System 1		Candidate System 2	
Unit acquisition cost	$45,000		$43,000	
Unit design life	6 years		6 years	
Unit salvage value at end of design life	$6,000		$5,000	
Unit operating cost:				
Energy and fuel	$600		$800	
Operating labor	500		700	
Preventative maintenance	400		400	
Other operating costs	400		400	
Age cohorts	MTBF	MTTR	MTBF	MTTR
0–1	0.16	0.04	0.18	0.04
1–2	0.21	0.04	0.21	0.04
2–3	0.26	0.05	0.25	0.05
3–4	0.26	0.06	0.25	0.05
4–5	0.26	0.06	0.23	0.06
5–6	0.24	0.06	0.20	0.06

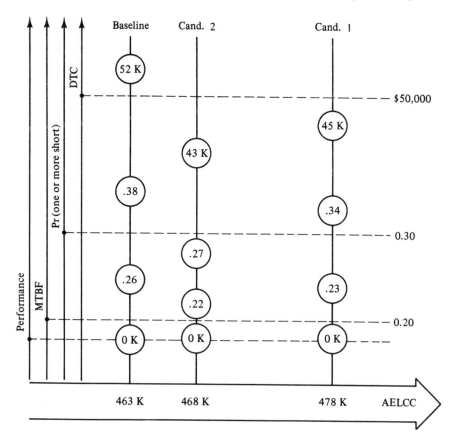

Figure 13.3   Design decision evaluation display for REPS.

parameters gives the results summarized in Table 13.5 for the candidate systems. Also included are the optimized results for the baseline design. The following observations are made:

1. Only candidate system 2 meets all design requirements.
2. Candidate system 2 has the lowest cost per unit and therefore the lowest investment cost for the deployed population.
3. Candidate system 2 has the highest probability of meeting the demand for 15 serviceable equipment units.
4. Candidate system 2 consumes the most energy and requires the highest expenditure for operating labor.
5. Candidate system 2 has an annual equivalent life-cycle cost penalty of $468,825 less $463,350 or $5,475 over the baseline design but has a lower investment cost than candidate system 1.

TABLE 13.5 Evaluation Summary for REPS Candidates

	Baseline Design	Candidate System 1	Candidate System 2
Number deployed, N	19	20	20
Repair channels, M	3	4	4
Retirement age, n	4	5	4
Unit cost, P	$52,000	$45,000	$43,000
Mean MTBF	0.26	0.23	0.22
Probability of no units short	0.622	0.663	0.730
Annual equivalent life-cycle cost	$463,350	$478,470	$468,825

There may be other candidate systems that meet all design requirements and which have life-cycle costs equal to or less than the LCC for candidate system 2. The objective of Design Problem II is to formalize the evaluation of candidates, with each candidate being characterized by its design dependent parameter values. Comparison of the candidates is made only after the optimized (minimized) values are found for life-cycle cost. This is in keeping with the idea of equivalence set forth in Equation 5.1.

13.5 CASE STUDY SUMMARY

This case study models and optimizes a repairable equipment population system composed of operational units and repair facilities used to keep the units operational. In System Design Problem I it is assumed that the units are procured with a predetermined MTBF and MTTR, with these values varying as a function of the age of units. The annual equivalent life-cycle cost is minimized by finding the population size, the replacement age, and the number of repair channels.

In System Design Problem II, an extension is made by considering units with MTBF and MTTR characteristics which are a function of the first cost of the units. Here it is assumed that improvements in MTBF and MTTR can be obtained at a price. This leads to the multiple application of the optimization routine for Design Problem I; an application to each possible MTBF and MTTR case. The result is the specification of MTBF and MTTR values for the units to be deployed.

Life-Cycle Cost Analysis Process

Part I of this text describes the basic concepts and theory upon which life-cycle cost and economic analysis is based. It is essential that these concepts be thoroughly understood prior to undertaking an economic analyses in any form. Part II builds on these concepts and theory in the context of life-cycle costing methodology and applications. Topics covered include cost estimating methods, the generation of cost profiles, the accomplishment of break-even analyses, the economic evaluation of alternatives, and so on. Part II also attempts to convert the theory into applications and identifies some useful tools appropriate for cost analysis. Part III extends concepts and applications one step further by developing and presenting two case studies. It is intended to show how the concepts and tools fit into the overall life-cycle cost and economic analysis process.

The objective of this Appendix is to summarize the material presented in this text by describing the overall life-cycle cost process in "generic" terms. (This is an expansion of the concepts presented in Figure 6.4.) When reviewing the various exercises and case studies, while the nomenclature and specific activities may vary from one example to the next, there is an overall series of steps that apply generally. The objective is to summarize the material presented in Parts I, II, and III by describing these steps in an integrated way.

The basic steps in a typical life-cycle cost analysis are illustrated in Figure A.1. These are described briefly below.

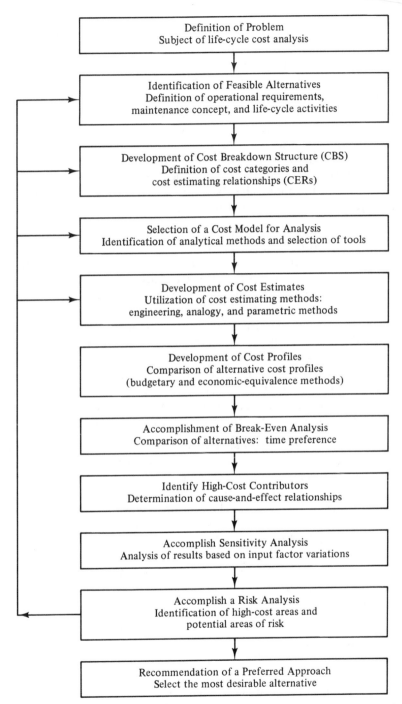

Figure A.1 The basic steps in a life-cycle cost analysis.

1. *Definition of problem.* An initial step involves the problem definition stage. Although this may appear to be intuitively obvious, it is not uncommon for one to delve into some in-depth analysis effort without first
having defined the problem in detail. In essence, there may be a requirement
for a life-cycle cost analysis in evaluating alternative technologies as part of a
feasibility study leading to a system design approach, alternative operational
scenarios, alternative maintenance and support policies, alternative packaging
schemes in equipment design, alternatives involving automation versus manual operations, alternative manufacturing approaches, alternative distribution
and transportation methods, and so on. The analyst needs to define the problem, and describe the approach to be followed in resolving the problem. There
are life-cycle implications in almost all instances. Refer to Section 6.1.

2. *Identification of feasible alternatives.* Critical in the accomplishment
of any life-cycle cost analysis is the identification of feasible alternatives and
the projection of each selected alternative in the context of the entire life
cycle. Associated with each alternative is a series of life-cycle activities in one
form or another: that is, research tasks, design and development tasks, production and/or construction tasks, distribution and system operation, sustaining maintenance and support, retirement, equipment recycling and/or disposal. As the costs associated with each phase of activity affect other phases,
it is necessary to view these activities in total. This, in turn, requires that the
analyst define the system operational requirements and the maintenance concept as envisioned at that time. Although the details may change, a baseline
must be established from the beginning. Activities affecting life-cycle cost are
discussed in Section 6.3. Also, the case studies in Part III illustrate the point.

3. *Development of cost breakdown structure (CBS).* Given the definition of alternative configurations (and associated activities) from a life-cycle
perspective, the next step is to develop a "structure" for the allocation/
collection of the costs as they related to the activities for each alternative being
evaluated (refer to Figure 2.5). The cost breakdown structures (CBS) must
consider *all* future costs, must cover *all* life-cycle activities, must be developed
to the depth required to provide the necessary visibility with regard to all
elements of the system and/or program activities, and must allow for the
presentation of costs on a *functional* basis. The CBS must be developed to
provide the sensitivity required for the analysis effort. Appendix B includes a
detailed example of a CBS.

4. *Selection of a cost model for analysis.* Within the CBS, there are
many different categories of cost, input–output parameter relationships, cost
estimating relationships (CERs), and so on. With this in mind, the analyst
needs to identify the appropriate analytical techniques/methods and a model
that can be utilized to facilitate the analysis process. Care must be exercised
to ensure that the tool selected is appropriate for the job at hand. There are

many models in existence, advertised as being "the answer to all things," that are not sensitive to the problem being addressed. This area of concern is discussed in Section 6.3.

5. *Development of cost estimates.* In response to the analysis requirements, the identified activities associated with the alternatives being evaluated, and the data structure within the CBS, the analyst proceeds with the cost estimating function. Cost estimates are developed using a combination straight engineering projection, estimating by analogy, using parametric methods, and so on. Cost estimating relationships (CERs), developed from data describing past experiences, are used to facilitate the estimating process. Cost projections are developed, including the effects of inflation, the utilization of learning curves, and so on. Cost estimating is covered in detail in Chapter 7.

6. *Development of cost profiles.* When projecting costs out into the future for each alternative configuration being evaluated, cost profiles are developed. For the purposes of accomplishing a life-cycle cost analysis, a typical profile might be presented in three different ways to include (a) a discounted profile, using the time value of money concepts described in Part I, for the comparison of two or more alternatives on an *equivalent* basis; (b) a budgetary profile using constant dollars to allow for the evaluation of a single profile on a year-to-year basis in terms of today's dollars; and (c) a budgetary profile using inflationary factors, effects of learning curves, and so on, to allow for the evaluation of a single profile in terms of possible resource or budgetary constraints. While an economic analysis effort requires the time value of money considerations, a manager will often want to look at a profile presented in budgetary terms prior to making a decision in selecting a specific alternative. Cost profiles are discussed in Section 6.4, and the comparison of alternatives is covered in detail in Chapters 9 and 10.

7. *Accomplishment of break-even analysis.* When comparing the alternative cost profiles on the basis of the individual cost summaries, delta costs, and so on, it may at first appear that one alternative is clearly favored over another. However, prior to arriving at a final decision, the analyst must determine the point in time when the preferred approach assumes the "position of preference." If *A* is preferred over *B* but *A* does not assume the preferred position until 11 years in the future, should *A* be selected as the preferred alternative? The analyst needs to develop a break-even analysis in order to determine the points in time when the different alternatives look good. The ultimate decision will not only be based on the cost profiles and the associated delta costs, but on the times in the life cycle when one looks better than the other. Of course, the analyst needs to consider such things as obsolescence, outside competition, and so on. Break-even analyses are covered in detail in Chapter 9.

App. A   Life-Cycle Cost Analysis Process

8. *Identify high-cost contributors.* Given the results of the life-cycle cost analysis, presented in a tabular form similar to Table 9.7 in Chapter 9, the analyst may wish to identify those areas of potential risk and where possible improvements can be introduced with the objective of reducing the overall life-cycle cost. Assuming that configuration *A* is tentatively selected based on the delta cost difference in Table 9.7 and the break-even analysis results in Figure 9.12, what can be accomplished leading to possible further improvements? Review of the tabular results indicates that there are two "high-cost" categories in the operations and maintenance area: "maintenance personnel and support cost," which constitutes 23.4% of the total, and "spare repair parts cost," which represents 11.5% of the total. When determining "cause-and-effect" relationships, it becomes obvious that the frequency of unscheduled maintenance (or the poor reliability) has a great impact on both areas. Assuming that there are opportunities for further design improvement, the analyst should identify several of the weaker links in the system from a reliability standpoint and make a recommendation for improvement. By improving reliability, the frequency of unscheduled maintenance will be reduced, the life-cycle cost will be reduced, and the overall effectiveness of the system or product will be increased. Further, when looking at personnel costs, the quantity of labor hours expended in the accomplishment of unscheduled maintenance and the skill levels required will also affect cost. Relative to spares costs, the packaging concepts and the diagnostic provisions incorporated in the design will affect this category. In other words, the analyst can review the initial results of the analysis, identify the high-cost areas, determine possible causes, and make recommendations for improvement leading to a lower overall life-cycle cost. This process can be facilitated through an understanding of the input factors to the cost categories in the CBS used in the analysis, as can be seen by reviewing the CBS in Appendix B.

9. *Accomplish sensitivity analysis.* When reviewing the output results of a life-cycle cost analysis, while identifying the high-cost contributors and the major "causes," the analyst should proceed further by identifying the specific input data elements that are used in the analysis process. These data elements, particularly those that can significantly affect the analysis results, should be investigated in terms of source, validity and reliability of the data, and so on. There may be certain input data elements, which have a large affect on the analysis results, that are highly "suspect" in terms of origin! An example may be the reliability MTBF factor, a major input data element leading to the results in Table 9.7, the origin of which is based on a poorly done reliability prediction exercise. To test the overall analysis results, the analyst may wish to vary the input MTBF factor over a designated range of values and determine the resultant impact on the output results. In other words, by varying selected input factors, what will be the impact on the results in Table 9.7? A second question pertains to the risk associated with the possible selection of configuration *A*. How much variation of the input MTBF can be tolerated before configuration *B* assumes the preferable position. The accomplishment of a sensitivity analysis is one of the most meaningful and useful steps in responding to the many "what if" questions that arise in life-cycle costing. This area is covered in detail in Chapter 8.

10. *Accomplish a risk analysis.* Potential areas of risk are reflected by those high-cost categories which, in turn, can be traced back to certain critical input factors. In the process of accomplishing life-cycle costing, including both the assessment and the feedback provisions for corrective action, it is the objective to identify the eliminate potential areas of risk early. However, if this process is not effective, the "outstanding" high-cost areas can be identified, noted in terms of probability of occurrence, and adequately addressed through an appropriate risk management program. Risk is covered at selected points in Part I and II.

A life-cycle cost analysis may be accomplished in addressing a wide variety of problems at different stages of the system/product life cycle. It is applicable in the initial structuring of system requirements, in the evaluation of design alternatives, and in the development of manufacturing/production approaches. It can be effectively utilized in assessing an existing system capability already in being by identifying high-cost contributors and costly problem areas. Life-cycle costing can be accomplished during conceptual design when limited input data are available and, of course, it can be accomplished later during detailed design and development when the system configuration is fairly well defined (refer to Section 6.2). In any event, the accomplishment of life-cycle analysis is iterative, ongoing, and must be "tailored" to the specific application. Regardless of the application, however, there are a series of general steps that are usually followed, even though the depth of coverage will vary. Figure A.1 and the discussion herein is intended to address these steps.

B

Cost Breakdown
Structure

In accomplishing a life-cycle cost analysis, one needs to develop a cost breakdown structure (CBS), or cost tree, to facilitate the initial allocation of costs (top-down) and the subsequent collection of costs on a functional basis (bottom-up). The cost breakdown structure must include consideration of all costs. It is intended to aid in providing overall cost visibility. The CBS is tailored to a specific system requirement, and the cost categories will vary somewhat in terms of depth of coverage, depending on the type of system being evaluated.

The cost breakdown structure, in the context of the life-cycle cost analysis, is discussed in detail in Sections 2.4 and 6.3. As a supplement, this section includes a sample cost breakdown structure in Figure B.1 and description of the numerous cost categories in Tables B.1 and B.2.[1] Through inspection, one can gain an appreciation for the many variables that must be addressed in a typical life-cycle cost analysis. Also, review of the different quantitative expressions in Table B.1 should lead to better understanding the relationships of the various input parameters.

---

[1] Figure B.1 and Tables B.1 and B.2 were adapted from B. S. Blanchard, *Logistics Engineering and Management,* 3rd ed. (Englewood Cliffs, NJ: Prentice–Hall, Inc., 1986).

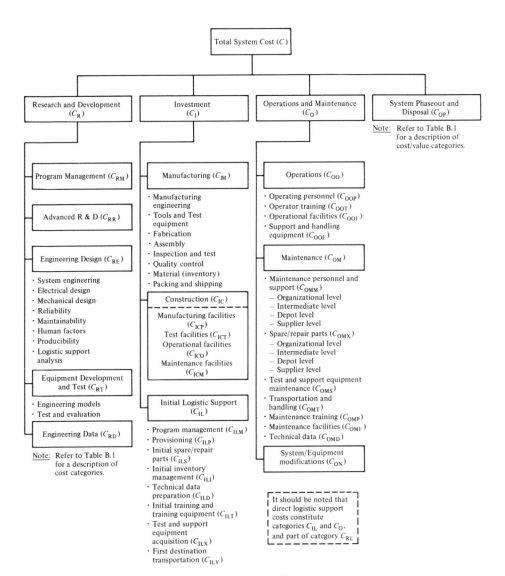

Figure B.1 A cost breakdown structure.

TABLE B.1 Description of Cost Categories

Cost Category (Reference Figure B–1)	Method of Determination (Quantitative Expression)	Cost Category Description and Justification
Total system cost (C)	$C = [C_R + C_I + C_O]$ $C_R =$ R&D cost $C_I =$ investment cost $C_O =$ operations and maintenance cost	Includes all future costs associated with the acquisition, utilization, and subsequent disposition of the system/equipment.
Research and development (C_R)	$C_R = [C_{RM} + C_{RR} + C_{RE} + C_{RT} + C_{RD}]$ $C_{RM} =$ program management cost $C_{RR} =$ advanced R&D cost $C_{RE} =$ engineering design cost $C_{RT} =$ equipment development and test cost $C_{RD} =$ engineering data cost	Includes all costs associated with conceptual/feasibility studies, basic research, advanced research and development, engineering design, fabrication and test of engineering prototype models (hardware), and associated documentation. Also covers all related program management functions. These costs are basically non-recurring.
Program management (C_{RM})	$C_{RM} = \sum_{i=1}^{N} C_{RM_i}$ $C_{RM_i} =$ cost of specific activity i $N =$ number of activities	Costs of management oriented activity applicable (across-the-board) to conceptual/feasibility studies, research, engineering design (including logistic support in the design process), equipment development and test, and related data/documentation. Such costs cover the program manager and his administrative staff; marketing; contracts; procurement; configuration management; logistics management; data management; etc. Management functions relate to C_{RR}, C_{RE}, C_{RT}, and C_{RD}.
Advanced research and development (C_{RR})	$C_{RR} = \sum_{i=1}^{N} C_{RR_i}$ $C_{RR_i} =$ cost of specific activity i $N =$ number of activities	Advanced research includes conceptual/feasibility studies conducted to determine and/or justify a need for a specific requirement. This includes effort oriented to defining mission scenarios, system operational requirements, preliminary maintenance concept, etc., accomplished early in a program.

Category		Description
Engineering design (C_{RE})	$$C_{RE} = \sum_{i=1}^{N} C_{RE_i}$$ C_{RE_i} = cost of specific design activity i N = number of design activities	Includes all initial design effort associated with system/equipment definition and development. Specific areas include system engineering; design engineering (electrical, mechanical, drafting); reliability and maintainability engineering; human factors; functional analysis and allocation; logistic support analysis; components; producibility; standardization; safety; etc. Design associated with modifications is covered in C_{ON}.
Equipment development and test (C_{RT})	$$C_{RT} = \left[C_{RDL} + C_{RDM} + \sum_{i=1}^{N} C_{RDT_i} \right]$$ C_{RDL} = cost of prototype fabrication and assembly labor C_{RDM} = cost of prototype material C_{RDT_i} = cost of test operations and support associated with specific test i N = number of identifiable tests	The fabrication, assembly, test and evaluation of engineering prototype models (in support of engineering design activity—C_{RE}) is included herein. Specifically, this constitutes fabrication and assembly; instrumentation; quality control and inspection; material procurement and handling; logistic support (personnel, training, spares, facilities, support equipment, etc.); data collection; and evaluation of prototypes. Initial logistic support for operational system/equipment is covered in C_{IL}.
Engineering data (C_{RD})	$$C_{RD} = \sum_{i=1}^{N} C_{RD_i}$$ C_{RD_i} = cost of specific data N = number of data items	This category includes the preparation, printing, publication, and distribution of all data/documentation associated with C_{RM}, C_{RE}, and C_{RT}, C_{RR}. This covers program plans; R and D reports; design data; test plans and reports; analyses; preliminary operational and maintenance procedures; and all effort related to a specific documentation requirement.
Investment (C_I)	$$C_I = [C_{IM} + C_{IC} + C_{IL}]$$ C_{IM} = system/equipment manufacturing cost C_{IC} = system construction cost C_{IL} = cost of initial logistic support	Includes all costs associated with the acquisition of systems/equipment (once that design and development has been completed). Specifically this covers manufacturing (recurring and nonrecurring); manufacturing management; system construction; and initial logistic support.

TABLE B.1 Description of Cost Categories (continued)

Cost Category (Reference Figure B–1)	Method of Determination (Quantitative Expression)	Cost Category Description and Justification
Manufacturing (C_{IM})	$C_{IM} = [C_{IN} + C_{IR}]$ C_{IN} = nonrecurring manufacturing cost C_{IR} = recurring manufacturing cost	This covers all recurring and nonrecurring costs associated with the production and test of multiple quantities of prime systems/equipments. Facility construction, capital equipment, and facility maintenance are covered under C_{IC}.
Nonrecurring manufacturing cost (C_{IN})	$C_{IN} = \left[C_{INM} + C_{INT} + C_{INA} + C_{INP} \right.$ $\left. + \sum_{i=1}^{N} C_{INQ} + \sum_{j=1}^{N} C_{INS} \right]$ C_{INM} = manufacturing engineering cost C_{INT} = tools and factory test equipment cost (excluding capital equipment) C_{INA} = quality assurance cost C_{INP} = manufacturing management cost C_{INQ} = cost of qualification test i C_{INS} = cost of production sampling test j N = number of individual tests	Includes all fixed *nonrecurring* costs associated with the production and test of operational systems/equipment. Specifically, this covers manufacturing management; manufacturing engineering; initial tooling and factory test equipment; quality assurance; first article qualification test (reliability test, maintainability demonstration, support equipment compatibility, technical data verification, personnel test and evaluation, interchangeability, environmental test) and related support; production sampling tests and related support. Logistic support for each individual qualification and sampling test is included in the cost of the individual test.
Recurring manufacturing cost (C_{IR})	$C_{IR} = [C_{IRE} + C_{IRL} + C_{IRM} + C_{IRI} + C_{IRT}]$ C_{IRE} = recurring manufacturing engineering support cost C_{IRL} = production fabrication and assembly labor cost C_{IRM} = production material and inventory cost	This category covers all *recurring* production costs to include fabrication; subassembly and assembly; material and inventory control; inspection and test; packing and shipping to the point of first destination. Sustaining engineering support required on a recurring basis is also included. Costs are associated with the produc-

	C_{IRI} = inspection and test cost C_{IRT} = packing and initial transportation cost	tion of prime equipment. Operational test and support equipment, training equipment, and spare/repair parts material costs are included in C_{IL}. Manufacturing management cost is included in C_{IN}.
Construction cost (C_{IC})	$C_{IC} = [C_{ICP} + C_{ICT} + C_{ICO} + C_{ICM}]$ C_{ICP} = manufacturing facilities cost C_{ICT} = test facilities cost C_{ICO} = operational facilities acquisition cost C_{ICM} = maintenance facilities acquisition cost For each item, one should consider the following. $C_{IC} = [C_{ICA} + C_{ICB} + C_{ICU} + C_{ICC}]$ C_{ICA} = construction labor cost C_{ICB} = construction material cost C_{ICU} = cost of utilities C_{ICC} = capital equipment cost	Includes all initial acquisition costs associated with manufacturing, test, operational and/or maintenance facilities (real property, plant, and equipment), and utilities (gas, electric power, water, telephone, heat, air conditioning, etc.). Facility costs cover the development of new building projects, the modification of existing facilities, and/or the occupancy of existing facilities without modification. Work areas plus family housing are considered. Category costs include preliminary surveys; real estate; building constructions; roads and pavement; railroad sidings; etc. Cost items include construction labor, construction material, capital equipment, and utility installation. (a) Manufacturing facilities support the operations described in C_{IM}, C_{IN}, C_{IR}. Initial and sustaining costs are included. (b) Test facilities cover any peculiar requirements (beyond that covered under existing categories) for evaluation test. (c) Operational facilities are required for system operation throughout its life cycle. Sustaining costs are covered in C_{OOF}. (d) Maintenance facilities are required to support the maintenance needs of the system throughout its life cycle. Sustaining costs are covered in C_{OMF}.

TABLE B.1 Description of Cost Categories (continued)

Cost Category (Reference Figure B-1)	Method of Determination (Quantitative Expression)	Cost Category Description and Justification
Initial logistic support cost (C_{IL})	$C_{IL} = [C_{ILM} + C_{ILP} + C_{ILS} + C_{ILI} + C_{ILD} + C_{ILT} + C_{ILX} + C_{ILY}]$ C_{ILM} = logistic program management cost C_{ILP} = cost of provisioning C_{ILS} = initial spare/repair part material cost C_{ILI} = initial inventory management cost C_{ILD} = cost of technical data preparation C_{ILT} = cost of initial training and training equipment C_{ILX} = acquisition cost of operational test and support equipment C_{ILY} = initial transportation and handling cost	Includes all integrated logistic support planning and control functions associated with the development of system support requirements, and the transition of such requirements from supplier(s) to the applicable operational site. Elements cover (a) Logistic program management cost—management, control, reporting, corrective action system, budgeting, planning, etc. (b) Provisioning cost—preparation of data which is needed for the procurement of spare/repair parts and test and support equipment. (c) Initial spare/repair part material cost—spares material stocked at the various inventory points to support the maintenance needs of prime equipment, test and support equipment, and training equipment. Replenishment spares are covered in C_{OMX}. (d) Initial inventory management cost—cataloging, listing, coding, etc., of spares entering the inventory. (e) Technical data preparation cost—development of operating and maintenance instructions, test procedures, maintenance cards, tapes, etc. Also includes reliability and maintainability data, test data, etc., covering production and test operations. (f) Initial training and training equipment cost—design and development of training equipment, training aids/data, and the

training of personnel initially assigned to operate and maintain the prime equipment, test and support equipment, and training equipment. Personnel training costs include instructor time; supervision; student pay and allowances; training facilities; and student transportation. Training accomplished on a sustaining basis throughout the system life cycle (due to personnel attrition) is covered in C_{OOT} and C_{OMP}.

(g) Test and support equipment acquisition cost—design, development, and acquisition of test and support equipment plus handling equipment needed to operate and maintain prime equipment in the field. The maintenance of test and support equipment throughout the system life cycle is covered in C_{ODE} and C_{OMS}.

(h) Initial transportation and handling cost (first destination transportation of logistic support elements from supplier to the applicable operational site).

Initial facility costs are identified in C_{IC}.

Specific logistic support requirements are defined in the Logistic Support Analysis (LSA) accomplished during engineering design.

Operations and maintenance cost (C_O)	$C_O = [C_{OO} + C_{OM} + C_{ON} + C_{OP}]$ C_{OO} = cost of system/equipment life-cycle operations C_{OM} = cost of system/equipment life-cycle maintenance C_{ON} = cost of system/equipment modifications C_{OP} = cost of system/equipment phaseout and disposal	Includes all costs associated with the operation and maintenance support of the system throughout its life cycle subsequent to equipment delivery in the field. Specific categories cover the cost of system operation, maintenance, sustaining logistic support, equipment modifications, and system/equipment phaseout and disposal. Costs are generally determined for each year throughout life cycle.

TABLE B.1 Description of Cost Categories (continued)

Cost Category (Reference Figure B-1)	Method of Determination (Quantitative Expression)	Cost Category Description and Justification
Operation cost (C_{OO})	$C_{OO} = [C_{OOP} + C_{OOT} + C_{OOF} + C_{OOE}]$ C_{OOP} = operating personnel cost C_{OOT} = cost of operator training C_{OOF} = cost of operational facilities C_{OOE} = cost of support and handling equipment	Includes all costs associated with the actual operation (not maintenance) of the system throughout its life cycle. Specific categories cover the costs of system/equipment operational personnel (system operator); the formal training of operators; operational facilities; and support and handling equipment necessary for system operation.
Operating personnel cost (C_{OOP})	$C_{OOP} = [(T_O)(C_{PO})(Q_{PO})(N_{PO}) \times$ (% allocation)] T_O = hours of system operation C_{PO} = cost of operator labor Q_{PO} = quantity of operators/system N_{PO} = number of operating systems	This category covers the costs of operating personnel as allocated to the system. A single operator may operate more than one system, but costs should be allocated on an individual system basis. Such costs include base pay or salary and allowances; fringe benefits (insurance, medical, retirement); travel; clothing allowances; etc. Both direct and overhead costs are included.
Operator training cost (C_{OOT})	$C_{OOT} = [(Q_{SO})(T_T)(C_{TOP})]$ Q_{SO} = quantity of student operators T_T = duration of training program (weeks) C_{TOP} = cost of operator training ($/student week)	Initial operator training is included in C_{ILT}. This category covers the *formal* training of personnel assigned to operate the system. Such training is accomplished on a periodic basis throughout the system life cycle to cover personnel replacements due to attrition. Total costs include instructor time; supervision; student pay and allowances while in school; training facilities (allocation of portion of facility required specifically for formal training); training aids, equipment, and data; and student transportation as applicable.

Cost category	Quantitative expressions	Description
Operational facilities cost (C_{OOF})	$C_{OOF} = [(C_{PPE} + C_U)(\% \text{ allocation}) \times (N_{OS})]$ C_{PPE} = cost of operational facility support (\$/site) C_U = cost of utilities (\$/site) N_{OS} = number of operational sites *Alternate Approach* $C_{OOF} = [(C_{PPF})(N_{OS})(S_O)]$ C_{PPF} = cost of operational facility space (\$/square foot/site); utility cost allocation is included S_O = facility space requirements (square feet)	Initial acquisition cost for operational facilities is included in C_{ICO}. This category covers the annual recurring costs associated with the occupancy and maintenance (repair, paint, etc.) of operational facilities throughout the system life cycle. Utility costs are also included. Facility and utility costs are proportionately allocated to each system.
Support and handling equipment cost (C_{OOE})	$C_{OOE} = [C_{OOO} + C_{OOU} + C_{OOS}]$ C_{OOO} = cost of operation C_{OOU} = cost of equipment corrective maintenance C_{OOS} = cost of equipment preventive maintenance $C_{OOU} = [(Q_{CA})M_{MHC})(C_{OCP}) + (Q_{CA})(C_{MHC}) + (Q_{CA})(C_{DC})](N_{OS})$ Q_{CA} = quantity of corrective maintenance actions (M_A); Q_{CA} is a function of (T_O)(λ) M_{MHC} = corrective maintenance labor hours/M_A C_{OCP} = corrective maintenance labor cost (\$/M_{MHC}) C_{MHC} = cost of material handling/corrective M_A C_{DC} = cost of corrective/maintenance documentation/M_A N_{OS} = number of operational sites	Initial acquisition cost for operational support and handling equipment is covered in C_{ILX}. This category includes the annual recurring usage and maintenance costs for those items which are required to support system operation throughout the life cycle (e.g., launchers, dollies, vehicles, etc.). The costs specifically cover equipment operation (not covered elsewhere); equipment corrective maintenance; and preventive maintenance. Spares and consumables are included in C_{OMX}. Corrective and preventive maintenance requirements are derived from the Logistic Support Analysis (LSA).

TABLE B.1 Description of Cost Categories (continued)

Cost Category (Reference Figure B-1)	Method of Determination (Quantitative Expression)	Cost Category Description and Justification
	$C_{OOS} = [(Q_{PA})(M_{MHP})(C_{OPP}) + (Q_{PA})(C_{MPH}) + (Q_{PA})(C_{DP})(N_{OS})$ Q_{PA} = quantity of preventive maintenance actions (M_A). Q_{PA} relates to fpt M_{MHP} = preventive maintenance man-hours/M_A C_{OPP} = preventive maintenance labor cost (\$/M_{MHP}) C_{MHP} = cost of material handling/preventive M_A C_{DP} = cost of preventive maintenance documentation/M_A N_{OS} = number of operational sites	
Maintenance cost (C_{OM})	$C_{OM} = [C_{OMM} + C_{OMX} + C_{OMS} + C_{OMT} + C_{OMP} + C_{OMF} + C_{OMD}]$ C_{OMM} = maintenance personnel and support cost C_{OMX} = cost of spare/repair parts C_{OMS} = test and support equipment maintenance cost C_{OMT} = transportation and handling cost C_{OMF} = cost of maintenance facilities C_{OMD} = cost of technical data	Includes all sustaining maintenance labor, spare/repair parts, test and support equipment, transportation and handling, replenishment training, support data, and facilities necessary to meet the maintenance needs of the prime equipment throughout its life cycle. Such needs include both corrective and preventive maintenance requirements at all echelons—organizational, intermediate, depot, and factory.
Maintenance personnel and support cost (C_{OMM})	$C_{OMM} = [C_{OOU} + C_{OOS}]$ C_{OOU} = cost of equipment corrective maintenance	Includes corrective and preventive maintenance labor, associated material handling, and supporting documentation. When a system/

	C_{OOS} = cost of equipment preventive maintenance Total cost is the sum of the C_{OMM} values for each echelon of maintenance.	equipment malfunction occurs or when a scheduled maintenance action is performed, personnel manhours are expended, the handling of spares and related material takes place, and maintenance action reports are completed. This category includes all directly related costs.
Corrective maintenance cost (C_{OOU})	$C_{OOU} = [(Q_{CA})(M_{MHC})(C_{OCP}) + (Q_{CA})(C_{MHC}) + (Q_{CA})(C_{DC})](N_{MS})$ Q_{CA} = quantity of corrective maintenance actions (M_A); $Q_{CA} = (T_O)(\lambda)$ M_{MHC} = corrective maintenance labor hours/M_A C_{OCP} = corrective maintenance labor cost (\$/M_{MHC}) C_{MHC} = cost of material handling/corrective M_A C_{DC} = cost of documentation/corrective M_A N_{MS} = number of maintenance sites Determine C_{OOU} for each appropriate echelon of maintenance.	This category includes the personnel activity costs associated with the accomplishment of corrective maintenance. Related spares, test and support equipment, transportation, training, and facility costs are covered in C_{OMX}, C_{OMS}, C_{OMT}, and C_{OMP}, respectively. Total cost includes the sum of individual costs for each maintenance action multiplied by the quantity of maintenance actions anticipated over the entire system life cycle. A maintenance action includes any requirement for corrective maintenance resulting from catastrophic failures, dependent failures, operator/maintenance induced faults, manufacturing defects, etc. The cost per maintenance action considers the personnel labor expended for direct tasks (localization, fault isolation, remove and replace, repair, verification), associated administrative/logistic delay time, material handling, and maintenance documentation (failure reports, spares issue reports). The corrective maintenance labor cost, C_{OCP}, will of course vary with the personnel skill level required for task performance. Both direct labor and overhead costs are included.

TABLE B.1 Description of Cost Categories (continued)

Cost Category (Reference Figure B-1)	Method of Determination (Quantitative Expression)	Cost Category Description and Justification
Preventive maintenance cost (C_{OOS})	$C_{OOS} = [(Q_{PA})(M_{MHP})(C_{OPP}) + (Q_{PA})(C_{MHP}) + (Q_{PA})(C_{DP})](N_{MS})$ Q_{PA} = quantity of preventive maintenance actions (M_A); Q_{PA} relates to fpt M_{MHP} = preventive maintenance labor hours/M_A C_{OPP} = preventive maintenance labor cost ($\$/M_{MHP}$) C_{MHP} = cost of material handling/ preventive M_A C_{DP} = cost of documentation/ preventive M_A N_{MS} = number of maintenance sites Determine C_{OOS} for each appropriate echelon of maintenance.	This category includes the personnel activity costs associated with the accomplishment of preventive or scheduled maintenance. Related spares/consumables, test and support equipment, transportation, training, and facility costs are covered in C_{OMX}, C_{OMS}, C_{OMT}, and C_{OMF}, respectively. Total cost includes the sum of individual costs for each preventive maintenance action multiplied by the quantity of maintenance actions anticipated over the system life cycle. A maintenance action includes servicing, lubrication, inspection, overhaul, calibration, periodic system check-outs, and the accomplishment of scheduled critical item replacements. The cost per maintenance action considers the personnel labor expended for preventive maintenance tasks, associated administrative/ logistic delay time, material handling, and maintenance documentation. The preventive maintenance labor cost, C_{OPP}, will of course vary with the personnel skill level required for task performance. Both direct labor and overhead costs are included.
Spare/repair parts cost (C_{OMX})	$C_{OMX} = [C_{SO} + C_{SI} + C_{SD} + C_{SS} + C_{SC}]$ C_{SO} = cost of organizational spare/ repair parts C_{SI} = cost of intermediate spare/repair parts	Initial spare/repair part costs are covered in C_{ILS}. This category includes all replenishment spare/repair parts and consumable materials (eg., oil, lubricants, fuel, etc.) that are required to support maintenance activities associated

		with prime equipment, operational support and handling equipment (C_{OOE}), test and support equipment (C_{OMS}), and training equipment at each echelon (organizational, intermediate, depot, supplier). This category covers the cost of purchasing; the actual cost of the material itself; and the cost of holding or maintaining items in the inventory. Costs are assigned to the applicable level of maintenance. Specific quantitative requirements for spares (Q_M) are derived from the Logistic Support Analysis (LSA). The optimum quantity of purchase orders (Q_A) is based on EOQ criteria. Support equipment spares are based on the same criteria used in determining spare part requirements for prime equipment.
	C_{SD} = cost of depot spare/repair parts C_{SS} = cost of supplier spare/repair parts C_{SC} = cost of consumables $$C_{SO} = \sum_{N_{MS}} [(C_A)(Q_A) + \sum_{i=1}(C_{Mi})(Q_{Mi}) + \sum_{i=1}(C_{Hi})(Q_{Hi})]$$ C_A = average cost of material purchase order ($/order) Q_A = quantity of purchase orders C_M = cost of spare item i Q_M = quantity of i items required or demand C_H = cost of maintaining spare item i in the inventory ($/\$ value of the inventory) Q_H = quantity of i items in the inventory N_{MS} = number of maintenance sites C_{SI}, C_{SD}, and C_{SS} are determined in a similar manner.	
Test and support equipment cost (C_{OMS})	$C_{OMS} = [C_{SEO} + C_{SEI} + C_{SED}]$ C_{SEO} = cost of organizational test and support equipment C_{SEI} = cost of intermediate test and support equipment C_{SED} = cost of depot test and support equipment $C_{SEO} = [C_{OOU} + C_{OOS}]$ C_{OOU} = cost of equipment corrective maintenance C_{OOS} = cost of equipment preventive maintenance	Initial acquisition cost for test and support equipment is covered in C_{ILX}. This category includes the annual recurring life-cycle maintenance cost for test and support equipment at each echelon. Support equipment operational costs are actually covered by the tasks peformed in C_{OMM}. Maintenance constitutes both corrective and preventive maintenance, and the costs are derived on a similar basis with prime equipment (C_{OOU} and C_{OOS}). Spares and consumables are included in C_{OMX}. In some instances, specific items of test and sup-

TABLE B.1 Description of Cost Categories (continued)

Cost Category (Reference Figure B–1)	Method of Determination (Quantitative Expression)	Cost Category Description and Justification
	$C_{OOU} = [(Q_{CA})(M_{MHC})(C_{OCP}) + (Q_{CA})(C_{MHC}) + (Q_{CA})(C_{DC})](N_{MS})$	port equipment are utilized for more than one (1) system, and in such cases, associated costs are allocated proportionately to each system concerned.
	$Q_{CA} = $ quantity of corrective maintenance actions (M_A) or	
	$Q_{CA} = (T_O)(\lambda)$	
	$M_{MHC} = $ corrective maintenance labor hours$/M_A$	
	$C_{OCP} = $ corrective maintenance labor cost $(\$/M_{MHC})$	
	$C_{MHC} = $ cost of material handling/corrective M_A	
	$C_{DC} = $ cost of documentation/corrective M_A	
	$N_{MS} = $ number of maintenance sites (involving organizational maintenance)	
	$C_{OOS} = [(Q_{PA})(M_{MHP})(C_{OPP}) + (Q_{PA})(C_{MHP}) + (Q_{PA})(C_{DP})](N_{MS})$	
	$Q_{PA} = $ quantity of preventive maintenance actions (M_A); $Q_{PA} = $ fpt	
	$M_{MHP} = $ preventive maintenance labor hours$/M_A$	
	$C_{OPP} = $ preventive maintenance labor cost $(\$/M_{MHP})$	
	$C_{MHP} = $ cost of material handling/preventive M_A	
	$C_{DP} = $ cost of documentation/preventive M_A	

	N_{MS} = number of maintenance sites (involving organizational maintenance) C_{SEI} and C_{SED} are determined in a similar manner.	Initial (first destination) transportation and handling costs are covered in C_{ILY}. This category includes all sustaining transportation and handling (or packing and shipping) between organizational, intermediate, depot, and supplier facilities in support of maintenance operations. This includes the return of faulty material items to a higher echelon; the transportation of items to a higher echelon for preventive maintenance (overhaul, calibration); and the shipment of spare/repair parts, personnel, data, etc., from the supplier to forward echelons.
Transportation and handling cost (C_{OMT})	$C_{OMT} = [(C_T)(Q_T) + (C_P)(Q_T)]$ C_T = cost of transportation C_P = cost of packing Q_T = quantity of one-way shipments $C_T = [(W)(C_{TS})]$ W = weight of item (lb) C_{TS} = shipping cost ($/lb) C_{TS} will of course vary with the distance (in miles) of the one-way shipment. $C_P = [(W)(C_{TP})]$ C_{TP} = packing cost ($/lbs) Packing cost and weight will vary depending on whether reusable containers are employed.	
Maintenance training cost (C_{OMP})	$C_{OMP} = [(Q_{SM})(T_T)(C_{TOM})]$ Q_{SM} = quantity of maintenance students C_{TOM} = cost of maintenance training ($/student-week) T_T = duration of training program (weeks)	Initial maintenance training cost is included in C_{ILT}. This category covers the *formal* training of personnel assigned to maintain the prime equipment, test and support equipment, and training equipment. Such training is accomplished on a periodic basis throughout the system life cycle to cover personnel replacements due to attrition. Total costs include instructor time; supervision; student pay and allowances while in school; training facilities (allocation of portion of facility required specifically for formal training); training aids and data; and student transportation as applicable.

348

TABLE B.1 Description of Cost Categories (continued)

Cost Category (Reference Figure B–1)	Method of Determination (Quantitative Expression)	Cost Category Description and Justification
Maintenance facilities cost (C_{OMF})	$C_{OMF} = [(C_{PPM} + C_U) \times (\% \text{ allocation})(N_{MS})]$ $C_{PPM} = $ cost of utilities (\$/site) $C_U = $ cost of utilities (\$/site) $N_{MS} = $ number of maintenance sites *Alternate Approach* $C_{OMF} = [(C_{PPO})(N_{MS})(S_O)]$ $C_{PPO} = $ cost of maintenance facility space (\$/square foot/site); utility cost allocation is included $S_O = $ facility space requirements (square feet) Determine C_{OMF} for each appropriate echelon of maintenance.	Initial acquisition (construction) cost for maintenance facilities is included in C_{ICM}. This category covers the annual recurring costs associated with the occupancy and support (repair, modification, paint, etc.) of maintenance shops at all echelons throughout the system life cycle. On some occasions, a given maintenance shop will support more than one (1) system, and in such cases, associated costs are allocated proportionately to each system concerned.
Technical data cost (C_{OMD})	$C_{OMD} = \sum_{i=1}^{N} C_{OMDi}$ $C_{OMDi} = $ cost of specific data item i $N = $ number of data items	Initial technical data preparation costs are covered in C_{ILD}. Individual data reports covering specific maintenance actions are included in C_{OOE}, C_{OMM}, and C_{OMS}. This category includes any other data (developed on a sustaining basis) necessary to support the operation and maintenance of the system throughout its life cycle.
System/equipment modification cost (C_{ON})	$C_{ON} = \sum_{i=1}^{N} C_{ONi}$ $C_{ONi} = $ cost of specific modification i $N = $ number of system/equipment modifications	Throughout the system life cycle after equipment has been delivered in the field, modifications are often proposed and initiated to improve system performance, effectiveness, or a combination of both. This category includes

		modification kit design (R&D); material; installation and test instructions; personnel and supporting resources for incorporating the modification kit; technical data change documentation; formal training (as required) to cover the new configuration; spares; etc. The modification may affect all elements of logistics.
System phase-out and disposal cost (C_{OP})	$C_{OP} = [(F_C)(Q_{CA})(C_{DIS} - C_{REC})]$ F_C = condemnation factor Q_{CA} = quantity of corrective maintenance actions C_{DIS} = cost of system/equipment disposal C_{REC} = reclamation value	This category covers the liability or assets incurred when an item is condemned or disposed. This factor is applicable throughout the system/equipment life cycle when phaseout occurs. This category represents the only element of cost that may turn out to have a negative value—resulting when the reclamation value of the end item is larger than the disposal cost.

TABLE B.2 Summary of Terms

C	Total system life-cycle cost
C_A	Average cost of material purchase order (\$/order)
C_{DC}	Cost of maintenance documentation/data for each corrective maintenance action (\$/M_A)
C_{DIS}	Cost of system/equipment disposal
C_{DP}	Cost of maintenance documentation/data for each preventive maintenance action (\$/M_A)
C_H	Cost of maintaining spare item i in the inventory or inventory holding cost (\$/dollar value of the inventory)
C_I	Total investment cost
C_{IC}	Construction cost
C_{ICA}	Construction fabrication labor cost
C_{ICB}	Construction material cost
C_{ICC}	Capital equipment cost
C_{ICM}	Maintenance facilities acquisition cost
C_{ICO}	Operational facilities acquisition cost
C_{ICP}	Manufacturing facilities cost (acquisition and sustaining)
C_{ICT}	Test facilities cost (acquisition and sustaining)
C_{ICU}	Cost of utilities
C_{IL}	Initial logistic support cost
C_{ILD}	Cost of technical data preparation
C_{ILI}	Initial inventory management cost
C_{ILM}	Logistics program management cost
C_{ILP}	Cost of provisioning (preparation of procurement data covering spares, test and support equipment, etc.)
C_{ILS}	Initial spare/repair part material cost
C_{ILT}	Cost of initial training and training equipment
C_{ILX}	Acquisition cost of operational test and support equipment
C_{ILY}	Initial transportation and handling cost
C_{IM}	Manufacturing cost
C_{IN}	Nonrecurring manufacturing/production cost
C_{INA}	Quality assurance cost
C_{INM}	Manufacturing engineering cost
C_{INP}	Manufacturing management cost
C_{INQ}	Cost of qualification test (first article)
C_{INS}	Cost of production sampling test
C_{INT}	Tools and factory equipment cost (excluding capital equipment)
C_{IR}	Recurring manufacturing/production cost
C_{IRE}	Recurring manufacturing engineering support cost
C_{IRI}	Inspection and test cost
C_{IRL}	Production fabrication and assembly labor cost
C_{IRM}	Production material and inventory cost
C_{IRT}	Packing and initial transportation cost
C_M	Cost of spares item i
C_{MHC}	Cost of material handling for each corrective maintenance action (\$/M_A)
C_{MHP}	Cost of material handling for each preventive maintenance action (\$/M_A)
C_O	Operations and maintenance cost
C_{OCP}	Corrective maintenance labor cost (\$/M_{MHC})
C_{OM}	Cost of system/equipment life-cycle maintenance

TABLE B.2 Summary of Terms (continued)

C_{OMD}	Cost of technical data
C_{OMF}	Cost of maintenance facilities
C_{OMM}	Maintenance personnel cost
C_{OMP}	Cost of replenishment maintenance training
C_{OMS}	Test and support equipment maintenance cost
C_{OMT}	Transportation and handling cost
C_{OMX}	Spare/repair parts cost (replenishment spares)
C_{ON}	Cost of system/equipment modifications
C_{OO}	Cost of system/equipment life-cycle operations
C_{OOE}	Cost of support and handling equipment
C_{OOF}	Cost of operational facilities
C_{OOO}	Cost of operation for support and handling equipment
C_{OOP}	Operating personnel cost
C_{OOS}	Cost of equipment preventive (scheduled) maintenance
C_{OOT}	Cost of replenishment training
C_{OOU}	Cost of equipment corrective (unscheduled) maintenance
C_{OP}	Cost of system/equipment phase-out and disposal
C_{OPP}	Preventive maintenance labor cost ($\$/M_{MHP}$)
C_P	Cost of packing
C_{PO}	Cost of operators labor ($\$$/hour)
C_{PPE}	Cost of operational facility support ($\$$/operational site)
C_{PPF}	Cost of operational facility space ($\$$/square foot/site)
C_{PPM}	Cost of maintenance facility support ($\$$/maintenance site)
C_{PPO}	Cost of maintenance facility space ($\$$/square foot/site)
C_R	Total research and development cost
C_{RD}	Engineering data cost
C_{RDL}	Prototype fabrication and assembly labor cost
C_{RDM}	Prototype material cost
C_{RDT}	Prototype test and evaluation cost
C_{RE}	Engineering design cost
C_{REC}	Reclamation value
C_{RM}	Program management cost
C_{RR}	Advanced research and development cost
C_{RT}	Equipment development and test cost
C_{SC}	Cost of consumables
C_{SD}	Cost of depot spare/repair parts
C_{SED}	Cost of depot test and support equipment
C_{SEI}	Cost of intermediate test and support equipment
C_{SEO}	Cost of organizational test and support equipment
C_{SI}	Cost of intermediate spare/repair parts
C_{SO}	Cost of organizational spare/repair parts
C_{SS}	Cost of supplier spare/repair parts
C_T	Cost of transportation
C_{TOM}	Cost of maintenance training ($\$$/student week)
C_{TOT}	Cost of operator training ($\$$/student week)
C_{TP}	Packing cost ($\$$/pound)
C_{TS}	Shipping cost ($\$$/pound)
C_U	Cost of utilities ($\$$/operational site)
fc	Condemnation factor (attrition)
fpt	Frequency of preventive maintenance (actions/hour of equipment operation)

TABLE B.2 Summary of Terms (continued)

λ	System/equipment failure rate (failure/hour of equipment operation)
M_{MHC}	Corrective maintenance hours/maintenance action (MA)
M_{MHP}	Preventive maintenance hours/maintenance action (MA)
N_{MS}	Number of maintenance sites
N_{OS}	Number of operational sites
N_{PO}	Number of operating systems
Q_A	Quantity of purchase orders
Q_{CA}	Quantity of corrective maintenance actions (MA)
Q_H	Quantity of i items in the inventory
Q_M	Quantity of i items required or demanded
Q_{PA}	Quantity of preventive maintenance actions (MA)
Q_{PO}	Quantity of operators/system
Q_{SM}	Quantity of maintenance students
Q_{SO}	Quantity of student operators
Q_T	Quantity of one-way shipments
S_O	Facility space requirements (square feet)
T_O	Hours of system operation
T_T	Duration of training program (weeks)
W	Weight of item (pounds)

C

Selected Definitions and Formulas

The majority of terms and definitions considered necessary for an understanding of the principles and concepts of life-cycle costing are included throughout this book. However, there are a few definitions that need some expansion, particularly in view of their relevance to life-cycle costing. The purpose here is to briefly expand in the areas of system effectiveness, reliability, maintainability, logistics, and so on. It is anticipated that a review of this material will facilitate an understanding of some of the key assumptions on which life-cycle cost estimates are based. This list is not intended to be all-inclusive.

C.1 SYSTEM EFFECTIVENESS

System effectiveness may be defined as the probability that a system or product can successfully meet an overall operational demand within a given time when operated under specified conditions. An alternative meaning pertains to the capability of a system to do the job for which it was intended. System effectiveness related to the ability of a system to fulfill a defined need and is a function of performance, capacity, availability, readiness, reliability, maintainability, supportability, dependability, and so on. System effectiveness, or some element thereof, is often related with life-cycle cost in the evaluation of systems or products.

C.2 RELIABILITY

Reliability is the probability that a product or system will operate in a satisfactory manner for a specified period of time when used under stated conditions. When related to the fulfillment of a given need, reliability may be defined as the probability of successfully meeting that need under specified use conditions. Reliability, sometimes equated to the probability of survival, may be determined from the equation

$$R = e^{-\lambda t} \tag{C.1}$$

where e is the Napierian or natural logarithm base (2.7183), λ is the failure rate in failures per hour ($\lambda = 1/\text{MTBF}$), and t is the total operating time in hours.

Reliability is usually related to the exponential function as illustrated in Figure C.1. Assuming that an item has a constant failure rate (λ), the reliability can be determined from the exponential distribution curve. Test and field data covering a variety of items have indicated that if the design of a system/product is mature, the failure rate (λ) is *relatively* constant throughout a defined period of the system's operational life. In addition, when an item is first produced and introduced into the field, there are usually more failures during a debugging period. Similarly, when an item reaches a certain age, there is a wear-out period when failures tend to increase. A typical failure rate curve is depicted in Figure C.2. However, it should be noted that this curve may vary considerably depending on the type of system, the operating conditions of the system, whether system modifications are introduced, and so on.

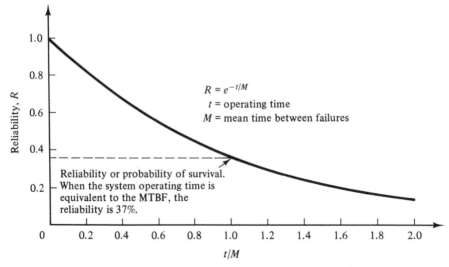

Figure C.1   Basic reliability function.

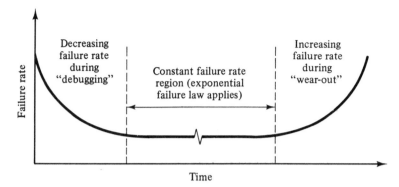

Figure C.2   Typical failure rate function.

The curve in Figure C.2 represents a *relative* set of conditions. Reliability, which is often expressed in terms of MTBF, basically reflects the frequency of unscheduled maintenance (i.e., $MTBM_u$). As such, this factor is a *major* parameter in determining O&S costs in life-cycle cost analyses. The analyst must acquire a basic knowledge of reliability if he or she is to accomplish life-cycle costing objectives. Additional sources covering reliability are indicated in the selected bibliography of Appendix E.

C.3 MAINTAINABILITY

Maintainability is an inherent characteristic of equipment design in installation which is concerned with the ease, economy, safety and accuracy in the performance of maintenance actions (i.e., scheduled and unscheduled maintenance). It is concerned with maintenance times, supportability characteristics in system/product design, and maintenance costs. Maintainability is the *ability* of a piece of equipment to be maintained, versus maintenance which constitutes a series of actions to be taken to restore or retain an item in a satisfactory operational state. Maintainability is a design parameter and maintenance is a result of design. Thus maintainability has a significant impact on life-cycle cost, particularly operation and support (O&S) cost. If the system/product design is not maintainable, the logistics support resources required in the accomplishment of maintenance actions are extensive, which, in turn, is costly. On the other hand, a prime objective in the design for maintainability is to minimize logistics support resource requirements in the event that maintenance actions are required.

Maintainability can also be defined in a more limited sense as "a characteristic of design and installation which is expressed as a probability that an item will be retained in or restored to a specified condition within a given period of time when maintenance is performed in accordance with prescribed procedures and resources." (Refer to MIL-STD-721, "Definition of Effectiveness Terms for Reliability, Maintainability, Human Factors, and Safety.") Maintainability can be specified, predicted, and measured. The primary measures of maintainability are in terms of a combination of maintenance times, supportability factors, and projected maintenance costs. Those measures most commonly applicable in life-cycle cost analyses are described below.

1. *Mean time between maintenance (MTBM)* is a function of both scheduled and unscheduled maintenance, and represents the average time between all maintenance actions for a specified period or for the life cycle. MTBM includes consideration of reliability MTBF and MTBR, and is determined from the equation

$$\text{MTBM} = \frac{1}{1/\text{MTBM}_u + 1/\text{MTBM}_s} \tag{C.2}$$

where MTBM_u is the mean interval of unscheduled (corrective) maintenance and MTBM_s is the mean interval of scheduled (preventive) maintenance. MTBM_u must consider (a) inherent reliability characteristics, (b) manufacturing or process defects, (c) wear-out characteristics, (d) dependent or secondary failures resulting from a chain reaction, (e) operator-induced failures, (f) maintenance-induced failures, and (g) equipment damage due to handling. Idealistically, MTBM_u should generally be equivalent to the reliability MTBF factor. The reciprocal of MTBM is the frequency of maintenance, which is a significant factor in deriving O&S costs.

2. *Mean time between replacement* (MTBR) is the mean interval of time between item replacements due to either scheduled or unscheduled maintenance actions, and usually generates spare/repair part requirements. MTBR is not necessarily synonymous with MTBM_u or MTBF.

3. *Mean corrective maintenance time* ($\overline{\text{M}}\text{ct}$) is the mean elapsed time to complete the corrective maintenance cycle for all unscheduled maintenance actions. The corrective maintenance cycle is illustrated in Figure A.1. $\overline{\text{M}}\text{ct}$ is expressed in the equation

$$\overline{\text{M}}\text{ct} = \frac{\Sigma\,(\lambda_i)\,(\text{Mct}_i)}{\Sigma\,\lambda_i} \tag{C.3}$$

where λ_i is the failure rate of the individual (*i*th) element of the item being measured, generally expressed in failures per item operating hour, and Mct_i is the elapsed time to complete the maintenance cycle for each individual (*i*th) maintenance action. $\overline{\text{M}}\text{ct}$ considers only active maintenance time, or that time which is spent working directly on the system or product, and is the weighted average of the individual Mct_i values.

4. *Mean preventive maintenance time* ($\overline{\text{M}}\text{pt}$) is the mean (or average) elapsed time required to perform preventive or scheduled maintenance on an item. This may include servicing, inspection, calibration, and overhaul; and can be accomplished when the system/product is in full operation, or could result in downtime. $\overline{M}pt$, resulting in downtime, can be determined from the equation

$$\overline{M}pt = \frac{\Sigma\,(fpt_i)\,(Mpt_i)}{\Sigma\,fpt_i} \tag{C.4}$$

where fpt_i is the frequency of the individual (ith) preventive maintenance action, generally expressed in actions per item operating hour, and Mpt_i is the elapsed time required for the ith preventive maintenance action.

5. *Mean active maintenance time* $\overline{M}$ is the mean or average elapsed time required to perform scheduled (preventive) and unscheduled (corrective) maintenance. It excludes logistics supply and administrative delay time, and is expressed in the equation

$$\overline{M} = \frac{(\lambda)\,(\overline{M}ct) + (fpt)\,(\overline{M}pt)}{\lambda + fpt} \tag{C.5}$$

where λ is the corrective maintenance rate and fpt is the preventive maintenance rate.

6. *Maintenance downtime* (MDT) is the total elapsed time that a system/product is not operationally available or in use due to scheduled or unscheduled maintenance. MDT includes active maintenance time ($\overline{M}$), downtime due to logistics support delays, and downtime due to administration delays of one form or another. Logistic delay time is that portion of nonactive maintenance time during which maintenance is delayed solely because of not having a spare part available, the unavailability of test and support equipment, the unavailability of facilities, and so on. Administrative delay time (or waiting time) is that portion of nonactive maintenance time during which maintenance is delayed for reasons of an administrative nature (i.e., personnel assignment priority, inadequate manning, organization constraint, etc.).

C.4 LOGISTICS

Logistics is the art and science of management, engineering, and technical activities concerned with requirements, design, and supplying and maintaining resources to support objectives, plans, and operations. The elements of logistics support include personnel and training, test and support equipment, supply support (provisioning, spare/repair parts, distribution, warehousing, inventories, etc.), transportation and handling, facilities, and technical data.

The term *logistics* is often employed in manufacturing and commerce to describe the broad range of activities concerned with the efficient movement of finished products from the end of the production line to the consumer, and in some cases includes the movement of raw materials from the source of supply to the beginning of the production line. The elements of logistics in this context include material acquisition or procurement, inventory requirements, warehousing, packing and containerization, physical distribution, transportation and traffic management, customer service, and so on.

In essence, logistics involves a broad range of activities throughout program planning, design, test and evaluation, production or construction, and sustaining system/product support. The impact of logistics on life-cycle cost is significant, particularly relevant to production/construction costs and operation and support (O&S) costs.

Logistics support analysis is an iterative analytical process that is employed throughout the system life cycle to (a) aid in the initial determination and establishment of logistics support criteria that influence on the system/product design; (b) aid in the evaluation of various configurations in terms of the inherent supportability characteristics already incorporated in the system/product design; (c) aid in the identification and provisioning of the various logistics support elements required for system/product sustaining life cycle support; and (d) to aid in the final analysis of the system/product design to assess its total logistics support effectiveness. An output of the LSA is the identification and documentation of maintenance frequencies (i.e., scheduled and unscheduled maintenance actions), and the logistics support resource requirements when maintenance actions occur. Resource requirements include test and support equipment, supply support (spares and repair parts, inventory control and maintenance, etc.) maintenance personnel and training transportation and handling, maintenance facilities and warehouse, and technical data. The LSA often includes maintenance analyses and the evaluation of various alternative support policies, and the results of this effort constitutes a significant input into life-cycle cost analyses.

D

Interest Factor Tables

Tables D.1 to D.14, interest factors for annual compounding values for seven interest formulas derived in Chapter 3, are given for interest rates from 5 to 30%.[1]

[1] Tables D.1 to D.14 are reproduced from W. J. Fabrycky and G. J. Thuesen, *Economic Decision Analysis,* 2nd ed. (Englewood Cliffs, NJ: Prentice-Hall, Inc., 1980).

TABLE D.1 5% Interest Factors for Annual Compounding

	Single Payment		Equal-Payment Series				Uniform Gradient-Series Factor
	Compound-Amount Factor	Present-Worth Factor	Compound-Amount Factor	Sinking-Fund Factor	Present-Worth Factor	Capital-Recovery Factor	
n	To Find F Given P $F/P, i, n$	To Find P Given F $P/F, i, n$	To Find F Given A $F/A, i, n$	To Find A Given F $A/F, i, n$	To Find P Given A $P/A, i, n$	To Find A Given P $A/P, i, n$	To Find A Given G $A/G, i, n$
1	1.050	0.9524	1.000	1.0000	0.9524	1.0500	0.0000
2	1.103	0.9070	2.050	0.4878	1.8594	0.5378	0.4878
3	1.158	0.8638	3.153	0.3172	2.7233	0.3672	0.9675
4	1.216	0.8227	4.310	0.2320	3.5460	0.2820	1.4391
5	1.276	0.7835	5.526	0.1810	4.3295	0.2310	1.9025
6	1.340	0.7462	6.802	0.1470	5.0757	0.1970	2.3579
7	1.407	0.7107	8.142	0.1228	5.7864	0.1728	2.8052
8	1.477	0.6768	9.549	0.1047	6.4632	0.1547	3.2445
9	1.551	0.6446	11.027	0.0907	7.1078	0.1407	3.6758
10	1.629	0.6139	12.587	0.0795	7.7217	0.1295	4.0991
11	1.710	0.5847	14.207	0.0704	8.3064	0.1204	4.5145
12	1.796	0.5568	15.917	0.0628	8.8633	0.1128	4.9219
13	1.866	0.5303	17.713	0.0565	9.3936	0.1065	5.3215
14	1.980	0.5051	19.599	0.0510	9.8987	0.1010	5.7133
15	2.079	0.4810	21.579	0.0464	10.3797	0.0964	6.0973
16	2.183	0.4581	23.658	0.0423	10.8378	0.0923	6.4736
17	2.292	0.4363	25.840	0.0387	11.2741	0.0887	6.8423
18	2.407	0.4155	28.132	0.0356	11.6896	0.0856	7.2034
19	2.527	0.3957	30.539	0.0328	12.0853	0.0828	7.5569
20	2.653	0.3769	33.066	0.0303	12.4622	0.0803	7.9030
21	2.786	0.3590	35.719	0.0280	12.8212	0.0780	8.2416
22	2.925	0.3419	38.505	0.0260	13.1630	0.0760	8.5730
23	3.072	0.3256	41.430	0.0241	13.4886	0.0741	8.8971
24	3.225	0.3101	44.502	0.0225	13.7987	0.0725	9.2140
25	3.386	0.2953	47.727	0.0210	14.0940	0.0710	9.5238
26	3.556	0.2813	51.113	0.0196	14.3752	0.0696	9.8266
27	3.733	0.2679	54.669	0.0183	14.6430	0.0683	10.1224
28	3.920	0.2551	58.403	0.0171	14.8981	0.0671	10.4114
29	4.116	0.2430	62.323	0.0161	15.1411	0.0661	10.6936
30	4.322	0.2314	66.439	0.0151	15.3725	0.0651	10.9691
31	4.538	0.2204	70.761	0.0141	15.5928	0.0641	11.2381
32	4.765	0.2099	75.299	0.0133	15.8027	0.0633	11.5005
33	5.003	0.1999	80.064	0.0125	16.0026	0.0625	11.7566
34	5.253	0.1904	85.067	0.0118	16.1929	0.0618	12.0063
35	5.516	0.1813	90.320	0.0111	16.3742	0.0611	12.2498
40	7.040	0.1421	120.800	0.0083	17.1591	0.0583	13.3775
45	8.985	0.1113	159.700	0.0063	17.7741	0.0563	14.3644
50	11.467	0.0872	209.348	0.0048	18.2559	0.0548	15.2233
55	14.636	0.0683	272.713	0.0037	18.6335	0.0537	15.9665
60	18.679	0.0535	353.584	0.0028	18.9293	0.0528	16.6062
65	23.840	0.0420	456.798	0.0022	19.1611	0.0522	17.1541
70	30.426	0.0329	588.529	0.0017	19.3427	0.0517	17.6212
75	38.833	0.0258	756.654	0.0013	19.4850	0.0513	18.0176
80	49.561	0.0202	971.229	0.0010	19.5965	0.0510	18.3526
85	63.254	0.0158	1245.087	0.0008	19.6838	0.0508	18.6346
90	80.730	0.0124	1594.607	0.0006	19.7523	0.0506	18.8712
95	103.035	0.0097	2040.694	0.0005	19.8059	0.0505	19.0689
100	131.501	0.0076	2610.025	0.0004	19.8479	0.0504	19.2337

TABLE D.2 6% Interest Factors for Annual Compounding

	Single Payment		Equal-Payment Series				Uniform Gradient-Series Factor
	Compound-Amount Factor	Present-Worth Factor	Compound-Amount Factor	Sinking-Fund Factor	Present-Worth Factor	Capital-Recovery Factor	
n	To Find F Given P $F/P, i, n$	To Find P Given F $P/F, i, n$	To Find F Given A $F/A, i, n$	To Find A Given F $A/F, i, n$	To Find P Given A $P/A, i, n$	To Find A Given P $A/P, i, n$	To Find A Given G $A/G, i, n$
1	1.060	0.9434	1.000	1.0000	0.9434	1.0600	0.0000
2	1.124	0.8900	2.060	0.4854	1.8334	0.5454	0.4854
3	1.191	0.8396	3.184	0.3141	2.6730	0.3741	0.9612
4	1.262	0.7921	4.375	0.2286	3.4651	0.2886	1.4272
5	1.338	0.7473	5.637	0.1774	4.2124	0.2374	1.8836
6	1.419	0.7050	6.975	0.1434	4.9173	0.2034	2.3304
7	1.504	0.6651	8.394	0.1191	5.5824	0.1791	2.7676
8	1.594	0.6274	9.897	0.1010	6.2098	0.1610	3.1952
9	1.689	0.5919	11.491	0.0870	6.8017	0.1470	3.6133
10	1.791	0.5584	13.181	0.0759	7.3601	0.1359	4.0220
11	1.898	0.5268	14.972	0.0668	7.8869	0.1268	4.4213
12	2.012	0.4970	16.870	0.0593	8.3839	0.1193	4.8113
13	2.133	0.4688	18.882	0.0530	8.8527	0.1130	5.1920
14	2.261	0.4423	21.015	0.0476	9.2950	0.1076	5.5635
15	2.397	0.4173	23.276	0.0430	9.7123	0.1030	5.9260
16	2.540	0.3937	25.673	0.0390	10.1059	0.0990	6.2794
17	2.693	0.3714	28.213	0.0355	10.4773	0.0955	6.6240
18	2.854	0.3504	30.906	0.0324	10.8276	0.0924	6.9597
19	3.026	0.3305	33.760	0.0296	11.1581	0.0896	7.2867
20	3.207	0.3118	36.786	0.0272	11.4699	0.0872	7.6052
21	3.400	0.2942	39.993	0.0250	11.7641	0.0850	7.9151
22	3.604	0.2775	43.392	0.0231	12.0416	0.0831	8.2166
23	3.820	0.2618	46.996	0.0213	12.3034	0.0813	8.5099
24	4.049	0.2470	50.816	0.0197	12.5504	0.0797	8.7951
25	4.292	0.2330	54.865	0.0182	12.7834	0.0782	9.0722
26	4.549	0.2198	59.156	0.0169	13.0032	0.0769	9.3415
27	4.822	0.2074	63.706	0.0157	13.2105	0.0757	9.6030
28	5.112	0.1956	68.528	0.0146	13.4062	0.0746	9.8568
29	5.418	0.1846	73.640	0.0136	13.5907	0.0736	10.1032
30	5.744	0.1741	79.058	0.0127	13.7648	0.0727	10.3422
31	6.088	0.1643	84.802	0.0118	13.9291	0.0718	10.5740
32	6.453	0.1550	90.890	0.0110	14.0841	0.0710	10.7988
33	6.841	0.1462	97.343	0.0103	14.2302	0.0703	11.0166
34	7.251	0.1379	104.184	0.0096	14.3682	0.0696	11.2276
35	7.686	0.1301	111.435	0.0090	14.4983	0.0690	11.4319
40	10.286	0.0972	154.762	0.0065	15.0463	0.0665	12.3590
45	13.765	0.0727	212.744	0.0047	15.4558	0.0647	13.1413
50	18.420	0.0543	290.336	0.0035	15.7619	0.0635	13.7964
55	24.650	0.0406	394.172	0.0025	15.9906	0.0625	14.3411
60	32.988	0.0303	533.128	0.0019	16.1614	0.0619	14.7910
65	44.145	0.0227	719.083	0.0014	16.2891	0.0614	15.1601
70	59.076	0.0169	967.932	0.0010	16.3846	0.0610	15.4614
75	79.057	0.0127	1300.949	0.0008	16.4559	0.0608	15.7058
80	105.796	0.0095	1746.600	0.0006	16.5091	0.0606	15.9033
85	141.579	0.0071	2342.982	0.0004	16.5490	0.0604	16.0620
90	189.465	0.0053	3141.075	0.0003	16.5787	0.0603	16.1891
95	253.546	0.0040	4209.104	0.0002	16.6009	0.0602	16.2905
100	339.302	0.0030	5638.368	0.0002	16.6176	0.0602	16.3711

TABLE D.3   7% Interest Factors for Annual Compounding

	Single Payment		Equal-Payment Series				Uniform Gradient-Series Factor
	Compound-Amount Factor	Present-Worth Factor	Compound-Amount Factor	Sinking-Fund Factor	Present-Worth Factor	Capital-Recovery Factor	
n	To Find F Given P $F/P, i, n$	To Find P Given F $P/F, i, n$	To Find F Given A $F/A, i, n$	To Find A Given F $A/F, i, n$	To Find P Given A $P/A, i, n$	To Find A Given P $A/P, i, n$	To Find A Given G $A/G, i, n$
1	1.070	0.9346	1.000	1.0000	0.9346	1.0700	0.0000
2	1.145	0.8734	2.070	0.4831	1.8080	0.5531	0.4831
3	1.225	0.8163	3.215	0.3111	2.6243	0.3811	0.9549
4	1.311	0.7629	4.440	0.2252	3.3872	0.2952	1.4155
5	1.403	0.7130	5.751	0.1739	4.1002	0.2439	1.8650
6	1.501	0.6664	7.153	0.1398	4.7665	0.2098	2.3032
7	1.606	0.6228	8.654	0.1156	5.3893	0.1856	2.7304
8	1.718	0.5820	10.260	0.0975	5.9713	0.1675	3.1466
9	1.838	0.5439	11.978	0.0835	6.5152	0.1535	3.5517
10	1.967	0.5084	13.816	0.0724	7.0236	0.1424	3.9461
11	2.105	0.4751	15.784	0.0634	7.4987	0.1334	4.3296
12	2.252	0.4440	17.888	0.0559	7.9427	0.1259	4.7025
13	2.410	0.4150	20.141	0.0497	8.3577	0.1197	5.0649
14	2.579	0.3878	22.550	0.0444	8.7455	0.1144	5.4167
15	2.759	0.3625	25.129	0.0398	9.1079	0.1098	5.7583
16	2.952	0.3387	27.888	0.0359	9.4467	0.1059	6.0897
17	3.159	0.3166	30.840	0.0324	9.7632	0.1024	6.4110
18	3.380	0.2959	33.999	0.0294	10.0591	0.0994	6.7225
19	3.617	0.2765	37.379	0.0268	10.3356	0.0968	7.0242
20	3.870	0.2584	40.996	0.0244	10.5940	0.0944	7.3163
21	4.141	0.2415	44.865	0.0223	10.8355	0.0923	7.5990
22	4.430	0.2257	49.006	0.0204	11.0613	0.0904	7.8725
23	4.741	0.2110	53.436	0.0187	11.2722	0.0887	8.1369
24	5.072	0.1972	58.177	0.0172	11.4693	0.0872	8.3923
25	5.427	0.1843	63.249	0.0158	11.6536	0.0858	8.6391
26	5.807	0.1722	68.676	0.0146	11.8258	0.0846	8.8773
27	6.214	0.1609	74.484	0.0134	11.9867	0.0834	9.1072
28	6.649	0.1504	80.698	0.0124	12.1371	0.0824	9.3290
29	7.114	0.1406	87.347	0.0115	12.2777	0.0815	9.5427
30	7.612	0.1314	94.461	0.0106	12.4091	0.0806	9.7487
31	8.145	0.1228	102.073	0.0098	12.5318	0.0798	9.9471
32	8.715	0.1148	110.218	0.0091	12.6466	0.0791	10.1381
33	9.325	0.1072	118.933	0.0084	12.7538	0.0784	10.3219
34	9.978	0.1002	128.259	0.0078	12.8540	0.0778	10.4987
35	10.677	0.0937	138.237	0.0072	12.9477	0.0772	10.6687
40	14.974	0.0668	199.635	0.0050	13.3317	0.0750	11.4234
45	21.002	0.0476	285.749	0.0035	13.6055	0.0735	12.0360
50	29.457	0.0340	406.529	0.0025	13.8008	0.0725	12.5287
55	41.315	0.0242	575.929	0.0017	13.9399	0.0717	12.9215
60	57.946	0.0173	813.520	0.0012	14.0392	0.0712	13.2321
65	81.273	0.0123	1146.755	0.0009	14.1099	0.0709	13.4760
70	113.989	0.0088	1614.134	0.0006	14.1604	0.0706	13.6662
75	159.876	0.0063	2269.657	0.0005	14.1964	0.0705	13.8137
80	224.234	0.0045	3189.063	0.0003	14.2220	0.0703	13.9274
85	314.500	0.0032	4478.576	0.0002	14.2403	0.0702	14.0146
90	441.103	0.0023	6287.185	0.0002	14.2533	0.0702	14.0812
95	618.670	0.0016	8823.854	0.0001	14.2626	0.0701	14.1319
100	867.716	0.0012	12381.662	0.0001	14.2693	0.0701	14.1703

TABLE D.4 8% Interest Factors for Annual Compounding

	Single Payment		Equal-Payment Series				Uniform Gradient-Series Factor
	Compound-Amount Factor	Present-Worth Factor	Compound-Amount Factor	Sinking-Fund Factor	Present-Worth Factor	Capital-Recovery Factor	
n	To Find F Given P $F/P, i, n$	To Find P Given F $P/F, i, n$	To Find F Given A $F/A, i, n$	To Find A Given F $A/F, i, n$	To Find P Given A $P/A, i, n$	To Find A Given P $A/P, i, n$	To Find A Given G $A/G, i, n$
1	1.080	0.9259	1.000	1.0000	0.9259	1.0800	0.0000
2	1.166	0.8573	2.080	0.4808	1.7833	0.5608	0.4808
3	1.260	0.7938	3.246	0.3080	2.5771	0.3880	0.9488
4	1.360	0.7350	4.506	0.2219	3.3121	0.3019	1.4040
5	1.469	0.6806	5.867	0.1705	3.9927	0.2505	1.8465
6	1.587	0.6302	7.336	0.1363	4.6229	0.2163	2.2764
7	1.714	0.5835	8.923	0.1121	5.2064	0.1921	2.6937
8	1.851	0.5403	10.637	0.0940	5.7466	0.1740	3.0985
9	1.999	0.5003	12.488	0.0801	6.2469	0.1601	3.4910
10	2.159	0.4632	14.487	0.0690	6.7101	0.1490	3.8713
11	2.332	0.4289	16.645	0.0601	7.1390	0.1401	4.2395
12	2.518	0.3971	18.977	0.0527	7.5361	0.1327	4.5958
13	2.720	0.3677	21.495	0.0465	7.9038	0.1265	4.9402
14	2.937	0.3405	24.215	0.0413	8.2442	0.1213	5.2731
15	3.172	0.3153	27.152	0.0368	8.5595	0.1168	5.5945
16	3.426	0.2919	30.324	0.0330	8.8514	0.1130	5.9046
17	3.700	0.2703	33.750	0.0296	9.1216	0.1096	6.2038
18	3.996	0.2503	37.450	0.0267	9.3719	0.1067	6.4920
19	4.316	0.2317	41.446	0.0241	9.6036	0.1041	6.7697
20	4.661	0.2146	45.762	0.0219	9.8182	0.1019	7.0370
21	5.034	0.1987	50.423	0.0198	10.0168	0.0998	7.2940
22	5.437	0.1840	55.457	0.0180	10.2008	0.0980	7.5412
23	5.871	0.1703	60.893	0.0164	10.3711	0.0964	7.7786
24	6.341	0.1577	66.765	0.0150	10.5288	0.0950	8.0066
25	6.848	0.1460	73.106	0.0137	10.6748	0.0937	8.2254
26	7.396	0.1352	79.954	0.0125	10.8100	0.0925	8.4352
27	7.988	0.1252	87.351	0.0115	10.9352	0.0915	8.6363
28	8.627	0.1159	95.339	0.0105	11.0511	0.0905	8.8289
29	9.317	0.1073	103.966	0.0096	11.1584	0.0896	9.0133
30	10.063	0.0994	113.283	0.0088	11.2578	0.0888	9.1897
31	10.868	0.0920	123.346	0.0081	11.3498	0.0881	9.3584
32	11.737	0.0852	134.214	0.0075	11.4350	0.0875	9.5197
33	12.676	0.0789	145.951	0.0069	11.5139	0.0869	9.6737
34	13.690	0.0731	158.627	0.0063	11.5869	0.0863	9.8208
35	14.785	0.0676	172.317	0.0058	11.6546	0.0858	9.9611
40	21.725	0.0460	259.057	0.0039	11.9246	0.0839	10.5699
45	31.920	0.0313	386.506	0.0026	12.1084	0.0826	11.0447
50	46.902	0.0213	573.770	0.0018	12.2335	0.0818	11.4107
55	68.914	0.0145	848.923	0.0012	12.3186	0.0812	11.6902
60	101.257	0.0099	1253.213	0.0008	12.3766	0.0808	11.9015
65	148.780	0.0067	1847.248	0.0006	12.4160	0.0806	12.0602
70	218.606	0.0046	2720.080	0.0004	12.4428	0.0804	12.1783
75	321.205	0.0031	4002.557	0.0003	12.4611	0.0803	12.2658
80	471.955	0.0021	5886.935	0.0002	12.4735	0.0802	12.3301
85	693.456	0.0015	8655.706	0.0001	12.4820	0.0801	12.3773
90	1018.915	0.0010	12723.939	0.0001	12.4877	0.0801	12.4116
95	1497.121	0.0007	18701.507	0.0001	12.4917	0.0801	12.4365
100	2199.761	0.0005	27484.516	0.0001	12.4943	0.0800	12.4545

TABLE D.5   9% Interest Factors for Annual Compounding

	Single Payment		Equal-Payment Series				Uniform Gradient-Series Factor
	Compound-Amount Factor	Present-Worth Factor	Compound-Amount Factor	Sinking-Fund Factor	Present-Worth Factor	Capital-Recovery Factor	
n	To Find F Given P $F/P, i, n$	To Find P Given F $P/F, i, n$	To Find F Given A $F/A, i, n$	To Find A Given F $A/F, i, n$	To Find P Given A $P/A, i, n$	To Find A Given P $A/P, i, n$	To Find A Given G $A/G, i, n$
1	1.090	0.9174	1.000	1.0000	0.9174	1.0900	0.0000
2	1.188	0.8417	2.090	0.4785	1.7591	0.5685	0.4785
3	1.295	0.7722	3.278	0.3051	2.5313	0.3951	0.9426
4	1.412	0.7084	4.573	0.2187	3.2397	0.3087	1.3925
5	1.539	0.6499	5.985	0.1671	3.8897	0.2571	1.8282
6	1.677	0.5963	7.523	0.1329	4.4859	0.2229	2.2498
7	1.828	0.5470	9.200	0.1087	5.0330	0.1987	2.6574
8	1.993	0.5019	11.028	0.0907	5.5348	0.1807	3.0512
9	2.172	0.4604	13.021	0.0768	5.9953	0.1668	3.4312
10	2.367	0.4224	15.193	0.0658	6.4177	0.1558	3.7978
11	2.580	0.3875	17.560	0.0570	6.8052	0.1470	4.1510
12	2.813	0.3555	20.141	0.0497	7.1607	0.1397	4.4910
13	3.066	0.3262	22.953	0.0436	7.4869	0.1336	4.8182
14	3.342	0.2993	26.019	0.0384	7.7862	0.1284	5.1326
15	3.642	0.2745	29.361	0.0341	8.0607	0.1241	5.4346
16	3.970	0.2519	33.003	0.0303	8.3126	0.1203	5.7245
17	4.328	0.2311	36.974	0.0271	8.5436	0.1171	6.0024
18	4.717	0.2120	41.301	0.0242	8.7556	0.1142	6.2687
19	5.142	0.1945	46.018	0.0217	8.9501	0.1117	6.5236
20	5.604	0.1784	51.160	0.0196	9.1286	0.1096	6.7675
21	6.109	0.1637	56.765	0.0176	9.2923	0.1076	7.0006
22	6.659	0.1502	62.873	0.0159	9.4424	0.1059	7.2232
23	7.258	0.1378	69.532	0.0144	9.5802	0.1044	7.4358
24	7.911	0.1264	76.790	0.0130	9.7066	0.1030	7.6384
25	8.623	0.1160	84.701	0.0118	9.8226	0.1018	7.8316
26	9.399	0.1064	93.324	0.0107	9.9290	0.1007	8.0156
27	10.245	0.0976	102.723	0.0097	10.0266	0.0997	8.1906
28	11.167	0.0896	112.968	0.0089	10.1161	0.0989	8.3572
29	12.172	0.0822	124.135	0.0081	10.1983	0.0981	8.5154
30	13.268	0.0754	136.308	0.0073	10.2737	0.0973	8.6657
31	14.462	0.0692	149.575	0.0067	10.3428	0.0967	8.8083
32	15.763	0.0634	164.037	0.0061	10.4063	0.0961	8.9436
33	17.182	0.0582	179.800	0.0056	10.4645	0.0956	9.0718
34	18.728	0.0534	196.982	0.0051	10.5178	0.0951	9.1933
35	20.414	0.0490	215.711	0.0046	10.5668	0.0946	9.3083
40	31.409	0.0318	337.882	0.0030	10.7574	0.0930	9.7957
45	48.327	0.0207	525.859	0.0019	10.8812	0.0919	10.1603
50	74.358	0.0135	815.084	0.0012	10.9617	0.0912	10.4295
55	114.408	0.0088	1260.092	0.0008	11.0140	0.0908	10.6261
60	176.031	0.0057	1944.792	0.0005	11.0480	0.0905	10.7683
65	270.846	0.0037	2998.288	0.0003	11.0701	0.0903	10.8702
70	416.730	0.0024	4619.223	0.0002	11.0845	0.0902	10.9427
75	641.191	0.0016	7113.232	0.0002	11.0938	0.0902	10.9940
80	986.552	0.0010	10950.574	0.0001	11.0999	0.0901	11.0299
85	1517.932	0.0007	16854.800	0.0001	11.1038	0.0901	11.0551
90	2335.527	0.0004	25939.184	0.0001	11.1064	0.0900	11.0726
95	3593.497	0.0003	39916.635	0.0000	11.1080	0.0900	11.0847
100	5529.041	0.0002	61422.675	0.0000	11.1091	0.0900	11.0930

TABLE D.6 10% Interest Factors for Annual Compounding

	Single Payment		Equal-Payment Series				Uniform Gradient-Series Factor
n	Compound-Amount Factor	Present-Worth Factor	Compound-Amount Factor	Sinking-Fund Factor	Present-Worth Factor	Capital-Recovery Factor	
	To Find F Given P $F/P, i, n$	To Find P Given F $P/F, i, n$	To Find F Given A $F/A, i, n$	To Find A Given F $A/F, i, n$	To Find P Given A $P/A, i, n$	To Find A Given P $A/P, i, n$	To Find A Given G $A/G, i, n$
1	1.100	0.9091	1.000	1.0000	0.9091	1.1000	0.0000
2	1.210	0.8265	2.100	0.4762	1.7355	0.5762	0.4762
3	1.331	0.7513	3.310	0.3021	2.4869	0.4021	0.9366
4	1.464	0.6830	4.641	0.2155	3.1699	0.3155	1.3812
5	1.611	0.6209	6.105	0.1638	3.7908	0.2638	1.8101
6	1.772	0.5645	7.716	0.1296	4.3553	0.2296	2.2236
7	1.949	0.5132	9.487	0.1054	4.8684	0.2054	2.6216
8	2.144	0.4665	11.436	0.0875	5.3349	0.1875	3.0045
9	2.358	0.4241	13.579	0.0737	5.7950	0.1737	3.3724
10	2.594	0.3856	15.937	0.0628	6.1446	0.1628	3.7255
11	2.853	0.3505	18.531	0.0540	6.4951	0.1540	4.0641
12	3.138	0.3186	21.384	0.0468	6.8137	0.1468	4.3884
13	3.452	0.2897	24.523	0.0408	7.1034	0.1408	4.6988
14	3.798	0.2633	27.975	0.0358	7.3667	0.1358	4.9955
15	4.177	0.2394	31.772	0.0315	7.6061	0.1315	5.2789
16	4.595	0.2176	35.950	0.0278	7.8237	0.1278	5.5493
17	5.054	0.1979	40.545	0.0247	8.0216	0.1247	5.8071
18	5.560	0.1799	45.599	0.0219	8.2014	0.1219	6.0526
19	6.116	0.1635	51.159	0.0196	8.3649	0.1196	6.2861
20	6.728	0.1487	57.275	0.0175	8.5136	0.1175	6.5081
21	7.400	0.1351	64.003	0.0156	8.6487	0.1156	6.7189
22	8.140	0.1229	71.403	0.0140	8.7716	0.1140	6.9189
23	8.953	0.1117	79.543	0.0126	8.8832	0.1126	7.1085
24	9.850	0.1015	88.497	0.0113	8.9848	0.1113	7.2881
25	10.835	0.0923	98.347	0.0102	9.0771	0.1102	7.4580
26	11.918	0.0839	109.182	0.0092	9.1610	0.1092	7.6187
27	13.110	0.0763	121.100	0.0083	9.2372	0.1083	7.7704
28	14.421	0.0694	134.210	0.0075	9.3066	0.1075	7.9137
29	15.863	0.0630	148.631	0.0067	9.3696	0.1067	8.0489
30	17.449	0.0573	164.494	0.0061	9.4269	0.1061	8.1762
31	19.194	0.0521	181.943	0.0055	9.4790	0.1055	8.2962
32	21.114	0.0474	201.138	0.0050	9.5264	0.1050	8.4091
33	23.225	0.0431	222.252	0.0045	9.5694	0.1045	8.5152
34	25.548	0.0392	245.477	0.0041	9.6086	0.1041	8.6149
35	28.102	0.0356	271.024	0.0037	9.6442	0.1037	8.7086
40	45.259	0.0221	442.593	0.0023	9.7791	0.1023	9.0962
45	72.890	0.0137	718.905	0.0014	9.8628	0.1014	9.3741
50	117.391	0.0085	1163.909	0.0009	9.9148	0.1009	9.5704
55	189.059	0.0053	1880.591	0.0005	9.9471	0.1005	9.7075
60	304.482	0.0033	3034.816	0.0003	9.9672	0.1003	9.8023
65	490.371	0.0020	4893.707	0.0002	9.9796	0.1002	9.8672
70	789.747	0.0013	7887.470	0.0001	9.9873	0.1001	9.9113
75	1271.895	0.0008	12708.954	0.0001	9.9921	0.1001	9.9410
80	2048.400	0.0005	20474.002	0.0001	9.9951	0.1001	9.9609
85	3298.969	0.0003	32979.690	0.0000	9.9970	0.1000	9.9742
90	5313.023	0.0002	53120.226	0.0000	9.9981	0.1000	9.9831
95	8556.676	0.0001	85556.760	0.0000	9.9988	0.1000	9.9889
100	13780.612	0.0001	137796.123	0.0000	9.9993	0.1000	9.9928

TABLE D.7   11% Interest Factors for Annual Compounding

	Single Payment		Equal-Payment Series				Uniform Gradient-Series Factor
	Compound-Amount Factor	Present-Worth Factor	Compound-Amount Factor	Sinking-Fund Factor	Present-Worth Factor	Capital-Recovery Factor	
n	To Find F Given P F/P, i,n	To Find P Given F P/F, i,n	To Find F Given A F/A, i,n	To Find A Given F A/F, i,n	To Find P Given A P/A, i,n	To Find A Given P A/P, i,n	To Find A Given G A/G, i, n
1	1.110	0.9009	1.000	1.0000	0.9009	1.1100	0.0000
2	1.232	0.8116	2.110	0.4739	1.7125	0.5839	0.4740
3	1.368	0.7312	3.342	0.2992	2.4437	0.4092	0.9306
4	1.518	0.6587	4.710	0.2123	3.1024	0.3223	1.3698
5	1.685	0.5935	6.228	0.1606	3.6959	0.2706	1.7923
6	1.870	0.5346	7.913	0.1264	4.2305	0.2364	2.1975
7	2.076	0.4817	9.783	0.1022	4.7121	0.2122	2.5860
8	2.305	0.4339	11.859	0.0843	5.1462	0.1943	2.9585
9	2.558	0.3909	14.164	0.0706	5.5371	0.1806	3.3145
10	2.839	0.3522	16.722	0.0598	5.8893	0.1698	3.6545
11	3.152	0.3173	19.561	0.0511	6.2066	0.1611	3.9789
12	3.498	0.2858	22.713	0.0440	6.4922	0.1540	4.2876
13	3.883	0.2575	26.212	0.0382	6.7499	0.1482	4.5823
14	4.310	0.2320	30.095	0.0332	6.9818	0.1432	4.8616
15	4.785	0.2090	34.405	0.0291	7.1906	0.1391	5.1268
16	5.311	0.1883	39.190	0.0255	7.3790	0.1355	5.3789
17	5.895	0.1696	44.501	0.0225	7.5489	0.1325	5.6183
18	6.544	0.1528	50.396	0.0198	7.7018	0.1298	5.8444
19	7.263	0.1377	56.939	0.0176	7.8394	0.1276	6.0578
20	8.062	0.1240	64.203	0.0156	7.9631	0.1256	6.2582
21	8.949	0.1117	72.265	0.0138	8.0749	0.1238	6.4487
22	9.934	0.1007	81.214	0.0123	8.1759	0.1223	6.6289
23	11.026	0.0907	91.148	0.0110	8.2665	0.1210	6.7972
24	12.239	0.0817	102.174	0.0098	8.3479	0.1198	6.9549
25	13.586	0.0736	114.413	0.0087	8.4218	0.1187	7.1045
26	15.080	0.0663	127.999	0.0078	8.4882	0.1178	7.2449
27	16.739	0.0597	143.079	0.0070	8.5477	0.1170	7.3752
28	18.580	0.0538	159.817	0.0063	8.6014	0.1163	7.4975
29	20.624	0.0485	178.397	0.0056	8.6498	0.1156	7.6119
30	22.892	0.0437	199.021	0.0050	8.6941	0.1150	7.7218
31	25.410	0.0394	221.913	0.0045	8.7329	0.1145	7.8199
32	28.206	0.0355	247.324	0.0040	8.7689	0.1140	7.9156
33	31.308	0.0319	275.529	0.0036	8.8005	0.1136	8.0019
34	34.752	0.0288	306.837	0.0033	8.8292	0.1133	8.0833
35	38.575	0.0259	341.590	0.0029	8.8550	0.1129	8.1586
40	65.001	0.0154	581.826	0.0017	8.9509	0.1117	8.4655
45	109.530	0.0091	986.639	0.0010	9.0082	0.1110	8.6777
50	184.565	0.0054	1688.771	0.0006	9.0416	0.1106	8.8182

TABLE D.8   12% Interest Factors for Annual Compounding

	Single Payment		Equal-Payment Series				Uniform Gradient-Series Factor
	Compound-Amount Factor	Present-Worth Factor	Compound-Amount Factor	Sinking-Fund Factor	Present-Worth Factor	Capital-Recovery Factor	
n	To Find F Given P $F/P, i, n$	To Find P Given F $P/F, i, n$	To Find F Given A $F/A, i, n$	To Find A Given F $A/F, i, n$	To Find P Given A $P/A, i, n$	To Find A Given P $A/P, i, n$	To Find A Given G $A/G, i, n$
1	1.120	0.8929	1.000	1.0000	0.8929	1.1200	0.0000
2	1.254	0.7972	2.120	0.4717	1.6901	0.5917	0.4717
3	1.405	0.7118	3.374	0.2964	2.4018	0.4164	0.9246
4	1.574	0.6355	4.779	0.2092	3.0374	0.3292	1.3589
5	1.762	0.5674	6.353	0.1574	3.6048	0.2774	1.7746
6	1.974	0.5066	8.115	0.1232	4.1114	0.2432	2.1721
7	2.211	0.4524	10.089	0.0991	4.5638	0.2191	2.5515
8	2.476	0.4039	12.300	0.0813	4.9676	0.2013	2.9132
9	2.773	0.3606	14.776	0.0677	5.3283	0.1877	3.2574
10	3.106	0.3220	17.549	0.0570	5.6502	0.1770	3.5847
11	3.479	0.2875	20.655	0.0484	5.9377	0.1684	3.8953
12	3.896	0.2567	24.133	0.0414	6.1944	0.1614	4.1897
13	4.364	0.2292	28.029	0.0357	6.4236	0.1557	4.4683
14	4.887	0.2046	32.393	0.0309	6.6282	0.1509	4.7317
15	5.474	0.1827	37.280	0.0268	6.8109	0.1468	4.9803
16	6.130	0.1631	42.753	0.0234	6.9740	0.1434	5.2147
17	6.866	0.1457	48.884	0.0205	7.1196	0.1405	5.4353
18	7.690	0.1300	55.750	0.0179	7.2497	0.1379	5.6427
19	8.613	0.1161	63.440	0.0158	7.3658	0.1358	5.8375
20	9.646	0.1037	72.052	0.0139	7.4695	0.1339	6.0202
21	10.804	0.0926	81.699	0.0123	7.5620	0.1323	6.1913
22	12.100	0.0827	92.503	0.0108	7.6447	0.1308	6.3514
23	13.552	0.0738	104.603	0.0096	7.7184	0.1296	6.5010
24	15.179	0.0659	118.155	0.0085	7.7843	0.1285	6.6407
25	17.000	0.0588	133.334	0.0075	7.8431	0.1275	6.7708
26	19.040	0.0525	150.334	0.0067	7.8957	0.1267	6.8921
27	21.325	0.0469	169.374	0.0059	7.9426	0.1259	7.0049
28	23.884	0.0419	190.699	0.0053	7.9844	0.1253	7.1098
29	26.750	0.0374	214.583	0.0047	8.0218	0.1247	7.2071
30	29.960	0.0334	241.333	0.0042	8.0552	0.1242	7.2974
31	33.555	0.0298	271.293	0.0037	8.0850	0.1237	7.3811
32	37.582	0.0266	304.848	0.0033	8.1116	0.1233	7.4586
33	42.092	0.0238	342.429	0.0029	8.1354	0.1229	7.5303
34	47.143	0.0212	384.521	0.0026	8.1566	0.1226	7.5965
35	52.800	0.0189	431.664	0.0023	8.1755	0.1223	7.6577
40	93.051	0.0108	767.091	0.0013	8.2438	0.1213	7.8988
45	163.988	0.0061	1358.230	0.0007	8.2825	0.1207	8.0572
50	289.002	0.0035	2400.018	0.0004	8.3045	0.1204	8.1597

TABLE D.9   13% Interest Factors for Annual Compounding

	Single Payment		Equal-Payment Series				Uniform Gradient-Series Factor
	Compound-Amount Factor	Present-Worth Factor	Compound-Amount Factor	Sinking-Fund Factor	Present-Worth Factor	Capital-Recovery Factor	
n	To Find F Given P F/P, i,n	To Find P Given F P/F, i,n	To Find F Given A F/A, i,n	To Find A Given F A/F, i,n	To Find P Given A P/A, i,n	To Find A Given P A/P, i,n	To Find A Given G A/G, i, n
1	1.130	0.8850	1.000	1.0000	0.8850	1.1300	0.0000
2	1.277	0.7831	2.130	0.4695	1.6681	0.5995	0.4695
3	1.443	0.6931	3.407	0.2935	2.3612	0.4235	0.9188
4	1.631	0.6133	4.850	0.2062	2.9745	0.3362	1.3480
5	1.842	0.5428	6.480	0.1543	3.5173	0.2843	1.7573
6	2.082	0.4803	8.323	0.1202	3.9976	0.2502	2.1469
7	2.353	0.4251	10.405	0.0961	4.4226	0.2261	2.5172
8	2.658	0.3762	12.757	0.0784	4.7987	0.2084	2.8683
9	3.004	0.3329	15.416	0.0649	5.1316	0.1949	3.2013
10	3.395	0.2946	18.420	0.0543	5.4262	0.1843	3.5162
11	3.836	0.2607	21.814	0.0458	5.6870	0.1758	3.8135
12	4.335	0.2307	25.650	0.0390	5.9175	0.1690	4.0932
13	4.898	0.2042	29.985	0.0334	6.1218	0.1634	4.3573
14	5.535	0.1807	34.883	0.0287	6.3024	0.1587	4.6048
15	6.254	0.1599	40.417	0.0247	6.4625	0.1547	4.8377
16	7.067	0.1415	46.672	0.0214	6.6037	0.1514	5.0548
17	7.986	0.1252	53.739	0.0186	6.7290	0.1486	5.2587
18	9.024	0.1108	61.725	0.0162	6.8399	0.1462	5.4492
19	10.197	0.0981	70.749	0.0141	6.9382	0.1441	5.6272
20	11.523	0.0868	80.947	0.0124	7.0249	0.1424	5.7923
21	13.021	0.0768	92.470	0.0108	7.1018	0.1408	5.9461
22	14.714	0.0680	105.491	0.0095	7.1695	0.1395	6.0880
23	16.627	0.0601	120.205	0.0083	7.2296	0.1383	6.2203
24	18.788	0.0532	136.831	0.0073	7.2828	0.1373	6.3428
25	21.231	0.0471	155.620	0.0064	7.3298	0.1364	6.4558
26	23.991	0.0417	176.850	0.0057	7.3719	0.1357	6.5623
27	27.109	0.0369	200.841	0.0050	7.4085	0.1350	6.6580
28	30.634	0.0326	227.950	0.0044	7.4410	0.1344	6.7468
29	34.616	0.0289	258.583	0.0039	7.4699	0.1339	6.8290
30	39.116	0.0256	293.199	0.0034	7.4957	0.1334	6.9054
31	44.201	0.0226	332.315	0.0030	7.5182	0.1330	6.9745
32	49.947	0.0200	376.516	0.0027	7.5381	0.1327	7.0375
33	56.440	0.0177	426.463	0.0023	7.5563	0.1323	7.0983
34	63.777	0.0157	482.903	0.0021	7.5717	0.1321	7.1509
35	72.069	0.0139	546.681	0.0018	7.5855	0.1318	7.1996
40	132.782	0.0075	1013.704	0.0010	7.6342	0.1310	7.3877
45	244.641	0.0041	1874.165	0.0005	7.6611	0.1305	7.5088
50	450.736	0.0022	3459.507	0.0003	7.6752	0.1303	7.5808

TABLE D.10 14% Interest Factors for Annual Compounding

	Single Payment		Equal-Payment Series				
	Compound-Amount Factor	Present-Worth Factor	Compound-Amount Factor	Sinking-Fund Factor	Present-Worth Factor	Capital-Recovery Factor	Uniform Gradient-Series Factor
n	To Find F Given P $F/P, i,n$	To Find P Given F $P/F, i,n$	To Find F Given A $F/A, i,n$	To Find A Given F $A/F, i,n$	To Find P Given A $P/A, i,n$	To Find A Given P $A/P, i,n$	To Find A Given G $A/G, i, n$
1	1.140	0.8772	1.000	1.0000	0.8772	1.1400	0.0000
2	1.300	0.7695	2.140	0.4673	1.6467	0.6073	0.4673
3	1.482	0.6750	3.440	0.2907	2.3216	0.4307	0.9129
4	1.689	0.5921	4.921	0.2032	2.9138	0.3432	1.3371
5	1.925	0.5194	6.610	0.1513	3.4331	0.2913	1.7400
6	2.195	0.4556	8.536	0.1172	3.8886	0.2572	2.1217
7	2.502	0.3996	10.730	0.0932	4.2883	0.2332	2.4834
8	2.853	0.3506	13.233	0.0756	4.6389	0.2156	2.8246
9	3.252	0.3075	16.085	0.0622	4.9463	0.2022	3.1462
10	3.707	0.2697	19.337	0.0517	5.2162	0.1917	3.4493
11	4.226	0.2366	23.045	0.0434	5.4529	0.1834	3.7336
12	4.818	0.2076	27.271	0.0367	5.6603	0.1767	3.9997
13	5.492	0.1821	32.089	0.0312	5.8425	0.1712	4.2494
14	6.261	0.1597	37.581	0.0266	6.0020	0.1666	4.4819
15	7.138	0.1401	43.842	0.0228	6.1421	0.1628	4.6989
16	8.137	0.1229	50.980	0.0196	6.2649	0.1596	4.9006
17	9.277	0.1078	59.118	0.0169	6.3727	0.1569	5.0883
18	10.575	0.0946	68.394	0.0146	6.4675	0.1546	5.2631
19	12.056	0.0829	78.969	0.0127	6.5505	0.1527	5.4247
20	13.744	0.0728	91.025	0.0110	6.6230	0.1510	5.5729
21	15.668	0.0638	104.768	0.0095	6.6872	0.1495	5.7119
22	17.861	0.0560	120.436	0.0083	6.7431	0.1483	5.8386
23	20.362	0.0491	138.297	0.0072	6.7921	0.1472	5.9551
24	23.212	0.0431	158.659	0.0063	6.8353	0.1463	6.0629
25	26.462	0.0378	181.871	0.0055	6.8729	0.1455	6.1607
26	30.167	0.0331	208.333	0.0048	6.9061	0.1448	6.2514
27	34.390	0.0291	238.499	0.0042	6.9353	0.1442	6.3348
28	39.205	0.0255	272.889	0.0037	6.9609	0.1437	6.4109
29	44.693	0.0224	312.094	0.0032	6.9832	0.1432	6.4800
30	50.950	0.0196	356.787	0.0028	7.0028	0.1428	6.5429
31	58.083	0.0172	407.737	0.0025	7.0200	0.1425	6.6004
32	66.215	0.0151	465.820	0.0022	7.0348	0.1422	6.6514
33	75.485	0.0132	532.035	0.0019	7.0482	0.1419	6.6997
34	86.053	0.0116	607.520	0.0017	7.0597	0.1417	6.7421
35	98.100	0.0102	693.573	0.0014	7.0701	0.1414	6.7829
40	188.884	0.0053	1342.025	0.0008	7.1048	0.1408	6.9286
45	363.679	0.0027	2590.565	0.0004	7.1230	0.1404	7.0175
50	700.233	0.0014	4994.521	0.0002	7.1327	0.1402	7.0714

TABLE D.11   15% Interest Factors for Annual Compounding

	Single Payment		Equal-Payment Series				Uniform Gradient-Series Factor
	Compound-Amount Factor	Present-Worth Factor	Compound-Amount Factor	Sinking-Fund Factor	Present-Worth Factor	Capital-Recovery Factor	
n	To Find F Given P $F/P, i, n$	To Find P Given F $P/F, i, n$	To Find F Given A $F/A, i, n$	To Find A Given F $A/F, i, n$	To Find P Given A $P/A, i, n$	To Find A Given P $A/P, i, n$	To Find A Given G $A/G, i, n$
1	1.150	0.8696	1.000	1.0000	0.8696	1.1500	0.0000
2	1.323	0.7562	2.150	0.4651	1.6257	0.6151	0.4651
3	1.521	0.6575	3.473	0.2880	2.2832	0.4380	0.9071
4	1.749	0.5718	4.993	0.2003	2.8550	0.3503	1.3263
5	2.011	0.4972	6.742	0.1483	3.3522	0.2983	1.7228
6	2.313	0.4323	8.754	0.1142	3.7845	0.2642	2.0972
7	2.660	0.3759	11.067	0.0904	4.1604	0.2404	2.4499
8	3.059	0.3269	13.727	0.0729	4.4873	0.2229	2.7813
9	3.518	0.2843	16.786	0.0596	4.7716	0.2096	3.0922
10	4.046	0.2472	20.304	0.0493	5.0188	0.1993	3.3832
11	4.652	0.2150	24.349	0.0411	5.2337	0.1911	3.6550
12	5.350	0.1869	29.002	0.0345	5.4206	0.1845	3.9082
13	6.153	0.1625	34.352	0.0291	5.5832	0.1791	4.1438
14	7.076	0.1413	40.505	0.0247	5.7245	0.1747	4.3624
15	8.137	0.1229	47.580	0.0210	5.8474	0.1710	4.5650
16	9.358	0.1069	55.717	0.0180	5.9542	0.1680	4.7523
17	10.761	0.0929	65.075	0.0154	6.0472	0.1654	4.9251
18	12.375	0.0808	75.836	0.0132	6.1280	0.1632	5.0843
19	14.232	0.0703	88.212	0.0113	6.1982	0.1613	5.2307
20	16.367	0.0611	102.444	0.0098	6.2593	0.1598	5.3651
21	18.822	0.0531	118.810	0.0084	6.3125	0.1584	5.4883
22	21.645	0.0462	137.632	0.0073	6.3587	0.1573	5.6010
23	24.891	0.0402	159.276	0.0063	6.3988	0.1563	5.7040
24	28.625	0.0349	184.168	0.0054	6.4338	0.1554	5.7979
25	32.919	0.0304	212.793	0.0047	6.4642	0.1547	5.8834
26	37.857	0.0264	245.712	0.0041	6.4906	0.1541	5.9612
27	43.535	0.0230	283.569	0.0035	6.5135	0.1535	6.0319
28	50.066	0.0200	327.104	0.0031	6.5335	0.1531	6.0960
29	57.575	0.0174	377.170	0.0027	6.5509	0.1527	6.1541
30	66.212	0.0151	434.745	0.0023	6.5660	0.1523	6.2066
31	76.144	0.0131	500.957	0.0020	6.5791	0.1520	6.2541
32	87.565	0.0114	577.100	0.0017	6.5905	0.1517	6.2970
33	100.700	0.0099	664.666	0.0015	6.6005	0.1515	6.3357
34	115.805	0.0086	765.365	0.0013	6.6091	0.1513	6.3705
35	133.176	0.0075	881.170	0.0011	6.6166	0.1511	6.4019
40	267.864	0.0037	1779.090	0.0006	6.6418	0.1506	6.5168
45	538.769	0.0019	3585.128	0.0003	6.6543	0.1503	6.5830
50	1083.657	0.0009	7217.716	0.0002	6.6605	0.1501	6.6205

TABLE D.12 20% Interest Factors for Annual Compounding

	Single Payment		Equal-Payment Series				Uniform Gradient-Series Factor
n	Compound-Amount Factor	Present-Worth Factor	Compound-Amount Factor	Sinking-Fund Factor	Present-Worth Factor	Capital-Recovery Factor	
	To Find F *Given P* *F/P, i, n*	*To Find P* *Given F* *P/F, i, n*	*To Find F* *Given A* *F/A, i, n*	*To Find A* *Given F* *A/F, i, n*	*To Find P* *Given A* *P/A, i, n*	*To Find A* *Given P* *A/P, i, n*	*To Find A* *Given G* *A/G, i, n*
1	1.200	0.8333	1.000	1.0000	0.8333	1.2000	0.0000
2	1.440	0.6945	2.200	0.4546	1.5278	0.6546	0.4546
3	1.728	0.5787	3.640	0.2747	2.1065	0.4747	0.8791
4	2.074	0.4823	5.368	0.1863	2.5887	0.3863	1.2742
5	2.488	0.4019	7.442	0.1344	2.9906	0.3344	1.6405
6	2.986	0.3349	9.930	0.1007	3.3255	0.3007	1.9788
7	3.583	0.2791	12.916	0.0774	3.6046	0.2774	2.2902
8	4.300	0.2326	16.499	0.0606	3.8372	0.2606	2.5756
9	5.160	0.1938	20.799	0.0481	4.0310	0.2481	2.8364
10	6.192	0.1615	25.959	0.0385	4.1925	0.2385	3.0739
11	7.430	0.1346	32.150	0.0311	4.3271	0.2311	3.2893
12	8.916	0.1122	39.581	0.0253	4.4392	0.2253	3.4841
13	10.699	0.0935	48.497	0.0206	4.5327	0.2206	3.6597
14	12.839	0.0779	59.196	0.0169	4.6106	0.2169	3.8175
15	15.407	0.0649	72.035	0.0139	4.6755	0.2139	3.9589
16	18.488	0.0541	87.442	0.0114	4.7296	0.2114	4.0851
17	22.186	0.0451	105.931	0.0095	4.7746	0.2095	4.1976
18	26.623	0.0376	128.117	0.0078	4.8122	0.2078	4.2975
19	31.948	0.0313	154.740	0.0065	4.8435	0.2065	4.3861
20	38.338	0.0261	186.688	0.0054	4.8696	0.2054	4.4644
21	46.005	0.0217	225.026	0.0045	4.8913	0.2045	4.5334
22	55.206	0.0181	271.031	0.0037	4.9094	0.2037	4.5942
23	66.247	0.0151	326.237	0.0031	4.9245	0.2031	4.6475
24	79.497	0.0126	392.484	0.0026	4.9371	0.2026	4.6943
25	95.396	0.0105	471.981	0.0021	4.9476	0.2021	4.7352
26	114.475	0.0087	567.377	0.0018	4.9563	0.2018	4.7709
27	137.371	0.0073	681.853	0.0015	4.9636	0.2015	4.8020
28	164.845	0.0061	819.223	0.0012	4.9697	0.2012	4.8291
29	197.814	0.0051	984.068	0.0010	4.9747	0.2010	4.8527
30	237.376	0.0042	1181.882	0.0009	4.9789	0.2009	4.8731
31	284.852	0.0035	1419.258	0.0007	4.9825	0.2007	4.8908
32	341.822	0.0029	1704.109	0.0006	4.9854	0.2006	4.9061
33	410.186	0.0024	2045.931	0.0005	4.9878	0.2005	4.9194
34	492.224	0.0020	2456.118	0.0004	4.9899	0.2004	4.9308
35	590.668	0.0017	2948.341	0.0003	4.9915	0.2003	4.9407
40	1469.772	0.0007	7343.858	0.0002	4.9966	0.2001	4.9728
45	3657.262	0.0003	18281.310	0.0001	4.9986	0.2001	4.9877
50	9100.438	0.0001	45497.191	0.0000	4.9995	0.2000	4.9945

TABLE D.13   25% Interest Factors for Annual Compounding

	Single Payment		Equal-Payment Series				Uniform Gradient-Series Factor
	Compound-Amount Factor	Present-Worth Factor	Compound-Amount Factor	Sinking-Fund Factor	Present-Worth Factor	Capital-Recovery Factor	
n	To Find F Given P $F/P, i, n$	To Find P Given F $P/F, i, n$	To Find F Given A $F/A, i, n$	To Find A Given F $A/F, i, n$	To Find P Given A $P/A, i, n$	To Find A Given P $A/P, i, n$	To Find A Given G $A/G, i, n$
1	1.250	0.8000	1.000	1.0000	0.8000	1.2500	0.0000
2	1.563	0.6400	2.250	0.4445	1.4400	0.6945	0.4445
3	1.953	0.5120	3.813	0.2623	1.9520	0.5123	0.8525
4	2.441	0.4096	5.766	0.1735	2.3616	0.4235	1.2249
5	3.052	0.3277	8.207	0.1219	2.6893	0.3719	1.5631
6	3.815	0.2622	11.259	0.0888	2.9514	0.3388	1.8683
7	4.768	0.2097	15.073	0.0664	3.1611	0.3164	2.1424
8	5.960	0.1678	19.842	0.0504	3.3289	0.3004	2.3873
9	7.451	0.1342	25.802	0.0388	3.4631	0.2888	2.6048
10	9.313	0.1074	33.253	0.0301	3.5705	0.2801	2.7971
11	11.642	0.0859	42.566	0.0235	3.6564	0.2735	2.9663
12	14.552	0.0687	54.208	0.0185	3.7251	0.2685	3.1145
13	18.190	0.0550	68.760	0.0146	3.7801	0.2646	3.2438
14	22.737	0.0440	86.949	0.0115	3.8241	0.2615	3.3560
15	28.422	0.0352	109.687	0.0091	3.8593	0.2591	3.4530
16	35.527	0.0282	138.109	0.0073	3.8874	0.2573	3.5366
17	44.409	0.0225	173.636	0.0058	3.9099	0.2558	3.6084
18	55.511	0.0180	218.045	0.0046	3.9280	0.2546	3.6698
19	69.389	0.0144	273.556	0.0037	3.9424	0.2537	3.7222
20	86.736	0.0115	342.945	0.0029	3.9539	0.2529	3.7667
21	108.420	0.0092	429.681	0.0023	3.9631	0.2523	3.8045
22	135.525	0.0074	538.101	0.0019	3.9705	0.2519	3.8365
23	169.407	0.0059	673.626	0.0015	3.9764	0.2515	3.8634
24	211.758	0.0047	843.033	0.0012	3.9811	0.2512	3.8861
25	264.698	0.0038	1054.791	0.0010	3.9849	0.2510	3.9052
26	330.872	0.0030	1319.489	0.0008	3.9879	0.2508	3.9212
27	413.590	0.0024	1650.361	0.0006	3.9903	0.2506	3.9346
28	516.988	0.0019	2063.952	0.0005	3.9923	0.2505	3.9457
29	646.235	0.0016	2580.939	0.0004	3.9938	0.2504	3.9551
30	807.794	0.0012	3227.174	0.0003	3.9951	0.2503	3.9628
31	1009.742	0.0010	4034.968	0.0003	3.9960	0.2503	3.9693
32	1262.177	0.0008	5044.710	0.0002	3.9968	0.2502	3.9746
33	1577.722	0.0006	6306.887	0.0002	3.9975	0.2502	3.9791
34	1972.152	0.0005	7884.609	0.0001	3.9980	0.2501	3.9828
35	2465.190	0.0004	9856.761	0.0001	3.9984	0.2501	3.9858

TABLE D.14 30% Interest Factors for Annual Compounding

	Single Payment		Equal-Payment Series				Uniform Gradient-Series Factor
	Compound-Amount Factor	Present-Worth Factor	Compound-Amount Factor	Sinking-Fund Factor	Present-Worth Factor	Capital-Recovery Factor	
n	To Find F Given P $F/P, i, n$	To Find P Given F $P/F, i, n$	To Find F Given A $F/A, i, n$	To Find A Given F $A/F, i, n$	To Find P Given A $P/A, i, n$	To Find A Given P $A/P, i, n$	To Find A Given G $A/G, i, n$
1	1.300	0.7692	1.000	1.0000	0.7692	1.3000	0.0000
2	1.690	0.5917	2.300	0.4348	1.3610	0.7348	0.4348
3	2.197	0.4552	3.990	0.2506	1.8161	0.5506	0.8271
4	2.856	0.3501	6.187	0.1616	2.1663	0.4616	1.1783
5	3.713	0.2693	9.043	0.1106	2.4356	0.4106	1.4903
6	4.827	0.2072	12.756	0.0784	2.6428	0.3784	1.7655
7	6.275	0.1594	17.583	0.0569	2.8021	0.3569	2.0063
8	8.157	0.1226	23.858	0.0419	2.9247	0.3419	2.2156
9	10.605	0.0943	32.015	0.0312	3.0190	0.3312	2.3963
10	13.786	0.0725	42.620	0.0235	3.0915	0.3235	2.5512
11	17.922	0.0558	56.405	0.0177	3.1473	0.3177	2.6833
12	23.298	0.0429	74.327	0.0135	3.1903	0.3135	2.7952
13	30.288	0.0330	97.625	0.0103	3.2233	0.3103	2.8895
14	39.374	0.0254	127.913	0.0078	3.2487	0.3078	2.9685
15	51.186	0.0195	167.286	0.0060	3.2682	0.3060	3.0345
16	66.542	0.0150	218.472	0.0046	3.2832	0.3046	3.0892
17	86.504	0.0116	285.014	0.0035	3.2948	0.3035	3.1345
18	112.455	0.0089	371.518	0.0027	3.3037	0.3027	3.1718
19	146.192	0.0069	483.973	0.0021	3.3105	0.3021	3.2025
20	190.050	0.0053	630.165	0.0016	3.3158	0.3016	3.2276
21	247.065	0.0041	820.215	0.0012	3.3199	0.3012	3.2480
22	321.184	0.0031	1067.280	0.0009	3.3230	0.3009	3.2646
23	417.539	0.0024	1388.464	0.0007	3.3254	0.3007	3.2781
24	542.801	0.0019	1806.003	0.0006	3.3272	0.3006	3.2890
25	705.641	0.0014	2348.803	0.0004	3.3286	0.3004	3.2979
26	917.333	0.0011	3054.444	0.0003	3.3297	0.3003	3.3050
27	1192.533	0.0008	3971.778	0.0003	3.3305	0.3003	3.3107
28	1550.293	0.0007	5164.311	0.0002	3.3312	0.3002	3.3153
29	2015.381	0.0005	6714.604	0.0002	3.3317	0.3002	3.3189
30	2619.996	0.0004	8729.985	0.0001	3.3321	0.3001	3.3219
31	3405.994	0.0003	11349.981	0.0001	3.3324	0.3001	3.3242
32	4427.793	0.0002	14755.975	0.0001	3.3326	0.3001	3.3261
33	5756.130	0.0002	19183.768	0.0001	3.3328	0.3001	3.3276
34	7482.970	0.0001	24939.899	0.0001	3.3329	0.3001	3.3288
35	9727.860	0.0001	32422.868	0.0000	3.3330	0.3000	3.3297

E

Selected References

1. Berliner, C., and J. Brimson, *Cost Management for Today's Advanced Manufacturing—The CAM-I Conceptual Design,* Harvard Business School Press, Boston, MA, 1988.

2. Blanchard, B. S., *Design and Manage to Life Cycle Cost,* Matrix Press, Chesterland, OH, 1978.

3. Blanchard, B. S., and W. J. Fabrycky, *Systems Engineering and Analysis,* Prentice-Hall, Inc., Englewood Cliffs, NJ, 1990.

4. Canada, J. R., and W. G. Sullivan, *Economic and Multiattribute Evaluation of Advanced Manufacturing Systems,* Prentice-Hall, Inc., Englewood Cliffs, NJ, 1989.

5. Collier, C. A., and W. B. Ledbetter, *Engineering Economic and Cost Analysis,* 2nd ed., Harper & Row, New York, 1988.

6. DARCOM P700-6 (Army), NAVMAT P5242 (Navy), AFLCP/AFSCP 800-19 (Air Force), *Joint-Design-to-Cost Guide: Life Cycle Cost as a Design Parameter,* U.S. Department of Defense, Washington, DC, 1977.

7. Dhillon, B. S., *Life Cycle Costing: Techniques, Models and Applications,* Gordon and Breach, Science Publishers, Inc., New York, 1989.

8. DOD Directive 4245.3, "Design to Cost," U.S. Department of Defense, Washington, DC.

9. DOD Guide LCC-1, *Life Cycle Costing Procurement Guide,* U.S. Department of Defense, Washington, DC.

10. DOD Guide LCC-2, *Casebook, Life Cycle Costing in Equipment Procurement,* U.S. Department of Defense, Washington, DC.

11. DOD Guide LCC-3, *Life Cycle Costing Guide for System Acquisitions,* U.S. Department of Defense, Washington DC.

12. DOD-HDBK-766, Military Handbook, *Design to Cost,* U.S. Department of Defense, Washington, DC.

13. DOD-STD-337, Military Standard, "Design to Cost," U.S. Department of Defense, Washington, DC.

14. Earles, M. E., *Factors, Formulas and Structures for Life Cycle Costing,* Concord, MA.

15. English, J. M. (ed.), *Cost Effectiveness—The Economic Evaluation of Engineering Systems,* John Wiley & Sons, Inc., New York, 1968.

16. Fabrycky, W. J., P. M. Ghare, and P. E. Torgersen, *Applied Operations Research and Management Science,* Prentice-Hall, Inc., Englewood Cliffs, NJ, 1984.

17. Fabrycky, W. J., and G. J. Thuesen, *Economic Decision Analysis,* 2nd ed., Prentice-Hall, Inc., Englewood Cliffs, NJ, 1980.

18. Fisher, G. H., *Cost Considerations in System Analysis,* American Elsevier, New York, 1971.

19. Grant, E. L., W. G. Ireson, and R. S. Leavenworth, *Principles of Engineering Economy,* 8th ed., John Wiley & Sons, Inc., New York, 1990.

20. Humphreys, K. K., and S. Katell, *Basic Cost Engineering,* Marcel Dekker, Inc., New York, 1981.

21. Jelen, F. C., and J. H. Black, *Cost and Optimization Engineering,* McGraw-Hill Book Company, New York, 1983.

22. Michaels, J. V., and W. P. Wood, *Design to Cost,* John Wiley & Sons, Inc., New York, 1989.

23. MIL-HDBK-259, Military Handbook, *Life Cycle Cost in Navy Acquisitions,* U.S. Department of Defense, Washington, DC.

24. MIL-STD-1390B, Military Standard, "Level of Repair," U.S. Department of Defense, Washington, DC.

25. OMB Circular A-76, "Cost Comparison Handbook," Office of the Management of the Budget, Washington, DC.

26. Ostwald, P. F., *Cost Estimating,* 2nd ed., Prentice-Hall, Inc., Englewood Cliffs, NJ, 1984.

27. Riggs, J. L., *Engineering Economics,* 2nd ed., McGraw-Hill Book Company, New York, 1982.

28. Stewart, R. D., *Cost Estimating,* John Wiley & Sons, Inc., New York, 1982.

29. Stewart, R. D., and A. L. Stewart, *Cost Estimating with Microcomputers,* McGraw-Hill Book Company, New York, 1980.

30. Stewart, R. D., and R. M. Wyskida, *Cost Estimator's Reference Manual,* John Wiley & Sons, Inc., New York, 1987.

31. Thuesen, G. J., and W. J. Fabrycky, *Engineering Economy,* 7th ed., Prentice-Hall, Inc., Englewood Cliffs, NJ, 1989.

32. White, J. A., M. H. Agee, and K. E. Case, *Principles of Engineering Economic Analysis,* 3rd ed., John Wiley & Sons, Inc., New York, 1989.

Index

A

Accounting data, 169
Acquisition:
  cost, 124
  phase, 2
Adjustment of cost data, 152
Advanced product planning data, 151
Allocation of cost, 128
Alternatives:
  break-even evaluation, 218
  comparisons based on total invest-
    ment, 84
  and decision making, 77
  do-nothing, 79
  equipment purchase, 195
  identification of, 132
  life-cycle cost optimization, 235
  life-cycle cost profiles, 139
  multiple, 201
  mutually exclusive, 81
  selection of automobiles, 201
  selection of capital equipment, 206
  selection of communication system,
    272

  selection of radio communication
    equipment, 212
  unequal lives, 89
Analogous cost estimating, 146, 148
Analysis:
  actual and constant dollar, 67
  approach, 202, 207, 276
  break-even, 199
  checklist, 270
  cost-effectiveness, 112
  geometric gradient inflation, 71
  guidelines and constraints, 131
  life-cycle cost, 130
  life-cycle economic, 12
  Monte Carlo, 186, 294
  process, 326
  sensitivity, 180, 217, 307, 330
Annual equivalent:
  amount, 56
  asset cost, 60
  evaluation, 196
  life-cycle cost (AELCC), 246, 314
Annual life-cycle cost (ALCC), 248
Annual percentage rate (APR), 37
Application of cost estimating
    methods, 147

H

High-cost contributors, 216, 330
High-interest-rate error, 176
Hurwicz criterion, 108

I

Identification of alternatives, 132, 328
Incentive:
  contracting, 267
  penalty plan, 268
Incremental investment:
  present equivalent, 86
  rate-of-return, 88
Independent proposals, 79
Indices, consumer and producer price, 62
Industrial engineering cost, 285
Inflation:
  factors, 137
  measures of, 62
  rate, 64
Inputs, economic, 17
Interest:
  compound, 35
  formula derivations, 41
  formulas, 34, 53
  rate, 35, 69
  simple, 35
  tables, 359
Interfaces, consumer/producer/supplier, 264
Intermediate maintenance, 277
Internal rate-of-return, 57
Investment:
  comparisons based on, 84
  incremental, 86

J

Judgment in estimating, 171

L

Laplace criterion, 106, 112
Learning:
  curves, 140, 157, 288

evaluation considering, 221
improvement due to, 156, 163
Lease-or-buy evaluation, 219
Life:
  economic, 250
  optimum equipment, 246
Life cycle:
  design for the, 2
  economic evaluations, 194
  product, 3
  system, 7
Life-cycle cost (LCC):
  actions affecting, 125
  analysis, 130
  analysis process, 326
  breakdown, 29, 215
  case studies, 201, 206, 212
  checklist, 271
  commitment, 13
  consumer/producer/supplier interfaces, 264
  data, 150
  economic analysis, 12
  methodology, 122
  models, 134
  optimization of alternatives, 235
  optimizing, 240
  organization for, 262
  profiles, 138
  program planning, 257
  program review and control, 263
  reporting, 259, 261
Logistics, 357
Logistic support:
  analysis (LSA), 358
  elements of, 112
  factors, 260

M

Maintainability, 5, 112, 260, 355
Maintenance:
  concept, 278
  cost, 293, 342
  downtime (MDT), 357
  factors, 298
  levels of, 277
  training cost, 347
Maintenance labor hours/operating hour (MLH/OH), 213, 308
Make-or-buy evaluation, 218